EXCALIBUR!

It was a time of violence and desperation. Britain reverberated with cries and clashing swords, a kingdom divided, longing for a leader to drive back the savage darkness. . . .

Into this crucial moment of history came Arthur, bastard son of Pendragon, the hero who would win a nation's love and loyalty, but never his heart's desire . . . Merlin the Druid, architect of the future, victim of a deadly lust . . . Lancelot and Guinevere, whose stormy passion yearned for a fulfillment their destiny defied.

From fabled Camelot to the slashing fury of Badon Hill . . . from the mysterious Hollow Hills to the final tragic confrontation between father and traitorous son, Gil Kane/John Jakes have created a masterful saga from an immortal legend.

Gil Kane is the creator of the Star Hawks comic strip. He is currently the artist for the Sunday Tarzan feature.

John Jakes is the author of the best-selling Kent Family Chronicle series, which has also been featured on TV.

EXCALIBUR!

Gil Kane
and
John Jakes

A DELL BOOK

Published by
Dell Publishing Co., Inc.
1 Dag Hammarskjold Plaza
New York, New York 10017

ISBN: 0-440-12291-0

Printed in the United States of America

First printing—March 1980

CONTENTS

EXCALIBUR!

CHAPTER 1

The Druid

The dying monk, his youthful face twisted in agony, dragged himself through the sand on his belly, leaving a bloody furrow. Over the murmur of the surf he heard the carnage behind him:

The gleeful howls of the attackers. . . .

The crashing of timbers cleaved by heathen war-axes. . . .

The shrieks of his brothers, being butchered.

And then, a dreadful roar.

Weeping, he recognized the sound of a growing holocaust. They were burning the abbey.

Staring ahead down the dark beach, he watched the sand redden. Then, as the fire intensified, he saw something else. . . .

A half-buried standard, rusted and rotting. An eagle of the Legions. And beyond it—the young monk gasped—a watching figure.

Gradually, as the firelight pushed back the darkness, he realized that the unmoving watcher wore neither the apparel nor the customary beard of a fighting man. The watcher was a plain enough fellow, even mild looking. Except for his eyes. . . .

Strange, restless eyes with flecked, multicolored

pupils. They set him apart. And made the monk shiver inexplicably.

At last the dying monk recognized the watcher's unusual garb: the distinctively simple wool gown, the cloak and runic brooch pinning it up at the right shoulder. He shuddered again, in genuine terror. With the abbey burning behind him, this traditional enemy in front of him was almost more than his soul could bear.

The monk panted: "Do you enjoy the sight, druid? You have won—"

"Because a temple of Christ burns?" Gently the druid priest shook his head. "No one wins now, save the Saxon invader." A hand pointed toward the destruction. "And he comes in greater numbers than ever before."

"Would you not rather see the old religions rise again?" the monk asked bitterly. "Your White Goddess? Your Earth Mother—?"

"They began to disappear when the Caesars brought the cross to this shore almost five centuries ago," said the other. "Rome opened the way for the earliest of your brethren, who brought the cross. And with it love, and charity for the weak, justice for all men—that is what I see perishing in the flames of your abbey, monk."

A maniacal Saxon yell down the wind punctuated the silence and the sibilance of the surf. The druid went on:

"We have both lost, you see, because the night is truly falling on our island. That the night can be held back is a small hope. But here—" Suddenly the fire-flecked, searching eyes returned to the doubled figure in the sand. "—let me see to your wound. I have some small skill—"

"No use. I—only fled—to spread the news. I—" The young monk felt fatal blood foaming from the stab in his belly. "—I do not think I will live sufficiently long even for that."

"I will carry the news," said the druid, walking forward. When the monk saw the stranger's right shoulder droop with each step, he cried out:

"I know of but one lame druid. The greatest of them. You—"

Before he could speak the name, a scream bubbled through the blood that suddenly filled his mouth. The monk's back arched. He shuddered, then lay still.

The druid knelt beside him, rested a tender hand on the cooling forehead. But his eyes roved up the shore to the big-sailed warships and, on the flame-lit headland, to the silhouettes of Saxons leaping and dancing in brutal celebration.

Presently he limped away up the beach, a new urgency in him, that driven, restless gaze searching the red horizon, as if for answers.

ii

Miles inland, just at dawn, the druid Merlin crouched in a ditch where thornbushes scratched his sandaled feet. He watched another band of Saxons torching and pillaging a small hill fort. From their garb, he could tell they came not from the sea but from villages in the district.

The fort's lord, a baron whose name Merlin did not know, had already been axed down and his head hoisted on a pole. Now his consort, well-fleshed but not unattractive, was dragged shrieking into the open.

One of the gore-spattered Saxons had found a red dragon banner somewhere. While the druid observed from his hiding place, the Saxons ripped the garments from the sobbing woman, then wrapped her in the stained flag, demeaning both.

The Saxons raised the woman over their heads and paraded her, their laughter thunderous. The druid's flecked eyes grew huge with rage; with sorrow; with his desperate sense of time running out. . . .

Still screaming, the baron's wife was borne into shadows beyond the torched fort. Saxon arm-rings flashed as thick-fingered hands reached to bare her body for the coming rape. The flag of Uther Pendragon fell to the ground.

Merlin's cave, high in the hills and sequestered by a screen of tangly brush at the entrance, was cold and moldy smelling when he reached it at noon. But he was grateful for the cool gloom; for sanctuary.

He struck flint with a dagger from his worktable, blew his tinder alight, and started a flame spurting in a bronze bowl of oil, shivering in memory of what he had seen since the previous sunset.

Strange and distorted, his peculiar eyes reflected in a giant, perfect sphere of solid crystal that sat among his pestles and earthen jars and Latin-writ scrolls. Merlin had lied to the murdered monk. He had gone to see the new Saxon onslaught for himself; there was no one to whom he meant to tell the tidings. They would reach the high king in Londinium soon enough.

And the other petty kings and barons—some of whom acknowledged the brother of Aurelius Ambrosius as high king, some who refused—they too would hear it and gabble over what to do, and in the end they would do nothing because of their divisive self-interest.

The distraught priest limped to the end of his bench, laid hands on one earthen jar, took from it a finger-length section of gnarled pinkish root. Slowly, using a stone, he ground the root in a pestle. To the particles he added cold mead from another jar. He stirred the mixture with his dagger, drank.

Then he retired to his couch in a chilly niche, a strange, still figure reflected in the sphere's curve.

He did not know the root's name. But in his experiments with natural science he had discovered its peculiar power to clarify his thoughts, to set his mind open to future possibilities. Soon he began to hear eerie ringing notes within his head. Began to see multicolored fogs blur away the cave's interior. . . .

His inner eye revealed Uther Pendragon, son of the dragon, twelve months the high king now. Uther was a brave enough man. But no more successful at stemming the Saxons than his predecessor, King Aurelius Ambrosius.

The vision shifted. . . .

He saw dead Vortigern, the foolish, frightened baron who had hired the first Saxon mercenaries from across the Narrow Sea, hurling them into battle against the fierce, hairy Picts pouring down over the fair island in sporadic raids out of the north.

The Pict threat had been pushed back. But the imported Saxons stayed, in their own settlements. Now, new shiploads of barbarians were crossing the waters to join those already present, join them in pillage that would bring down the dark that Rome had staved off for a short time during her occupation. . . .

He saw Roman garrison towns, abandoned as the empire withdrew because of threats to its home borders. And he saw the Christian fathers who had brought the new faith. The abbeys they founded were being decimated by the Saxon fire, the Saxon sword. . . .

Again Uther floated in Merlin's thoughts. The vision turned frosty and dreadful: surrounded by hundreds of glowing candles, Uther lay on a bier of mourning.

The high king's throne-chair appeared. *Empty*. . . .

Sweating and trembling, Merlin woke from the trance.

He had seen the future. Unless someone intervened, Uther would die without issue. And Merlin knew with even more certainty that Pendragon could never work the miracle of holding back the island's destruction. Only a new king might. . . .

The *next* king. Carefully instructed. Taught the arts of mercy as thoroughly as the arts of might—which were the only ones rough Uther understood.

The *next* king . . . prepared for his sacred mission by Merlin himself.

Merlin limped to the sphere, laid his palm on its chill curvature. He stared at it a long while, hoping that the face of the new king would be revealed. The effort proved fruitless. His mind kept distracting him with images of Uther, who had no consort—and no heirs.

"There must be a son," Merlin breathed. "And the son must be Uther's without question, or the barons and kings will never rally to him. Even then, they may not—at first. It must be arranged so they do—"

His course was clear. King Uther must be persuaded to find a wife to bear that child. He felt the conviction with a mystic certainty—just as he knew that he, not Uther, would be the prime mover.

He put both hands on the sphere and again tried to see the boy's face, but could not.

He knew what the boy must be, though. A fighter of strength, yet a lord of wisdom and compassion—

His face wrenching, his flecked eyes flaring, he gripped the sphere and whispered a second time:

"There *must* be a son."

It was almost a prayer that he would have the strength to bring it about.

iii

The hall at Londinium rang with laughter for the first time since the Saxon invasion. The room was filled with the lively notes of minstrels' strings merrily plucked, bustled with the activity of poorly clad servants bearing in the heaped trenchers and overflowing mead jars. At the table of honor, behind the silver chalice of precious, costly salt, big-chested and bearded Uther sopped up the last of his thrush pie with bread, heedless of food-gobbets in his beard.

Minor kings, barons, their women—and their attractive daughters—packed the trestle tables. But Uther, a little drunk, had eyes for only one female.

He bent to whisper to the plump-breasted, warm-eyed, and richly dressed young woman he had contrived to have seated on his left. She clapped a hand to her cleavage, flushing in response to the high king's private remark.

On her left a thin old man with a sharp nose and a straggle of white chin-beard said sullenly:

"May it please the king to share his jest with my wife with all of us?"

Annoyed, Uther glanced past the suddenly pale young woman.

"No, it doesn't please me to do so, my good Cornwall."

Seated on Uther's right, Merlin put a hand across his oddly flecked eyes. It was all going wrong. . . .

Uther had agreed in principle to taking another wife in the hope of begetting a lawful heir. But in the week-long festivity arranged for bringing the fairest daughters of the barons and the petty kings to Uther's attention in Londinium, one noble, Cornwall, had appeared without his female offspring, who were too small.

But he had brought his wife, Ygrayne. And damnably, it was *her* bold eye, *her* ample figure that had caught Uther's fancy.

"My lord," Ygrayne of Cornwall said, turning to the man so far past his prime, "the king shared only an innocent frivolity. There is no need for wrath. Or jealousy," she added in a pointed way.

"I have a different opinion," Cornwall exclaimed, pushing aside his trencher. It fell off the trestle, crashing, splattering raw oysters, and bringing immediate silence to the hall. Cornwall rose. "He pays excessive heed to you, and you to him."

Uther's face, scar-ridged, grew ugly. "I would remind the duke that the high king is entitled to appropriate attention when he speaks to any subject, male or female."

"When the purpose is not indecent," Cornwall said.

The words fell like stones into a pool of audible gasps. A torch popped; a minstrel dropped his instrument; discordant twanging echoed and reechoed as burly Uther likewise pushed up from the trestle with both hands. Ygrayne turned pink with shame, then pale from fear.

"Speak plainly to me, my lord," Uther demanded.

Cornwall pointed a veined hand at Merlin. "I have heard of the druid's scheme to catch you a wife." The finger swung to Ygrayne. "And I have seen the rash and foolish heat in her eyes—"

"Put there, perhaps, by an unfortunate lack of heat in yours," Uther retorted. "Young girls do not happily—or willingly—wed men your age. I know my lady's father arranged the match—"

Merlin reached out. "I beg you to hold your temper, your majesty—"

Uther flung off the hand without glancing around.

"You claim to be high king—" Cornwall began, sneering.

"I *am* high king! As was my brother Ambrosius before me!"

Cornwall—never very loyal to the house of Ambrosius anyway, Merlin knew—refused to be cowed:

"—and therefore you also claim to be a Christian, forswearing adultery."

Uther's hand dropped to his sword pommel. The guests cringed at his roar:

"There is no adultery, my good duke. If you are saying otherwise—"

"I say there is none as yet. Nor shall there be any." Quavering a little under Uther's truculent stare, he swung to Ygrayne:

"Gather your ladies. We will be gone from this place by midnight."

Uther shook his head. "Not without the high king's leave."

"Do I have that leave?"

"You do not, Cornwall."

"Then I will make departure without it!"

He snatched at his wife's arm, literally dragged her up from her chair, while Uther watched speechless.

Ygrayne cast a frightened, sorrowing glance back over her shoulder; a glance for Uther that Merlin didn't miss as he clambered to his feet, bent to whisper in Uther's ear:

"Let him go. Let him leave the hall without disgrace."

Uther's hand held the sword pommel so tight that veins bulged. "But not Londinium. Not in defiance of my authority."

Unsteady of step, one arm around his wife's waist, the Duke of Cornwall hurried Ygrayne from the hall. Merlin ranged his glance over the faces along the tables. Here he saw an expression of doubt that dismayed him; there, the beginning of a smirk that did so doubly—

"A word in private," he begged, luring the high king from the dais. Uther was beside himself with anger—Merlin felt the trembling—and perhaps that was why he permitted hands on his person; allowed himself to be directed into a small room off the rear of the hall. Merlin slammed its door thunderously.

"Your majesty, you have asked my advice in times past, so please heed it now. Coveting that woman, you will undo the tenuous hold you've won on the loyalty of your barons—choose another!"

"There is no other woman I want," Uther answered in his rumbling bass voice. "And loyalties, which root only in the soil of fear—"

"Not the highest loyalties," Merlin murmured, unheard.

"—are already dangerously undone because I let Cornwall defy me. To tie them up again, I will permit him to ride from Londinium—" Abruptly Uther's stained beard cracked with a cruel smile. "—and punish him in a more appropriate setting. A battlefield."

He stormed out.

iv

From a tower parapet where he had been led by the alarmed servant who woke him, Merlin heard the cocks crow in the meadows along the great river outside the old Roman wall. He heard, then saw, the foot troops tramping out through the wall gate in double column, Uther in iron cap and leather and link-mail on horseback at their head.

Within the hour, although he despised horse travel and sat any mount badly, the druid was cantering through the mist along the great river's bank, following the clear trail of Uther's army. That the high king had an uncontrollable lust for Ygrayne he could no longer doubt. It sickened and disheartened him; fate was already twisting his plan toward ruin.

Only by following the king could he keep that plan's ruin from becoming total. So he rode through the sweet-smelling dawn fields in pursuit of the dust cloud of the army, while black rooks, flushed by the racketing of hoofs, rose around him like flapping omens of evil.

V

"I *had* the rebellious traitor!" Uther raged, his fist clenching. "Had him caught between our lines and the hills. I was close enough to see that fur-trimmed mantle the peacock wears in battle—!"

Merlin crouched over a brazier; the pavilion was chilly. Its cloth walls snapped, and its poles swayed in the night wind. From outside, rowdy camp noises and an occasional cry of an injured man punctuated the strained silence.

Uther started pacing. The supple leather of his breeches and high war boots bore dried bloodstains. Near the pavilion's entrance, three captains, all as gore-spattered as the high king, endured Uther's rage stoically.

Finally one captain said, "It was to be expected that Cornwall would fear pursuit and send for more foot soldiers—"

"But if they'd only swarmed across the hilltops an hour later—!"

"Majesty, we caught the duke just a short time before

sunset. Even if the reinforcements hadn't arrived, today's action would have been brief."

"Brief!" Uther sneered. "Yet we lost how many?"

Flecked eyes staring into the flames, Merlin said, "Fifty."

"And Cornwall lost only a fraction of that before he retreated across the river!"

Glumly another of the captains said, "Surely we'll finish him when we attack at dawn—" Merlin understood the continuing resentment of Pendragon's men. They knew the high king fought for no vital purpose, but only to gain revenge for injured pride, frustrated lust—

"I have decided there will be no dawn attack because even a simpleton would expect just that." Uther knuckled a long, clotted gash on his cheek. "Keep the men awake after they finish their meal. Permit no drunkenness. We'll cross the river at moonrise. The sky's clear—it should be almost like fighting in daylight."

One of the weary officers started to protest. Uther gestured him silent:

"Spread the order! And keep the campfires bright—the men singing. So Cornwall thinks we *are* waiting until dawn."

Merlin continued to stare into the brazier as the sullen captains slammed right fists against their leather chest-armor and left.

"And now I suppose I'll get a moralistic lecture from you," the king said. Merlin glanced up, momentarily unnerved by Uther's perception of his mood.

"No, majesty. Only a fool prostrates himself in front of the stone gathering momentum on a hillside. I know your feelings about Lady Ygrayne."

"I'll have her here by the cock's crow."

"I must beg leave to disagree."

Raising a mead jar, Uther scowled across the rim.

"You doubt I can pull Cornwall's flag down in battle?"

"Not at all. But during this afternoon's short combat,

certain men were serving as my eyes and ears. While the duke's reinforcements marched over the hills, another party slipped away. Several armed men—and one woman. Cornwall has sent his wife to safety."

Fury showed on Uther's scarred face. "Then we'll change the plan! Circle wide and strike for the duke's hill fort—"

Uther spun toward the pavilion entrance, stopped as Merlin rose and exclaimed:

"Cornwall may be in his dotage, but he's no fool. Only two of the party will ride to his fort, there to collect his two daughters. Mother and children will be reunited at what Cornwall fancies is a safer haven. Tintagel abbey."

"How do you know?"

"You've never questioned my reports before, majesty—or even demanded to know how I came by them. The information is correct."

"Then I'll go to her at the abbey once Cornwall's killed!"

Merlin sighed. "You plan to lay siege to a house of the Christian god? If so, you'll have even less support among the petty kings and barons than you do now."

Infuriated by Merlin's impertinence, Uther treated the druid to scathing mockery:

"What do you suggest in your wisdom? You know I intend to have the woman. And to beget the heir you're always carping about—"

"I know." Merlin nodded. "I have planned a way for you to enter the abbey." He concealed his trepidation as he said the rest: "When the moon's up, you'll have one more soldier in the van of your attack than you counted on."

vi

The river shone like rippled silver under the huge white globe of moon. Screened from the enemy by underbrush along the far shore, Uther's men waded across in silent files, long-bladed Roman swords tucked under their arms to prevent a telltale flash, tough shields of whitewashed leather held up out of the water. The shields bore the device of the dragon.

Third in his file, Merlin shivered as the water lapped the boots and breeches he'd donned. The river purled and, occasionally, the link-mail that the soldiers wore beneath their tunics clinked. But the wind was blowing cold in Merlin's face. With luck, the sounds wouldn't carry to enemy sentries.

The men were fording the river in ten parallel files. Because of his limp, Merlin had difficulty keeping up. So did a few others, older or heavier. To his right, a stout man stumbled, cursed, inadvertently struck the water with his war-axe, and flailed up a fan of silver droplets.

On shore branches crackled. One of Uther's captains cried softly:

"You fool, you roused a sentry!"

From a spit of land on Merlin's left, the sentry's cry split the night. Far on the druid's right, Uther Pendragon lunged forward at the head of his file, heedless of noise now. His spatha shone as he pointed it heavenward. Behind him, a dragon-flag unfurled, held aloft by a stripling. Uther bellowed the command for the attack.

Merlin splashed ahead. More warning cries rang from Cornwall's camp behind the screen of foliage. Uther's soldiers broke formation, spilling up the loamy riverbank and hurling through the brush with swords and spears poised, slings loaded, axes raised—

Uther's surprise strike caught most of Cornwall's camp asleep. That was a brief advantage. The druid and the others encountered no resistance until they passed through the brush. Beyond, shadow-figures scrambled up from spread blankets. One of their number shrieked as Uther reached him and gored him through the throat with his spatha.

Cornwall's soldiers stumbled into crude protective formations. Enemy shields caught the moonlight. Each carried the painted image of a griffin.

Then, all around Merlin the battle exploded, a confusion of screams, moon-sheened metal, grunting, pushing—a pandemonium in which the blades of friends and foemen were hard to tell apart.

Near a grove at the fringe of the fighting, Merlin spied a spindly figure, a man vainly trying to rally several fleeing soldiers. A mantle tufted with white fur belled in the wind as the old man laid about him with his sword. The cowards squealed and covered their heads.

An enemy spearman lunged at Merlin. He shifted position awkwardly, turned sidewise, and raised his shield. A soldier behind him hacked the enemy spear in half with one stroke. The attacker fled.

Merlin fitted a stone in his sling, whirled the sling around and around, watched the spindly figure—

The stone missed.

Hands slick with sweat, the druid fitted another. An axe glanced off his shield, burying in the ground. Merlin kicked the attacker below the waist, pushed him over, reluctant to kill. Agonized screams all around him signaled no similar reluctance among the rest of Uther's men.

Merlin whirled the sling and released one end. The stone sped true. The mantled figure cried out, swayed. The sword fell to the ground. The cowards fled into the grove. Merlin hurled himself forward as fast as his infirmity permitted.

Some of Cornwall's men saw their commander down. Several started to rush to his aid. Merlin reached the stunned, mumbling old man a step or two ahead of the others. Cornwall's eyes grew huge in the moonlight as what appeared to be an enemy towered over him—

No deathstroke took the astonished duke. Instead, the druid knotted a hand in Cornwall's fur-trimmed cloak, tore—

The brooch pin snapped loose. A second later Merlin had the cloak in his hand.

But Cornwall's rescuers were upon him. A diamond-headed spear point raked Merlin's shield as he bent low and darted back into the melee. Dodging spears and swords, he worked his way toward the river, stepping over fallen bodies—some decapitated, some with limbs hacked off. He hardened his senses to the stench of wounds and the moans of the dying.

With no further thought for the battle, he waded into the glittering river, the precious mantle bundled under his arm.

vii

Merlin heard the high king enter, turned to see him limned against the radiance of dawn. Uther's leather chest-armor was even bloodier than it had been last evening. Another huge gash reddened one cheek.

The king's face broke into a coarse smile at the sight of the druid adjusting the cowled mantle on a frame of poles.

"It will be dry shortly," Merlin said. "Has Cornwall fallen?"

"His flag fell. And he took a deep wound. But his captains got him away to a hilltop. We have him pinned there."

"You'll let the others finish him, then?"

"Aye." Uther grinned. "I have business at an abbey."

Unholy business, Merlin thought uneasily, disturbed by the direction his plan was taking. Still, he would not change it now. If Uther would accept only Ygrayne as the mother of his heir, it was Merlin's task to see that the union was accomplished.

The druid looked into the high king's eyes and touched Cornwall's mantle.

"Yes," he said. "And now you have the means to conduct it."

Fog shrouded the rocky headland, muffling the stamp of the half-dozen horses. Cowled, so that his face was concealed, Merlin limped to the gate in the wall.

The night's chill seemed to reach into the marrow of his bones. But he was cold for a reason other than the weather. This was a sanctuary of the Christian God, and Merlin didn't believe in mocking any deity, no matter what earthly name He went by—

Only the desperation of the island's plight gave him the courage to walk those last few steps to the gate. *Cornwall will die on the field if he hasn't already*, he thought. *And now adultery to compound the sin. For a holy end, we entwine ourselves in evil means—*

The sea boomed at the base of the headland. Restless cattle lowed in the abbey's stable beyond the wall. Merlin knocked loudly, the sound sharp over the distant, eerie notes of the brothers chanting a prayer in the Celtic tongue.

A shivering novitiate answered. The youth's hair was cut in the Celtic tonsure: a wide strip shaved across the top of his head from one ear to the other. He raised his lantern, but Merlin's face remained hidden by the cowl.

"Brother gatekeeper, we're Cornwall's men. Come to find his wife and children."

The novitiate peered beyond Merlin to the dim figures standing beside their horses in the curling mist. "We had heard the good duke had perished. Murdered by the high king—"

Merlin gestured. "Does that look like a ghost, brother? Surely you recognize the duke's war mantle."

On cue, Uther took a step forward, his face likewise concealed by his cowl. But the white fur trimmings of the cloak were unmistakable.

The novitiate hesitated. "The duke escaped the battlefield, then?"

"As darkness fell." Merlin nodded. "Come, don't

keep my lord shivering out here all night. He wants to see his family."

"But weapons aren't welcome here. You'll have to leave your long swords in the gatehouse."

Impatiently Merlin growled, "There's no objection. But these, we take with us."

He thrust his left arm forward. The lantern light fell across a whitewashed shield bearing Cornwall's griffin.

The novitiate's eyes darted to the painted emblem. Something disturbed him. He reached out—

Merlin whirled away, preventing the gatekeeper from touching the shield and discovering that the pigments had not yet fully dried.

"Two of you stay with the horses," he ordered. "Two more in the gatehouse with the weapons. I'll accompany the duke to his family, then rejoin you—"

The gatekeeper stood aside. Merlin and Uther followed the bobbing lantern across the abbey's huge yard.

Buildings loomed in the fog. Merlin clenched his teeth, struggling to keep up with the high king. At any moment he feared the gatekeeper would glance around, notice him limping—

But the fur-trimmed mantle and the repainted shields had evidently allayed the novitiate's suspicion. He led the two toward the guest house located beside the wall halfway to the point of the headland. On the point the abbey proper glowed with lamps, misty circles in the drifting fog. The Celtic singing had a strange, hollow sound that counterpointed the crash of the surf far down in the estuary. Merlin's nostrils filled with the ripe aroma of straw and manure from the stables.

Slot windows in the guest house radiated light. "There is no need to announce us," Merlin said, slipping around Uther and rapping on the door. It opened a moment later. Busy watching the novitiate, the druid suddenly heard Ygrayne's soft, startled intake of breath.

"Husband?"

In that one word there was a question, a doubt. She knew instantly that the proportions of the man before her were all wrong, no matter what mantle he wore or what shield hung from his forearm.

Uther's cowled head nodded. The novitiate continued to stare. Merlin waved him off:

"Privacy for the duke, if you please, brother!" The gatekeeper headed back for the outer wall. Merlin felt safe in limping inside, following the king.

He closed the door on the plainly furnished chamber. A small child asked a sleepy question from behind a gauzy hanging that closed off an alcove. Another alcove held a rude bed. Uther handed his shield to Merlin, reached for his cowl. Merlin's flecked eyes narrowed with inexplicable fear—

The hanging on the first alcove seemed to stir. Were the children awake—?

Slowly Uther pushed back his cowl. The oil lamps in the chamber lit his scarred face. Ygrayne gasped softly, darted a glance at the hanging, then at Merlin. Finally her confusion gave way to a rush of color in her cheeks. Uther's mouth curved into a smile.

The smell of lust was almost palpable. The druid felt ashamed.

Remembering her manners, Ygrayne managed a curtsey:

"My lord does me honor by this visit."

Without looking around Uther said, "You may leave us."

Even as Merlin turned toward the door, the high king reached out with one hand and closed his fingers on Ygrayne's slender forearm.

ix

Behind the gauzy hanging, two small girls huddled in a cold bed.

One, only five, whimpered and fretted. The other, eight, made no sound. She had wakened and felt a thrill at the sight of her father's war mantle. And then the man had revealed his face—

A flash of lamplight showed her the other visitor as well. Although she didn't know the second man's name, she would never forget his appearance—particularly his odd, flecked eyes. Her own gray ones were huge and almost animallike as she pressed fingers over her sister's mouth and watched the high king conduct her mother to the other alcove, there to snuff two lamps.

From the alcove's darkness came muted laughter, muffled sounds whose meaning she perceived dimly. Something hardened within her as she watched and listened—

Slowly her large, lynxlike eyes filled with hatred.

x

In the yard Merlin saw the last of the guest house lamps go dark. He shivered.

He had to keep remembering what he believed so implicitly: that out of this night's wickedness—conducted in the very shadow of the images of the Christian God—would come the island kingdom's only hope of staving off destruction by the invaders.

Yet he was depressed, filled with foreboding as he limped back toward the gate. High purpose and mortal sin were now fatefully and irrevocably mingled in his plan. He was powerless to change that, but he feared the consequences. And he was certain one or both of Ygrayne's daughters had been watching behind the hanging.

Somehow he couldn't shake off the certainty that terrible retribution had been set in motion by the adulterers coupling in the guest house—with his complicity.

xi

Winter ice cracked on the eaves of the long house. The night seemed as endless as the cold weather. The river Cam had been frozen for half a month. Snow mixed with rain fell almost daily. The soldiers and servants and their women were waiting for the high king's wife to be delivered of her child—

Uther is drinking far too much, Merlin thought, watching the high king slop down more mead. Uther's gaze was fixed on the griffin flag, bloodied and ragged now. The flag had been pinned to the log wall of the king's solar, his private chamber, at a north corner of the fort's long main building.

Merlin listened, caught the sound of a moan from a nearby chamber. To relieve the king's nervousness, he said:

"The midwife assures me she will be delivered by daylight."

Uther shook his head. "But she's so slow. Laboring since dawn this morning—" Unhappily the high king looked at the druid. "Did you know two more of the barons came to me this afternoon?"

"Yes, I saw them ride through the gate."

"Everywhere it's the same, they say. The high king called filthy names, and Ygrayne too."

"You wed her before the duke was a week in the ground. That was your wish."

"And yours, wasn't it?" Uther challenged.

Merlin bowed his head in troubled, wordless assent. Uther flung the mead jar to the table. "Christ preserve us, what a way to celebrate the eve of the Savior's birth! Sick with worry for her—"

A sharp scream broke the end of his sentence. Uther rushed past Merlin, who seized his arm:

"The midwife will care for her—!"

"Damn you, she may be dying!"

"She will not die," the druid said. "The child will come—whole and sound. He will be a king of surpassing mighty dominion."

Uther peered into the flecked eyes. "You seem to know a great deal about it."

"I do. I ask you to stay here."

Uther flung off the druid's hand but didn't leave the chamber. By the fire his hunting hound raised its long yellow head, lolled its tongue, then went back to sleep. On the roof a slab of ice cracked loose and fell—

xii

At the breaking of daylight the child was born. Merlin and Uther stole in to see the stout, lusty boy howling in the crooked arm of his drowsing, pale-cheeked mother.

As Merlin peered over Uther's shoulder he felt an almost supernatural shiver of expectancy. The weary midwife stole in behind them, wiping her hands on her stained apron:

"The sun is coming. A fit present for the new king, eh, masters?"

Uther bent over his wife and his child as Merlin stole out to the fort's yard. He heard cheerful halloos from the huts clustered under the great walls of earth and stone. Over the eastern wall, light was breaking. The light of Christmas Day—

In an almost ecstatic state Merlin paced the muddy yard until the sun was fully up. His doubts and fears at Tintagel were forgotten. Great icicles fell from the eaves of the long house and crashed into the yard. From the smokeholes of the huts came the delicious aroma of wood burning, meat roasting—

Merlin felt the warmth of the earth rising around him; the evil weather had broken. His eye was suddenly arrested by the reflection of the sun in a pool of melting water. In the center of an expanse of thawing mud, the pool seemed to glow and shimmer. For a moment, spikes of light played over the surface.

In the water Merlin saw a strange and miraculous image. It seemed as if a cross of light burned like a sign of hope—

He blinked. The vision in the pool was gone.

As families opened their hut doors to greet each other with Christmas wishes, Merlin returned to Uther's solar in high spirits. There the thunderblow fell:

"What you said before, Merlin—that the boy will be a king—"

"Of surpassing mighty dominion, your majesty."

Peering at the flag of dead Cornwall, Uther shook his head. "I have thought long on it, and it must not come to pass." He swung around. "My position is shaky enough as it is. The barons and petty kings will never recognize an heir conceived before the queen and I were properly married."

Stunned, Merlin argued, "Very few know—"

"Everyone knows! If I knew the name of the traitor who talked, I'd open a second mouth for him. It must be one of the men who was with us at Tintagel. But which one—?"

Angry, he shook his head.

"It could be someone else," Merlin said, thinking of the presence he'd sensed behind the gauzy hanging.

"It makes no difference. I will not give the throne to a child whose legitimacy is in question. That would undo all I've worked and fought for—you'll have to wait another year for that son you want so badly, druid. The second one won't have any scandal attached to his name. His claim will be clear—"

Terrified, Merlin exclaimed, "Majesty, there is no time to wait—!"

"What do you mean, there's no time?" Uther roared. "Ygrayne is well. She can bear again—"

"But—"

Merlin's words broke off. How could he speak to Uther, a man of practical realities, about the icy vision of the empty throne he'd seen in the crystal sphere? How could he tell the high king that he would never conceive a second son? How could he convince him that *this* son, yelling loudly as the brilliant Christmas sunlight suffused the solar, was the destined one?

"There's no arguing," Uther declared. "My mind's made up. The kings and barons will recognize my *second* son."

"If—if that is your vow, majesty," Merlin said, "then I ask a boon. A gift in honor of this festive day."

Uther scowled. "What gift?"

"That you let me have the boy and see to his care and upbringing."

Now it was Uther's turn to be troubled. "He will *not* be a king, druid. No matter how many visions you see—or how much you wish for it."

"If he's not a king, he'll have no favored place in your house. And I might make something of him—"

"A pedant? A soothsayer?" Uther scoffed. More cordially, he laid a huge hand on the druid's wool-clad sleeve. "See here. I don't mean to be so curt. It's only your timetable that's awry."

No, Merlin thought, *yours. The king who will hold back the night is already born and lies suckling beyond that wall. He must be reared as a king, not as some peasant's yard-boy, hardly noticed or cared for—*

But Merlin only said, "Then let me take this one after he's weaned."

"Very well."

"Have you named him?"

"I think a good Roman name like my brother's would suit," Uther mused. "He has a burly look to him, tiny as he is—yes, I favor Artorius, the Bear."

xiii

The road from the hill fort at Cam was muddy with spring rain and sweet with flowers blooming under the budding trees. Merlin rode with the seventeen-month-old infant squalling in a carrying-sleeve fastened over his shoulders with leather straps.

Uncomfortable on horseback, the druid still felt a sense of elation—of a reprieve won. Little Artorius was growing a set of lusty lungs, which he exercised as Merlin cantered along on his journey to a destination already arranged—

Uther had been correct about one thing. The scandal

concerning the boy's conception remained widespread. And with Uther's position so tenuous the selfish local kings and barons were not ready to acknowledge a bastard. They preferred to talk about themselves as Uther's successors since the claim of Artorius was no claim at all—

But in the long, troubled year that had passed since Merlin saw his first tangible sign of the boy's destiny—the flash of cruciform light on Christmas morning—Uther had not managed to fill his consort's belly with a second heir. He still spoke hopefully—when he was available to speak. He and his troops were away from the hill fort more than they were present. The Saxon depredations were spreading.

And each time Pendragon did return home, he looked more haggard. He complained that his failure to beget another son was due to the draining rigors of endless riding, skirmishing, fretting, and trying to outthink the barbarian invaders—

Well, there was still time to convince Pendragon that the boy must be acknowledged his heir—the king Merlin knew him to be. Then the druid would have to convince the barons to recognize the child as well. At the moment, however, his concern was the infant's upbringing.

Pondering thus, Merlin failed to see the trio of men skulking in trees to the left of the road. He only became aware of their presence when an arrow hissed by the muzzle of his horse.

The horse neighed in terror, started to rear—and only that saved Merlin from taking a second quarrel in the throat. It missed him by a hand's width.

Artorius bellowed at the sudden jouncing. The horse's forefeet jolted back on the gummy road. Merlin bent low over the animal's neck and dug in his knees. Another arrow whispered past his bowed back. The horse stretched his legs, galloping and splattering up great slops of mud—

Twisting his head around, Merlin squinted in the

sunlight. He saw the three assassins scrambling for their own mounts. How had they known he was leaving Cam with the boy? Someone had been rewarded for that information, obviously. It was not exactly a secret among Uther's folk.

Yet Merlin had never imagined that any threat such as this would materialize. And a very real threat it was: three mounted figures swung into the road some distance behind, gaining speed as the druid's horse splashed across a creek and into a thick wood.

To remain on the road would invite capture and death. He could not outride the younger, more adept horsemen. But ahead—

The road dipped down through a gully. Merlin turned his horse's head up the gully to the right, into the greening, dappled shadows. He heard the drumming hoofbeats of his pursuers coming closer. He reined in, struggled to the ground as the boy-child wailed in the leather sleeve.

Merlin whacked the horse across the flank to send it pounding out of sight along the gully. He scrambled up the bank and crouched in the underbrush, the sleeve in his arms and the hem of his gown wrapped around the baby's head to muffle its cries—

He watched the assassins ride by, pursuing the runaway horse down the gully. They were rough, heavily armed men with shields on their arms—

Shields that bore the griffin device of Cornwall.

The murderers disappeared. Merlin limped back toward the road, intending to press ahead along the shoulder so as to leave no trail. He was overwhelmed with a new and dreadful fear:

Already someone was seeking revenge for Cornwall's death and Ygrayne's adultery. Cornwall had left no heirs except his two small daughters. Merlin remembered the gauzy hanging, the sense of impending evil—

A child against a child? Merlin thought gloomily. One of the girls must have seen Uther's face at Tintagel. How old was she?

Old enough to understand and to hate. And he didn't even know what she looked like—

Hobbling beside the muddy road, Merlin cradled the baby boy protectively against his chest. Now Artorius must be raised not only apart but in secret. The druid hadn't intended to conceal the infant's whereabouts, but that had become a necessity. Somehow he felt that the unexpected turn of events was the beginning of that retribution he had anticipated at Tintagel.

The beginning, he thought as he hurried along, mocked by the cheerful trilling of bright birds in the trees. *The beginning—but where will it end?*

xiv

On a summer morning five years later, old Baron Hector stumped into the yard of his fort in the mid-country mountains and was well pleased with what he saw:

Two stocky boys in coarse shirts and trousers were rolling and pummeling each other in the dirt. Hector, a man with a pie face and a battle-broken nose, watched the boys and smiled. He was convinced once again that he had made a shrewd if peculiar bargain with Pendragon's druid.

The cattle and grain that Merlin arranged to be delivered annually helped defray the poor yield of Hector's own meager fields; he could never content himself with farming anyway. His head was too full of memories of the days when he rode with Ambrosius. In those times driving back the Saxons was an adventurous lark, not the desperate and often futile task it had become in recent years—

But there was a second benefit to his bargain with the druid. At age sixty Baron Hector had at last managed to birth a boy-child, born of a serving wench of pleasing temperament. Hector had married her and had cared for her faithfully until her death two springs ago. Now his son, Kay, the shorter of the two boys wrestling on the ground, had a companion his own age.

The other boy was bright haired and surpassingly strong, with powerful shoulders and long, cleanly shaped limbs. And his mind—the very thought made old Hector sigh with pleasure.

Just then Kay jumped on his friend's stomach and pinned his arms:

"I've trapped you, Bear! Admit you're caught!"

Motionless, the other boy appeared to surrender. Kay grinned and wiped a dusty cheek. A few paces away, Hector, delighted, used his left hand to clap two scrolls against his left leg. Hector's right sleeve was empty from the elbow down and pinned up at the shoulder with a brooch. Young Kay would get a good lesson any moment, Hector saw—

The boy Artorius doubled his knees and knocked his opponent into the dust. In a moment it was Artorius on top and Kay pinned.

"Who's trapped now?" Artorius chortled. A second later Kay admitted his defeat. The other boy extended a hand to help him up. Hector waddled forward:

"A good match and well fought! Now, my young stallions, shall we have the daily lesson?" He waved the scrolls.

"Do we start the lives of the holy saints today?" Artorius asked. Kay made a face.

"Yes, as soon as we spend an hour with the Romans."

The high king's bastard was afire with eagerness. Kay merely gazed at the clouds in the summer sky.

Sometimes old Hector wished his own offshoot had the keen wits of the strong, intense boy who was his constant companion. Kay had no interest in the venerable Latin of the scrolls. Artorius was already able to pick out some hundred different words—and was eager for more.

"Dull old books," Kay grumbled as they made for the fort's long house.

"Old they may be," Hector replied amiably, tucking the scrolls under his stump of an arm. "But far from dull. They hold the world's wisdom and truth, and so they're doubly precious in these times. The barbarians from the Narrow Sea throw scrolls like these into the flames. My library becomes more valuable with every fort that falls!" Hector tried to say that lightly. But there was a grim undertone nonetheless.

"Most of the barons can't read, can they, sir?" Artorius asked as the trio entered the cool, gloomy chamber where some eighty to a hundred scrolls were stored in a hand-built compartmentalized cabinet.

"No, they think it's of little worth—like this rattlehead." Affectionately Hector ran a hand through Kay's hair. "Unless you show a little more interest in your lessons, Kay, when you and Artorius are men, there'll be no doubt about who will lead and who will follow."

"Oh, that's been plain a long time," Kay said, without rancor. "Bear can already swing a spatha twice as hard as I can."

It was true, Hector admitted. In everything Artorius excelled. What strange ambition burned in the boy, Hector could not guess. But the druid must suspect its existence, having handed the lad into Hector's care.

The old man gazed into the bright, luminous eyes of his pupil while Kay yawned again. Artorius was a vessel waiting to be poured full. Hector in his old age relished the task:

"Today we shall listen to Flavius Primex, who authored this treatise on the use of cavalry. That means soldiers on horseback, Kay," Hector added, receiving another yawn in reply. "Our countrymen have forgotten that Rome used horse troops to great advantage—"

Kay dozed as Hector began to read. The Bear sat cross-legged in a bar of sunlight falling through a slot window. Odd how the lad always sought the bright places, Hector reflected during a pause. The boy always wanted to be out of doors or near windows—as if he had some unconscious affinity for the blazing radiance of heaven. That same light gave his handsome young face the glow of polished metal. Hector lóved his son Kay. But this Bear—this was a child he admired. There was a vast difference.

"How many men rode in a Roman horse troop?" Artorius asked eagerly. Just as eagerly, Hector told him.

XV

Twice a year, sometimes oftener, Merlin appeared at the great gates of Hector's fort and spent a few days in company with Artorius. One such visit occurred in the autumn of the boy's tenth year. On a chilly evening the two climbed to the watch tower beside the gate. From its platform they gazed out on the color-splashed mountains. From beyond one low peak, a smoke column rose.

"The barbarians have found some new victims," Merlin said, pointing.

Artorius nodded. "Baron Hector and his captains rode out at first light to protect the roads and to make sure the Saxons don't come this far."

Touching the boy's shoulder, Merlin said, "You will have a part to play in the long war, Artorius. That's why Hector is teaching you to ride and to swing the spatha. You do very well, he tells me."

"I expect to go out with Hector when I'm twelve or thirteen. It's everyone's duty to protect the land from those who'd lay it to waste."

Merlin's flecked eyes narrowed. "You'd kill the Saxons in battle, then?"

The boy's face was turned toward the sunset light. He pondered, then said:

"Well, sir, I'd kill them to win a battle, but once they were beaten, no, I'd only send them home if they would go."

A great sense of pride and satisfaction filled the graying druid. Hector was teaching wondrously well, exactly along the lines Merlin had outlined to him. Discourses on war were balanced against the holy texts in Latin. There was courage in Artorius, but there were the seeds of an understanding of mercy as well—

Merlin limped up beside the boy, who asked suddenly, "How is my father?"

"Not well. The constant fighting wearies him."

"I'll gladly take up his sword when I'm older."

No, Merlin thought, *I have another sword in mind.* "You'll have a great deal more than a sword to take up, Artorius. You will have a great role to play—"

"In the war, you said."

"Greater than that." Merlin stared down into the scarlet-washed face. "You are going to be the high king, Artorius. Would something like that make you afraid?"

The boy thought again, then whispered, "Now—yes."

"And later—?"

"No," said Artorius, his eyes almost like an old man's as he stared at the druid. "I guessed a long time ago that I was being taught for some purpose—"

"A purpose vaster than any of you ever dreamed," Merlin whispered, immensely gratified when the boy did not seem alarmed but only turned and stared thoughtfully toward the column of smoke climbing beyond the mountains.

CHAPTER 2

Pict Hall

Darkness reigned in the Pictish Hall.

The outside Fortren night, in the misty highlands, seemed to focus into colder blackness within the king-place. A blackness of the spirit. . . .

"So," bellowed Huil, son of Caw. Huil was chieftain now of this tribe, two months after he had buried his Scot blade deep in the previous leader's paunch. His presence seemed charged with lightning, and his self-confidence was overwhelming. Now he wished to overwhelm all he could. "You are the magic man of Northumbria. Let us see if your magic—and your life—holds any interest to our cause."

In the midst of the gathering snapped a fire, asputter about a spit of charred wild boar. The fire shuddered, quivering like a frightened stranger in this omnipresent dark. Two Picts, painted in bluish spirals from brow to ankle, shoved their captive toward the smoky huddle of light, before their fearsome leader.

A thin man, the captive was gaunt and bedraggled. He fell to bloody knees in the greasy dirt. Huil's piercing eyes raked the sight of him, assaying his potential. Not much, it seemed. . . .

The prisoner's clothes were but a twist of cloth upon his tortured frame; a memory of warmth and happiness wrapped about pale nakedness. "Untie my bonds, and I will do my best," he said.

Huil sneered, showing teeth like a healthy wolf's. "Is not your magic great enough to release yourself?" Tossing away his dripping boar's shank, he clutched his mead jar. A film spread over his eyes . . . ruminating. Taking over the Picts tribe by tribe was such a slow process. He had three under his command now. A thousand warriors. . . .

But the other tribes were wary of him and threatened to band together against him. Give him time with each tribe to assert his charisma, and his overbearing power of leadership would curl them around his fingertips. If not, his warriors could subdue them. Time was growing short, though. He had barely enough strength to match his forces against all the others. He needed aid. Magical aid of a most uncommon sort to bend all clans and tribes of this land to his conquering, visionary will.

A land of the Picts. Under his control, his alone . . . and soon to come. So near.

"It is magic of the hands," replied the beaten man. "You think if I had the power to tear these leather straps I would be here now?" A spark of defiance and hatred flared in his Celtic eyes. This was the sort of man that Huil would have to deal with eventually, when he moved down to conquer the southern lands. A brave man. And valiant. But the Celts were a stubborn lot. They would not take to serving under a leader of a different race.

The chieftain's eyes seemed to glare the color of his flamelike hair. But only for a moment. . . .

He barked a laugh. His eyes narrowed with a low cunning. "Yes, Northumbrian. I like you. I hope you are the one we seek." He nodded to a hulking man squatted beside him. The tawny man drew a dirk and sliced off the thongs that bound the Celt's arms behind his back.

The Celt rubbed blood back into whitened hands. "I wondered why I was not butchered like the rest of my brethren during your heathen raid. I knew it stemmed from no mercy on your part. We were but a poor, peaceful village—"

"My warriors needed sport to prepare them for bigger assaults, scrawny one." The big, muscled Scot sucked a noisy draft of mead, leaned toward the Celt intently. "You were spared because word has reached me of your magic hand. Why we desire it is no concern of yours. Now *show* me—no more of this South-people talk!"

The Celt stared at the peat and bracken fire a moment, the flames reflecting desolation in his bluish eyes. But then he smiled. "I have a bag. I need it."

"No bag!" the chieftain growled.

"No magic."

In a flurry of ragged wolfskin and fox fur, Huil leaped to unshod feet. The blade of a captured spatha gleamed beneath the Celt's throat. Little restraint showed in the swelling cords of the leader's brawn.

The Celt closed his eyes and faltered: "Dead, I can certainly be of no help to you. Surely my bag has been searched by now and has yielded no weapons."

Reluctantly Huil lowered the sword. With chilled cobalt eyes, he searched the faces of the Picts who had brought the man. The warriors shook their unkempt heads, tersely responding.

"Very well. Give him his bag."

A doeskin pouch was thrust into the Celt's arms.

Digging into it, he proclaimed: "This magic came with the Romans. I learned it from my dead father, who learned it from his father's father." From the bag, he drew a birch branch. "Observe, good people—a *whole* stick. Now, such a stick is known for its strange properties. *This* one is special. Even if you break it, it becomes whole again. Watch!" The man snapped the stick into four pieces. Held them aloft with one hand. "You see. It is broken, But wait! *Is* it?" Folding the pieces into his hands, he rubbed them.

He lifted a whole stick.

The astonished Picts gasped. Except for Huil, whose face was stone. "Is this all you can do? It is *tiny* magic."

"I must limber my abilities," the man replied, stepping over to the tall Pict beside Huil. "I observe, chieftain, that one of your men is most peculiar. He has stones in his ears!"

Deftly the Celt plucked a pebble from the Pict's left ear. Another. And another. The big man's eyes bulged with surprise. He poked a thick finger past the lobe, probing—finding nothing. The others laughed.

A wizened old warrior stood. "I told you, Huil, great one! Good magic, no?"

"Houndson!" Huil growled, hurling his earthenware jar at the man. The old one dodged. The bowl fell, cracking its lip. Immediately Huil was handed a brimmed jar by a cowering servant in his shadow. "This is nothing! I want magic to wake the lightning in the clouds. To cast thunderbolts upon my enemies! I want spells and sorcery that will bring the whole of Pictland quaking under my leadership. But this! This is boar's dung!"

A fevered grimace contorted his features. His body seemed to radiate raw power.

"This wretched Celt is not to see tomorrow's light. See that his cries disturb the entire night!"

The Celt retreated into the curling smoke. "B-but your highness. I implore! I have not finished yet. Is it lightning that you want? Thunderbolts and sorcerous spells to crack the air with their power?"

Huil glowered, considering. Suspicion darkened his brutishly craggy face. But beneath and in his eyes glimmered a ray of hope. "You can do these things?"

"But surely! I can set the earth to rumbling! Yes—that is what I will show you. But I need certain witch tools."

"*What?*" Huil frowned. "Witch tools?"

"Oh, merely trifles for the potion." Biting a bloody fingernail, he scanned the disheveled pottery, the tattered blankets in the thatched shadows of corners.

"Hmm. That discarded bowl there. Old man—give it."

The old Pict rose and handed the chipped bowl to the Celt.

"Now, I shall need elements for my potion. A swallow of bracken brew! A dollop of dirt touched by the moon. A newly laid hen's egg! Fresh water from a stream and old manure from a horse! Fetch me these things in this hard clay jar, and I promise, the earth will shake and the true Huil, son of Caw, will be revealed."

Huil grasped his servant woman, thrust her to the Celt. "Take it. Obtain the things he desires. Quickly!"

The dark woman grabbed the bowl and melted into the darkness.

The Celt stood mute. Head high, eyes closed. Preparing himself.

Huil quaffed his brownish mead, his eyes thin slits of desire. "Yes, Celt. I have always known that if I should find the right instrument the powers of the dark would be mine. And as that dark serves me, so shall I *it*, until we spread over this foul isle like fog, and all its people *worship* me with their bodies and their souls. This is my dream, Celt!" The Scot from the Western Island rose to full height. He lifted aloft a clenched hand. His fierce eyes shone, ice cold.

"And our nightmare," muttered the Celt under his breath. Moments passed in silence. The woman returned.

The Celt took the slopping, noisome jar from her hands. Tense and unsmiling, holding the mess with one hand, he stirred it slowly with his birch stick, moaning softly. "Oh, Sky God! You have seen the heathen axes of war rend the limbs from my innocent daughter and son. You have heard the dreadful cries of dear Myrra, my wife, as she was raped by these barbarian swine, who would as soon rut snake holes! You have the stench of our burned homes yet in your nostrils and the agony of our dying still in your heart." He withdrew the stick, let it drop. He brought the loathsome vessel close to his mouth. "Take my essence—" He spat into the bowl. "—and shake this earth with your fury and your curse!" His blazing eyes opened wide. In a blur of action, he threw the noxious stew square in Huil's astonished face.

"Now," the Celt screamed, face contorted. "Watch the earth shake and may God rot you all!" He stood tall, bracing himself up.

Huil wiped a hand down his face. Stinking droplets hung in his hair and his beard. Huil's eyes burned molten. With an inhuman shriek, he wrenched himself up, grabbed his spatha by its horn hilt, and streaked thunderously up to the Celt. Firelight flashed on the blade. Beaten iron sang through air and chunked sickeningly into flesh. In a spray of crimson, the Celt's head tumbled from his shoulders and rolled away into the shadows.

The headless body staggered. Dropped into the fire. Huil hacked and slashed until sweat popped on his forearms, until the body lay in a gore-heap of flesh and bones cracking and glistening in the flames.

With harsh breaths and trembling frame, Huil straightened from the carnage. He threw his blood-drenched sword into the dirt and growled: "Clean my blade of this Celtic filth. Throw these bones out for the dogs to gnaw!"

He plumped down on a blanket and rubbed his face clean.

"The bastard was a clever one, cheating us of his torture! But he did show me that I, Huil, *can* make the earth move! And I *will* move it to get my magician!"

He tossed down the rest of his heather-mead in one gulp, and when he lifted the jar from his mouth, a man separated himself from the shadows to stand before him.

"What is it, Brys, son of Bradman—my captain, my eyes into the south?" Huil said, impatiently, grinding his teeth.

"You seek a magician."

"Aye."

"And tonight's games show you that only the best of that brood will do. *Not* some trickster fool you properly killed."

The scarred, thickset captain was disguised as a Celtic soldier: leather cuirass, brown breeches, a shield stamped with a cross.

"Down in the southwest, in the place called the Hollow Hills, a man lives. He is of the old race, a druid. I have heard that of all men on this island he knows of the arcane magics, Huil."

"You know *where* he lives?"

"Aye. Alone, in a cave. Simple prey with enough men. But we need to go in like disguises. . . ." He smoothed a hand down his cuirass. "With horses, we can slip through the country like ghosts and spirit him away back here for your pleasure."

Huil spat into the fire. "Go then. Get this druid. Bring him here, unharmed, and your reward will be great, Brys."

The captain nodded, pivoted, and stamped toward the door.

"Hold a moment, Brys. What does this man call himself?"

Framed in the doorway, against the starry night, tendriled with mist, Brys turned and smiled. "His name, great leader," he said, "is Merlin."

ii

. . . a flash of sword iron, horse hoofs pawing the moonlight, the salty tang of blood, the close stench of unwashed bodies wrapped in night fog.

The aging druid clamped his hands harder to the cold crystal sphere.

A shudder ripped through Merlin's back. The spasm wrenched his tough hands from the glass. A cool sweat dotted his flushed face. His breathing came in ragged spurts.

A careless arm swiped down, knocking over the mortar and pestle, which had ground the dreamroot, upsetting the bowl that held the dregs of the liquid that had surged through the man's mind, pointing to visions leaping from the heart of the crystal like unchained evil spirits.

The sheep tallow candle's flame guttered on its wick, throwing fretful spatters of light along the worktable against a dank cavern wall.

Merlin seized hold of his thoughts, and his fright felt like dew under dawn's sun.

"Fate," he muttered. He heaved a sigh as he raised his pained bones from the oaken stool and wrapped his cowhide cape closer to his purple tunic. "I cannot control you as well as I would like. But perhaps . . . perhaps I *can* use you!"

A faint glimmer of mirth lit his flecked eyes.

Humming to himself, he padded to a wood cabinet from which he obtained a clean scroll of yellowed parchment, his tarnished Roman inkwell, and his goose quill. Damning the rheumatism that hampered his movement at damp times like this, he limped back to his table and proceeded to scribble Latin words on the paper.

When he finished, he rerolled the paper, tying it fast with a leather strip.

He emerged from his cave's mouth past the thornbushes that concealed it and searched the hills, painted with sunset.

There he was, the little fellow . . . on the round, grassy summit of a neighboring hill. The shepherd's son, Garfon—tending his ailing father's folds.

Merlin negotiated the crooked paths through the brushy heather and the rainworn thrusts of rock. Through the tart trampled bracken and the sweet briar that clustered on his beloved hills. Down one, up the next, through furze mottled with shadow. Until he reached the hilltop.

Scattered ewes and rams and lambs cropped the ample grass, bawling with content, munching. Crook in hand, the twelve-year-old sat against a mossy boulder, nibbling a piece of goat's cheese.

"Whoa ho, Merlin!" the lad cried, eyes brightening at the sight of his friend. "Have you come to share the sunset with me this evening?"

"Na. Na, Garfon. I have need of you, if you be willing. . . ."

"Of course," the boy said, rising to offer the druid his comfortable seat. "You have eased my father's pain and set him on the road to health. I will do anything to repay—"

Merlin waved the notion away. He sat on the soft moss, peering out at the sinking sun's bands of color. Turquoise, reddened with orange tonight. . . . "I would have done that for the fine man in any event. It is not repayment I want. Just a simple favor."

"Name it!" A breeze frolicked through Garfon's brown curls.

Merlin sighed, his limbs aching from the climb. Blast it, anyway! He was no youngster, but neither was he ancient. He took out the scrolled parchment from the folds of his tunic. "Take this. Keep it safe. Do you know where Watling Fort is—the home of Hector and his son Kay. And the young man Artorius?"

"You have spoken of the place many times, and I know the way if only from your many words on the subject."

"Yes." Merlin chuckled. "I suppose sometimes my ramblings come to good cause. But listen. Should something happen to me. . . ."

Garfon frowned with alarm. "But what—?"

"Now, now . . . nothing may come of it, but I've had troublesome visions lately. Should bad tidings knock on my door . . . take this and present it to Artorius. Borrow a horse from a farm. Here . . . you'll need a coin or two for that. . . ." He picked a pair of old Roman gold coins from his pouch, tucked them into Garfon's palm. ". . . and speed you to the home of Baron Hector. This is all I ask."

"You have my vow, Merlin."

"Good enough." The druid arose, aching in his joints. "Damned damp. You'd think I was a derelict or something. I've got a score of years left me, I swear I do."

"Many score, if God listens to my prayers," said the youth. "But please, Merlin. Stay and share some cheese and mead with me! To celebrate. The ewes are perky, and the rams are beside themselves with lust. We will have many new sheep before long."

"Na. Thanks to you all the same, but there are preparations I must make. Tomorrow, I start off to see Artorius myself. It is time he had another teaching."

The boy showed surprise. "But why not give him this message yourself then . . . not that I object to traveling with it."

Merlin tousled the lad's hair fondly. "Perhaps one day I can explain this to you. You will understand." He bade farewell and began the return journey back to his cave. Keeping his back to the setting sun.

Another sunset, he knew, would bring the barbaric hordes from all around, dragging the sun of civilization down farther and farther into the dark.

To keep that sun up, enriching the lives of gentlefolk like Garfon and his father . . . was this not an ambition in life worthy of dedication and struggle?

Merlin looked up at the blackening sky to the east, the direction from which the Saxons had swarmed.

Salt tears blurred his vision.

Swallowing back his emotion, he turned his sight back upon the narrow pathway and limped back to his home in the hill.

iii

The bow was bent.

Its catgut string was taut, firm.

"Now, Kay! Now!" whispered Artorius, excited.

Tensed arms and squinted eye adjusted the aim. Slender fingers let go.

The shaft flew, whistling in the dappled wood, toward the deer.

And thunked resoundingly into tree bark.

The white-throated buck started. Its pointed ears pricked up alongside the horny beginnings of antlers.

"Oh, Kay! Kay! Kay!" Frustrated, Artorius grabbed the small bow from his friend's hands. He jerked another arrow from the quiver on Kay's back, set feathered end against string.

The deer's nose sniffed the air as it moved away. Catching a strange scent, its walk turned to a run. Before Artorius could even aim it streaked toward a low-branched copse of fir trees.

"Oh, curse," Kay said, teeth clenched. "I know you wanted venison tonight, Bear."

The tall, lithe fourteen-year-old holding the bow returned sharply: "I still do. And I'm going to get it, too."

He darted after the deer, holding the arrow still cocked.

"But Bear! You can't catch a running—"

"I bet a week's worth of chores I can!" Artorius yelled.

"Done!" bellowed Kay. "And that includes swilling the hogs!"

This really is a hopeless chase, thought the proud young Artorius. He did not look forward to assuming Kay's tasks for a *day* much less a week. But by all that was holy, how it rankled to taste the prospect of juice-filled roast venison in one's mouth—to have it abruptly yanked away by a stupid deer. Already, failure was not something the boy took well.

A flash of milk-colored tail.

The rattle of bushes.

The beast was not far then! Artorius lunged through the firs, which seemed to swipe at him with their thick prickly branches to detain him and save their brother of the wild. With all his might, Artorius the Bear, bastard son of Uther Pendragon, pushed through the fir trees, fists tight around his weapon. A clearing opened before him. He stumbled over a dead branch, righted himself. A field. Studded with wildflowers. The scent of lilies wafted into his nostrils.

On the other side of the grassy expanse the buck sprinted for the shelter of gorse and sycamore. The break in foliage had provided a chance—and if Artorius did not grasp that chance now, there would be none other.

Halting, he lifted the bow and arrow, sighted, pulled back on the string—let the arrow soar through the air. It arced and dove like a thin, short-feathered hawk.

The buck thrust through the gorse bushes. Finishing its fifty-yard flight, the shaft vanished into the brush as well.

Had it sped true? Only one way of finding out. Artorius jogged through the high-bladed grass to look.

Stopping, he craned his neck over the froth of gorse.

Lying on the ground near the sycamore trees, an arrow cleanly skewering its neck, lay the deer.

Artorius whooped. "Kay! Oh, Kay! I got him! I got him!" Joyously he tossed the bow over his head and swarmed through the bushes to examine his kill.

He could almost taste the succulent roast in his mouth—feel the luxury of a choreless week. . . .

Kneeling by the buck he unsheathed his dagger. If the animal was yet alive, it must be released from any suffering. But it was dead: opened eyes glazed, thick red oozing from the wound.

Strange. The shaft . . . the arrow . . . it looked *different*. Much thicker. Blue and yellow feathers instead of red. And the head, protruding from the other side. Barbed!

This, Artorius realized, was not the arrow he had shot!

Laughter thundered from the dense foliage. A throaty merriment. Artorius reared up, dagger before him for protection, eyes darting. He couldn't see anything. . . .

From behind a sycamore trunk a man emerged, holding an empty bow in both hands as a gesture of peace. A tall, hefty man in brown roman *braccae* and a tattered cuirass. A leather quiver of blue and yellow arrows was slung on his broad back.

"Who are you?" demanded Artorius, standing straight.

"Well, now." The tanned man chuckled, a smile showing through a black bushy beard. "That's a question worthy of philosophers. Who am I? A fleshy vessel for a wandering spirit? Or perhaps a self-deluded ghost doomed to stalk these woods, cheating sportsmen of their kills? Maybe even a figment of your addled imagination!"

His hazel eyes twinkled amusement.

"Na. Na, stranger," Artorius said, relaxing, realizing the man meant no harm. "Your name! Your business. You bear the mark of a hotter country's sun. Your clothes have seen much wear and appear to be of Roman origin. What are you doing in Britain?"

"Questions, questions! Where to begin answering?" The man rubbed his beard in mock bemusement.

Just then Kay stumbled through the gorse, tripped over a root, and sprawled in a pile of dead leaves. He looked up and saw the slain buck. "You *did* it, Bear! You *got* it!"

Artorius shook his head and pointed at the newcomer. "No. *He* did."

The man bowed curtly. "As I was saying, my name is Amlodd. I've come to abide awhile with my uncle—"

"Cousin Amlodd!" cried Kay, awkwardly gaining his feet. "It's me! Kay!"

Amlodd shook his head and grinned. "By Jove's toes, I haven't seen you since you were a wee bairn, Kay! How do you recognize my name?"

"Oh! Father talks of his nephew Amlodd all the

time. Fighting for the Romans against the Huns! He was afraid you were dead. I'm so glad you're not."

"So am I!" The big man stooped over the deer. He plucked the bloodied arrow from its neck as though it were merely a pricking thorn. He slung the dead beast over his broad shoulders. "By the by, Kay, who's this stern lad who challenged me so fiercely?"

"Oh, I'm sorry!" Kay brushed the loam and leaf bits from his tunic. "This is Bear! I mean, Artorius, son of the high king! *We* call him Bear, though."

"He certainly growls enough for one. Greetings, Bear!"

Artorius could not help but smile. What an amusing fellow! "Greetings, Amlodd."

"Shall we go to Baron Hector? I've not seen the splendid Godsman for years. My heart aches for some of his famous mead."

They traipsed through the wood.

"Wait a moment!" Kay chortled. "Bear, if *you* didn't kill the deer, then you have to do my chores! I've finally beaten you in a bet!"

"What is this?" Amlodd asked. "Not kill the deer? Why of course he did. The arrows struck simultaneously." He pulled Artorius' arrow from his quiver. Blood covered it.

"You see, Kay?" Amlodd winked at Artorius, who was confused. Kay scratched his head. "I don't understand. Bear said—"

"Since there is some question," interrupted Amlodd, "why don't you just call off this bet. With sure bellyfuls of buck meat tonight, we've *all* won, haven't we?" He jerked his head to where the deer's lolling snout hung. "What did you say, Sir Buck? Ah?" He turned to Artorius and Kay. "The deer objects to my last statement. *He* didn't win." Amlodd let go a resonant, belly-shaking laugh. The boys joined in, and together they marched back to Baron Hector's fort.

iv

Amlodd quaffed his seventh goblet of mead and smacked his lips. "Divine! Do ye know what the Romans call their mead? Nectar of the gods. Well, I'd trade all the water grape swill in the world for a cask of Hector's mead." He eyed the empty cup. "Ah, by Jove, the cup is yet thirsty. Drunken vessel. But it *will* have its drink, so why deny it? Pour, lad, pour. Perhaps the golden stuff will pry another story out of me."

Eagerly Artorius lifted the ceramic pitcher from the wooden bench, dumping swirls of mead into the yawning mouth while Amlodd looked on, eyes glimmering approval.

Outside, spring night hung lightly in the air, pierced by a silver-coin moon and winking stars. An ash branch swished against a half-closed shutter, stirred by a breeze that breathed mountain scents into the room. Candles guttered, throwing a wash of light onto the assembled party: Baron Hector, snoring in his armchair; Kay, his son, passed out on a bearskin rug, by a fallen cup, a spill of mead.

Victims of the potent brew.

Artorius clasped his own goblet. The goblets were beautiful: bronze, sparkling with gems, which Hector had taken out of his closet to celebrate his nephew's homecoming. The boy sipped at the tangy sweetness. His three cups of the stuff had long since sent their warmth through his sinews. Artorius realized blearily that for the first time in his life he was drunk.

As was Amlodd, who set his cup down and licked his lips.

"Your story, soldier!" demanded Artorius, comically toasting his new friend. The alcohol lent him the feeling of bold abandon. Along with a sensation of camaraderie with the hairy man.

"Ah, yes! One of my very best," Amlodd proclaimed. He scratched his nose, considered the sleeping forms of Kay and his father. "A shame these dullards could not survive the night. But the story bears repeating. They'll just have to wait."

Scraping back his chair, he stood, leaning upon the roughened wood of the table, palms flat. "It was in Germany that this happened. I was commanding a phalanx of mercenaries against the crazed Huns, a bunch of heathens to make the Saxons puppies by comparison. My squadron was ambushed in a glade by swarms of the whoresons. Pitifully outnumbered we were, and the ruckus was so tremendous I could not shout orders for assembly. It was every mother's child for himself, and I was the first to see that. I hacked a few of the scum—and then, miraculously, an opening appeared in that fearsome crowd. 'Amlodd,' say I to meself. 'You have a choice. Stay and be cut to bits for a cause that you care not for—and is paying less every day in the bargain. Or retreat honorably and save this life for whatever good Fate has planned for it.' Actually the question came up even as I dashed away and was only a philosophical exercise. Well, I didn't see much wrong with this—but one precious Roman general did. That night in the strategy meeting he claimed that I was a coward and a traitor. Foolhardy man . . . the Romans needed every man they had. There was no sense in ridding themselves of a valuable leader. But this worthy hated me. Even though the others tried to discourage him, he swaggered up to me, spit in my face, and demanded, in the name of holy honor, that I immediately fall on my sword, in the hallowed tradition of Roman suicide. Fall on my sword! The very words he used." Amlodd pounded on the table. "And so I did!"

Artorius gasped.

"Yes, I did, and I'll show you!" Amlodd grabbed up his spatha from its place beside him.

"No," cried Artorius, alarmed. "Don't . . . you're drunk. You might hurt yourself." Concerned, some of his inebriation phased away. He stood, holding out an imploring hand.

Amlodd shook his head and chuckled. "No, lad. Don't worry. This is what I did." Lightly he laid the spatha on the wood floor of the great hall, blade flat. Then he thunked to his knees and let his torso descend to meet the iron sword. His head twisted around, wearing a silly grin.

Bemused, Artorius blinked. Then the joke communicated.

He laughed uproariously. Tears started from his eyes. His sides ached, he laughed so much. "And . . . and you got away with *that*?" he managed to gasp.

Instantly Amlodd shot to his feet and draped a friendly arm over Artorius' shoulders, his voice assuming a confidential tone. "Did I get away with it? The Romans laughed as hard as you. That great captain was humiliated. I left a couple of weeks later anyway, but that little jest saved my neck right there." He twitched his bristled mustache. "But here. Mead is notorious for weakening one's cunning. Let's exercise our wits awhile more before we rest our heads." His eyes glittered mischievously. "And while we're at it, let's put our arms to one more cup of mead's worth of work, eh lad?"

Reassuming his seat, Artorius poured out the last dregs of mead.

Amlodd's eyes shone with affection through half-closed lids. His big hands folded around his goblet, but he did not drink. "You hold your drink well, Bear. That's the Celt in you. We are a hard-drinking people. And yet it does not inflame your senses, nor do you drowse as is usually the case."

"You have had more than I, bottomless one!" Artorius said.

Amlodd's eyes, reflecting the lights, seemed to part curtains. For a moment, Artorius saw them blaze, like red-hot copper. "I have had very little tonight, lad. My capacity for drink is immense. And when I am truly drunk. . . ." The curtain seemed to shut. The fires in them dimmed, and the premature wrinkles in the face deepened. ". . . it is then that the ancestry of our breed shows forth. I have killed many a man in fair fights, Artorius. And not remembered their names or the cause of argument the next morning." He smiled and shrugged. "But that was years ago. Perhaps the Romans have civilized me, eh?"

His paw of a hand whacked Artorius' shoulder. He gulped the rest of his drink and rose from his chair, like a towering crag of hard rock jutting up from the floor. Artorius felt a twinge of awe and even fright. Perceived an inkling of power before him, raw and neutral, that owned roots beyond the mere being of this affable, brutish man. "Come on. Let's get some sleep. I've got some things I want to show you in the morning."

Without further words, Amlodd lumbered toward the chamber where Hector had stored his sleeping mat.

Artorius woke his sleeping friends one at a time, helped them to their bedchambers, and finally surrendered to sleep himself.

▼

The noon sun glittered on the polished blade of the spatha. It made a sweeping arc. Straight for him.

Straining muscles he had only recently discovered, Artorius jerked his own sword up to parry. The weapons clanged. Artorius' sword seemed determined to rip itself away from his tortured hands. The sweat that had been beading on his forehead this past hour dripped. But he held firm and did not lose the sword.

Looking cool and collected, Amlodd, his sparring partner, backed away. He grinned as he noticed how hard Artorius was breathing: gasps and sighs.

"Enough for now. You're doing better today, lad. I've only hacked you in half five times to yesterday's ten."

Artorius wiped his brow on his tunic sleeve and sought the shade of an elm nearby. "And I beheaded *you* once! Don't forget that, Amlodd."

A burst of laughter. "Luck! Luck, you arrogant snot!"

"Once is all it takes, Amlodd." Artorius breathed deep of the woodsy air. His limbs ached. His lungs burned. His cheeks were hot. His soaked armpits smelled even to him.

But he had never felt so exhilarated in his life.

Amlodd used his spatha as though it were an extension of his arm. And he was teaching Artorius that skill. No. That *art*. This was no child's play of stick swords. This was the real thing, with a veteran warrior.

Artorius had been cut two days ago. A small, ragged slash on the arm. It had stung, hurt, and now only ached. But he treasured it. This would be his first scar.

Amlodd had wounded him accidentally the first time they had actually test-fought. The man did not notice the wound until they had finished. But when he saw the dripping blood, he examined the cut without apology. He had taken Artorius' blade then and nicked his own arm. Blood trickled down the elbow. Stunned, Artorius watched as the man smeared his own blood on Artorius' wound. "There," Amlodd had said. "To hurt you now, I would be wounding myself." He winked. "And same with you."

The following days had seen several other practice fights, but no accidents. Often Amlodd's sword would come within a finger's length of Artorius' skin—but always at the last moment it checked . . . and never touched him again. In these moments, helpless, his life at the whim of that silvery blade, Artorius perceived anew the restrained energy in the man. Restrained only because of friendship.

Five days Amlodd had been there.

They had been astounding days.

Used to chores and study, with few pleasures in between, Artorius' world was being opened. The big man took a special interest in the lad. His studies had been forgotten. Amlodd had cajoled both Artorius and Kay from most chores so that they could game and hunt and carouse with him. The days had been filled with sport. Amlodd had taught them all manner of Roman games. Had played their own favorites . . . hurley by day, fidchell by firelight. The man fountained with humor, bawdy poems, epic tales of heroes and monsters, animal energy, and good cheer. Artorius suspected that in these past five days he had consumed more drink than all of his previous fourteen years combined.

Even now Amlodd hefted a goatskin of mead mixed with honey to his lips. It splashed down on his bare, hairy chest with abandon.

They stood in a glade about two hundred yards from Hector's fort. Kay was doing chores. His turn to spar would come during Artorius' chores. But with Kay, Amlodd wrapped his sword in cloth.

Suddenly Artorius realized that Amlodd stood beside him. He was offering the much depleted goatskin. Artorius accepted and drank the stuff. Cool. Sticky. But wet enough to satisfy.

When Artorius had quaffed his fill, Amlodd said, "You're good with a sword, Bear. There's a fire in your handling I've not seen before. In anyone."

Artorius' chest filled with pride. This was the first serious comment that Amlodd had given him. "Thank you."

"But you lack, lad."

"Lack?" He couldn't hide the disappointment in his eyes.

"Oh, I'm not faulting your technique or potential power. You will grow. You will learn. But there's *more* there. I can sense it . . . you lack something very important."

"But what, Amlodd. What?"

The man shrugged his broad shoulders. "Jove knows. Maybe the right sword. You use Hector's extra spatha like an amputated man uses a wooden leg. You get around all right, but the sword play's not *whole* yet."

"I don't understand."

"Neither do I. Neither do I. But. . . ." He sucked in

the fresh air as though it were his favorite wine. ". . . by the time I leave, you'll be able to beat any man of this island."

"Leave? Don't go yet, Amlodd. You haven't been here a week."

"Oh, no! You misunderstand, Bear." Amlodd grinned. "I'll stay here as long as Uncle Hector feeds me. . . . And I'm amused. Then I'll move on. I don't like to stay in one place too long. Confining."

"I've never known anyplace other than this." Artorius let a small gesture encompass the pleasant green, the nodding trees, the black mountains in the misty distance. A gesture of newly formed discontent. "I want to see more."

Amlodd was silent a moment, cleaning his spatha with a rag. In nearby branches a sparrow trilled. A breeze soughed through the trees, the gorse bushes, the grassy fields. "You'll never see any place finer, lad," Amlodd said finally. "When I was away, I ached for it."

Artorius shook his head. "No. I want to see the other countries. I want to ride the seas. I want to eat at a Roman feast—and see the lands of the far east. I want—"

"So many wants in such a small head!" proclaimed Amlodd heartily. "But right now my stomach wants its supper. Did I spy some cheese in the larder this morning. Let's go make sure it's not there this night!"

Amlodd strode off.

"Hey wait!" Artorius cried. He struggled to his feet and fell into step alongside the giant.

To keep pace was wearisome work. Amlodd was taller, his legs hoisting the barrel torso a surprising portion of his height. A relaxed stride, for Amlodd, was the equal of two lunges by Artorius.

He did not slow his pace for the lad, but made him work to keep up. He smiled at the boy's intensity. "You are a strange one, Artorius." His base voice filled with amusement. "So young and already so old. Enjoy your youth. Don't be so serious. Learn to laugh and savor the moment. *Live* the day. Don't act like it's a rehearsal for tomorrow."

Hector's small fort was perched upon a hill, lending it good defensive position. The wooden gate yawned open into the well-kept courtyard. Laughing and joking with his new companion, Artorius entered.

Within the yard, still and quiet as some ominous cairn of rocks, towered Merlin upon a spotted mare. Long gray beard stirring in the breeze. Multicolored eyes bearing no trace of emotion.

Artorius halted, surprised.

A twinge of guilt irked him. He pushed it away and smiled at the druid wrapped in his threadbare cloak. Their eyes locked. Artorius could almost feel his soul being searched.

Nonsense. For all his knowledge Merlin was a man . . . just like anyone else.

"Merlin!" Artorius cried, breaking the strained moment. "I forgot that it was getting on time for your week. Welcome!" For the life of him he could not contain feeling ill-at-ease, nor revealing it in his voice. Stupid voice, anyway. It squeaked. How he longed for the day when it had the body, volume, and timbre of Amlodd's.

The brawny man raised ragged eyebrows. "Ah ha! So this is your druid, Bear. I'd hate to tell you what the Romans have to say about Britain's druids." He turned. "Tell me, citizen Merlin. Do you dance widdershins?"

Merlin smiled so slightly that his mouth seemed no more than another of his many wrinkles. "Only on the graves of barbarians, my friend."

Amlodd unbridled an appreciative laugh. "Well said!" He tapped Artorius' shoulder. "Well, lad. Introductions!"

"Merlin, this is Kay's cousin. Amlodd. He's just back from Roman campaigns. He has been teaching me a great deal."

"The lad takes to lessons like a baby beaver to the river." Amlodd beamed proudly, almost as though he were boasting of his own son. Nonchalantly he scratched his beard. The rumbling of his stomach signaled his impatience to get on with supper.

"Yes, of course," Merlin said. "I am glad you have come. It is a pleasure." His burning, questioning gaze swiveled to Artorius. Was that jealousy Artorius saw in those strangely flecked eyes? Sadness? Happiness? Resignation? A mixture of all these and more? So difficult to read the druid's emotions. . . . But one feeling the young man could definitely perceive whenever Merlin was around: caring. Unworded concern. A father's love to a boy who hardly knew his true father, the high king.

Feelings warred in Artorius' mind. Somehow he resented the blanketing, smothering love he felt when Merlin was near. It was a love of attachment. What Artorius wanted now was to be free, unfurl his wings of youth that Amlodd revealed, and flap away—just to savor the flight itself. The reminder of obligations born before *he* was rankled. Didn't *he* get a say in the whole business?

"Good day to ye, Merlin!" The cry burst from the door of the house. From Baron Hector himself—beloved old Hector, happily shuffling forward to greet the new arrival.

Merlin did not swerve his studying gaze. "Hadn't you better help this wrinkled carcass off his horse, Artorius?" The ironic smile was in Merlin's eyes now. Inexplicably Artorius felt a weight lift from his heart.

As Artorius assisted his teacher from his mount Merlin again addressed Amlodd. "You look like a drinking man, Amlodd."

Amlodd's attention was caught. He smirked. "Aye. I wish I had a coin for every Roman I drank under the table!"

Merlin patted a hairy goatskin slung on his saddle. "What say you then to fermented mare's milk?"

The hairy man could not contain a grin of expectation.

vi

"I have the feeling," announced Merlin, scanning the low mountains, "that one such as those will be my burial mound." The druid shifted his weight. His buttocks pained him from all that riding. How he loathed it! From his seat atop a lichened boulder he looked down to Artorius, leaning against its dewy side. Artorius did not answer. Merlin sighed and prodded the lad's shoulder gently with his walking staff. Artorius started and stared up at his teacher with a reproachful gaze. *Ah, pride grows in the youngster's breast*, Merlin thought to himself. *I can see his father in him finally*.

"I heard!" said Artorius. "The notion is just too stupid to consider. You'll outlive me—maybe even these mountains. You're too stubborn to die."

Laughing, Merlin reached down and rubbed Artorius' hair affectionately. "I'll live long enough to see you on the throne. That is all I ask."

Their horses were tethered to bushes in the valley. They had hiked the winding trail to watch the dawn, as was their custom when Merlin visited. Undisturbed, they would talk all morning, wandering the mountain paths.

But today Artorius was moody. Nervous as a newly bridled colt. Or rather one that has just discovered that the bit in his mouth from birth is not a natural part of his existence.

False dawn had washed the horizon in oranges and yellows. Now sunlight gushed up to fill in the dark between the stars. Merlin's nose was full of the drifting mist smells, the scents of the bracken, the moss, the heather. The breeze that rustled his cape tasted surprisingly salty, as though the sea were much closer than it was. Perhaps the pirates from the West were bringing the mysterious deep with them.

"I invited your friend along, you know."

Artorius scraped greenish-gray lichen from rock with a hunting knife. "Amlodd likes to sleep late."

"I should think so, with the amount of drink he took last night."

The brown locks bounced as Artorius' head jerked up. "You don't like him, do you?"

"One chooses one's own friends, Artorius. He has many admirable qualities. He will do much to teach you to be a king."

"King! King! King! Can't we talk about something else?" Artorius kicked at a rock, dislodging it. The stone tumbled down the cliff, causing a small, rattling landslide.

He sheathed his knife. Folded his arms across his chest.

"Very well, my boy."

"I'm not your boy."

"Whose are you now, then?"

"My own. And I'm not a boy anymore, in case you haven't noticed."

"Oh, indeed I have noticed. You are growing well." Merlin lifted himself from his sitting position and stood atop the boulder. "Come on. Let's walk."

Artorius joined him on the path. They walked awhile in silence. Occasionally Artorius would pick up a stone and hurl it with all his might into the valley, where the sparse trees were rapidly growing shadows as the sun rose.

"As for being your own man," said Merlin. "Well, that is quite the truth. I'm glad you realize that."

"You mean I don't have to be king?" Artorius' eyes were wide with surprise.

"Not if you don't want to. Most *would* want to, Artorius. But very few come along that have your qualities who are also privileged to such duties."

"I've got awhile yet to decide," said Artorius with finality.

Don't you realize, thought Merlin. *You were born to be king. It's in your blood, your bones. Every sinew of your body bears the power that can keep back the dark, Artorius.*

He was wise enough to say nothing.

"If you're not king, Bear, what do you plan to do?" Merlin continued finally.

Artorius shrugged. "I don't know. I haven't decided anything yet."

"A farmer perhaps? That would be nice. Or a servant. Servants have no responsibilities to anyone but their masters. A pleasant life, I should think, letting another run one's life. Or perhaps you'd like to freeboot like Amlodd."

"Maybe."

He brings his characteristic intensity to everything, even the spurious, thought Merlin. He can deny it all he likes, but he is of kingly stock.

"I want to see the world, Merlin," Artorius continued, suddenly enthused. "I don't want responsibilities."

"We all have responsibilities, young man. If only to ourselves."

"Exactly!" Artorius beamed. "You understand! Talking with Amlodd, I see just how much there is to *do* in this world. Why, we're just in a little, unimportant corner of it—we're *nothing*! I want—I want to do *everything* before I die!"

"Yes," Merlin said, gazing absently down at the fog pockets in the valley, clearing under the burning sun. "Quite true. But just what comprises ourselves, Artorius?" He touched Artorius' cheek. It was warm with youth. "Certainly the homes of our souls—these heads of ours. Our ancestors believed that the individual lives on awhile after death in his head, did you know that? Many of our race still do—myself included. But is that all we are? Or are we all more? How about our family? Friends? Those that we care for? Are they not a part of us—and we a part of them? And this fine air that fills our breasts, and this island beneath our feet with its beauty and its love for us. Is all this not a part of us as well? And our culture. Our legends, Artorius. Our history, our art—the monuments to our forebears. When the darkness comes, Artorius, when the winds of chaos finally swoop in from their three directions, more will die than our lives. You say you resent the responsibility you bear. Don't you think you should grab it with both hands and be glad of it?"

"You *don't* understand!" Artorius mumbled. Without another word he ran ahead of the druid.

"You can't run away from it, Artorius," Merlin muttered to himself. A gentle smile appeared. "Nor, in the end, will you want to."

Through the fine mountain morning, through smells of wild mountain flowers, of bracken and heather, through the chilled mist, Merlin limped on, knowing that in only a few minutes Artorius would be back, full of apology.

Not even the searing fires of adolescence could change his iron character, Merlin knew.

And the fires would get hotter.

vii

Limned by the dim shuddering peat fire in the hovel's center, the limber young man shed his clothes.

Already divested of hers, Morgan le Fay stealthily drew her dagger from beneath a mound of tattered, molding furs. A glimmer of sharp, pitted metal. And then the weapon was tucked away beneath the dry straw sleeping mat. The muttering fire gleamed in lynxlike eyes as Morgan surveyed the wanderer's body appreciatively. A fine strapping speciman of manhood, yes indeed, she mused. The rich blood that pulsed through that thin-drawn face, those muscular arms and legs working in the muted red lighting . . . that blood would forge a strong link in the chain-spell.

The spell-curse that would be the Hated One's undoing. . . .

The fair-haired young man jerked the last leg of his coarse breeches off, brusquely tossed them down by the fire. He swung around to face her, and she smiled to see the stiff evidence of the potent love potion she'd slipped in his herb soup. Merely as a precaution, however; she was quite aware of the natural magic her firm full breasts, slender waist, and sloping hips worked on hot-blooded males, stirred with her inviting smile.

"You are a beautiful young boy." Her eyes traveled the muscular lines silhouetted by fire and smoke. She could not see his eyes, and that was a shame, for they looked like happy pools of blue water, friendly and open. She parted her long dark hair as she might a curtain before a stage of delight, and she stretched in a calculatedly provocative manner. "But come, dear boy. The night is dark, and I am cold. Warm me."

The man came to her in smooth movements. Skin whispered on skin, and the straw crackled as he kneeled beside her, half-reverence and half-desire tensing his position. She leaned over and brushed his fine curling hair with her lips as her light fingers traced love-messages in his wealth of chest hair. "Relax," she murmured. "Relax, dear Garroch of Powys. The night is all ours, and we shall make the sun rise." The tips of her fingers touched his groin teasingly . . . and her own desires uncoiled in her belly like some dark serpent. . . . Suddenly he was upon her, all wet kisses and sighs.

She giggled. *Silly folk, these Celts*, she thought as she accepted his groping hands and fondled a buttock to keep his surging spirit up. They say they are civilized, and yet at the flash of a woman's thigh, they melt into heaving beasts.

She'd found Garroch of Powys wandering in her glade, smiling and carefree, a sack of food, wine, and clothing upon his broad back. She herself had been wandering in search of root and spider and herb for her attempts at sorcery, and the finding of this lanky lad had been most fortunate.

After restrained greeting she had pulled his destination from him.

"Nowhere, my lady," he had said. "I simply walk and enjoy."

"Nowhere?" she returned, cocking her head in scolding disbelief. "Is this not somewhere, and are you not here now?" And then she had given him her very best guileless smile, the one practiced before her sole, cracked looking glass for so long. "Come and take some drink with me and rest your weary feet awhile. It is not often that travelers stumble upon Sharwyn Wood."

Innocence lighting his face, he had accepted gladly, falling under the spell of her charm quite easily. Beside her modest hut, she had brewed him strong herb tea, inquiring as to his origin and his name.

"Garroch of Powys, madam. Son of Aberderon, a lord of small yet gentle means." Garroch had found himself gifted with a week's worth of leisure and had decided to enjoy it by hiking the summer landscape. "A beautiful land, is it not? It fills my soul with wonder."

She assented, but she lied, for in truth she yearned for the craggy coast of Cornwall with its dark booming sudden squalls and the smell of ancient magic in the air. A bastion of the dark religion, it was the home of her childhood.

Now she lived from place to place, scrabbling about for the learning that would give her power and the power that would give her vengeance. Vengeance and release from the driving ambition that rose like constant bile from the dark pit of her soul. This forest, this leafy wood of Hereford, she'd divined as a place of power. The learning and the practicing of sorcery would here be strengthened.

But of course, she gave simple Garroch no inkling of the real reason for her presence. She'd merely coyly intimated that she was a maiden of the trees, pining for a lover lost to the Saxons. He'd swallowed it all, including her invitation to linger for supper, to talk half the night (and thus she gleaned much important information of his land that she might one day use for her own means). And then she had prevailed upon him to shelter her . . . and finally, she had seduced him into sharing her bed.

He was a clumsy lover but sincere in his attempts, and Morgan was troubled at the way her breasts tingled and hardened with his rough handling, the pleasure she received as his tongue probed her ear. He smelled of new-scythed hay and fresh brooks, and his moans and implorations were sweet and many.

An alien tenderness moved in her heart, and for a moment, as the sweet, murky scent of their mingled sweat was claiming hold of her nostrils and the warmth of his body made her feel alive and wanted, she thought that she might let this young man leave with his life.

But then his urgency quickened his movements. Morgan was reminded of the barbarity of men. With no gentleness at all he lurched back and grasped her legs. Morgan felt a sweet pain as he jerkily parted her thighs. The pain lost its sweetness as she remembered her mother's moans of pleasure, rutting foully with Pendragon, her dear father's enemy and murderer. . . .

Garroch fumbled for the device of his lust's consummation. . . . And Morgan remembered vividly the Celt soldiers who had stolen her maidenhood long ago. The soldiers that were to have guarded her after Tintagel of Cornwall had rebelled and been recaptured, when she was only eleven. Afterward, they said, they would kill her if she told.

She swallowed. A tear of grief and loss slipped down the side of her face, taking the last of her warmth.

With feigned passion, she whispered, "Here. Let me help." Her squirming into better position masked the darting of her hand to beneath the mat. The shadows hid the progress of the dagger.

Leaning on his arms, Garroch lowered himself, eyes closed, anticipating pleasures. Morgan raised the knife point upward with her right hand.

"My dearest," murmured Garroch.

Face contorting into a grim parody of pleasure, Morgan drove her dagger up. Garroch's gasp melted with the sickening slash sound as the dagger buried deep in flesh and bone.

Garroch's scream did not drown Morgan's words as bright blood spurted upon her hands. "How does *that* feel?"

The man's eyes were wide as his head whipped back, spraying wild hair. He fell on his back, almost into the fire, and his fine blond hair began to singe. The stink filled the small hut.

Morgan sprang up. Sweat glistening on her naked body, she picked up a brass cup from the floor and turned a fierce gaze to her victim. Garroch sprawled before her, paralyzed with pain, half conscious, fear and loathing brimming his eyes. "Good," Morgan said. "You're still alive."

She bent and partly filled her cup with his seeping blood. She held it up to the rooftop and to the night and to beyond, and old words flowed from her mouth.

The powers she sought were quixotic, fickle as the weather, for their anchor was nothingness, their home nowhere. But when the organized beings of life served their ways of ambiguity, delved into their black ways, and forced order into being swallowed by disorder, as when life kills life, these forces would hover nearby. Perhaps to view the proceedings, perhaps merely to suck the somethingness into their emptiness, Morgan le Fay knew not. She knew only that when one touched the lands of the living, part of its power would be discharged there. And Morgan would use that power to twist the channels of fate.

The atmosphere of the wood and mud hovel suddenly owned the charge of a threatening lightning storm.

Morgan le Fay knew the powers she craved were near at hand.

A groan.

Morgan looked down. The Celt attempted to right himself, crawl away, leaving a trail of blood as a snail trails ooze.

With a sneer she pounced upon him.

He had more life in him than she had reckoned. Desperately the effort bringing bands of sinew to tautness in his neck, Garroch of Powys grasped her ankle and tugged. She lost her balance, almost tumbling to the packed-dirt hut floor. A glance told her the Celt was gripping the dagger with a blood-smeared hand, attempting to wrest it out, use it in defense.

Morgan le Fay, although seemingly slight, had powers born of obsession, and the trickle of strength from the chaos nearing. With a lunge, she turned her fall into a kick, smashing the Celt's nose to ruin. His head crashed back, and he lay still, softly moaning away what was left of his life.

Morgan regained her feet, her breath coming in ragged gasps, her long hair in wanton disarray as it slid down her sweaty nakedness.

The peat fire shuddered and grew bright. Through the wavering smoke escaping the chimney hole above, bright stars peered down, like astonished voyeurs.

A grin of hate marring her beauty, Morgan le Fay proceeded with the sacrifice.

viii

The sun dawned upon blood.

Ruddy light slipped through the sky, spilling down upon the forest through the larch leaves, the juniper buds. Illuminating the elm bark and the moss tufts that grew beside the tumbled cairn of rocks in Morgan's glade.

Falling upon the Celt's grave—the specks of dried blood still upon her hands.

She had buried him by the magic place just before false dawn, a final offering.

But she'd felt a need to be swift with the task. She had a premonition of further visitors.

Brushing the bits of leaf and musky dirt from her hair, she walked back to her makeshift hut, the need for breakfast and sleep strong.

The murder had been almost symbolic for her distaste of the Celts.

Once, she knew, they had been as wild as the wind. Relics of their pact with the spurious elemental powers that Morgan so craved littered the countryside. But that had been before the decadent Romans had conquered much of Britain. Their unifying power had forced upon the diverse peoples and tribes a civilization of principles in direct opposition to nature . . . and its masters.

Now the Celts were weaklings, their individuality gone. Even their once-savage druids bore the taint of Christianity in their philosophies. A foul religion that had swept in with the Romans like disease after vermin.

Druids like Merlin.

Back at her home Morgan washed her hands in a rough wood basin. She unbanked her outside fire. Plumes of smoke curled up. Coals glowed to her blowing—just as the coals of her soul rekindled once more at the thought of that despised name.

Merlin.

Not that Merlin was Christian.

No. But his religion, whatever it was, was no friend to darkness and chaos. No ally of the forces Morgan wooed.

He was like that village carpenter who Morgan had hired to build her a hut far off in the wood. The lout was a bumbler whose progress was slow and wearying.

His materials had to be obtained from the surrounding trees and fields. The tools he used were primitive, and often the sweating man had to rely upon chanced-upon fallen branches or unearthed stone. But he worked hard, a definite design in mind. Arnoc the carpenter had created from the wilderness a pleasant residence for her stay here.

Oh, the *joy* she would have burning it down before she departed!

Merlin was such an architect. Painstaking and fumbling, his purpose opaque to such as Morgan. But she hated him. Hated everything he stood for, just as she loathed the product of his machinations, her half-brother.

Artorius.

Bastard of her mother Ygrayne's foul congress with the outlander, the chief dragon, Uther.

Her life was dedicated to the boy's downfall.

And his teacher's as well.

As she cooked the remains of the stoat caught in her trap yesterday, the Picts arrived.

They were a swarthy, mean-eyed lot. They fidgeted uncomfortably atop their mounts as though infested with itching fleas. Their reddish hair were all tangles. Stains and splotches from past meals covered their hide jerkins. The stench of their ill-bathed bodies advanced before them.

An aroma like death.

Morgan le Fay's first reaction was uneasiness.

As they approached their yellowed teeth were bared in wolflike hunger. Their eyes gleamed much as her Celt guards' had in torchlight, before they had taken her. A woman, alone in the forest with a group of barbarians. The prospect bode ill.

Nonetheless, she felt her power and was confident she could match them strength for strength.

Then she recognized the foremost of their number, and a vixen smile came to her lips. They had met in a dim drinking hall. She had answered all his questions . . . told him about the great Merlin. . . .

And where she might be found if he needed her. . . .

Her lynxlike eyes gleamed yellow with good humor.

"So, Northman. You have come back!"

The man was a patchwork of scars. He grunted a gruff monotone reply and dismounted. Short, stout. Undoubtedly powerful. And many such men under his command. Good. Very good.

"I had not expected to see you again," Morgan said demurely, thinking it best not to show her natural defiance and spite before these particular men.

"My chief shows much interest in the great wizard you spoke of," replied Brys simply.

"That would be Huil, no?"

"Yes. He has sent me to seek the wizard's—" Pause, a feral glint invaded his eye. "—services."

"Merlin serves himself." She tossed away a bone contemptuously. "He will not come along willingly."

"Woman, we are good negotiators."

She laughed shrilly. "And so you are."

"Would you care to assist? A woman's wiles are always to the good in such cases." Brys folded arms across a broad chest.

Morgan considered. Should she? Her vengeance could be partly achieved, and she would help destroy this land. A villain like Huil would soon sweep down mightily from the north, vanquishing many of those she thought of as enemies.

But no. The time was not ripe. Any revenge obtained now would be unfulfilling. The true beauty of her plot would only come to fruition with time. In the meantime perhaps she could savor the torture visited upon Merlin, maybe even upon the bastard Artorius.

"I think not, my friend." She poked her fire with a charred stick. "You have enough aid. The forces that the druid opposes. . . . They will surely watch with interest. I can do nothing. I merely, from time to time, *see* things."

"You have seen well for us."

She nodded slowly, then turned to fix him with her gaze. "But is this why you have sought me out, to ask for woman's aid?"

"Yes," replied Brys bluntly. "And to inquire as to the actual place where Merlin's cave rests."

"Ah ha," she said, licking her lips. "That information I will gladly give." She turned suddenly, frowning. "But I hope that dear Merlin will come to no irreparable harm. I should not like that."

She saw Brys shudder at the fervor of her words,

heard the awed mutter of his companions as they felt her intensity.

No. Merlin was for her. They could torture him as they pleased. But she would come for the man who stole the prize of vengeance from her grasp.

"That is not what we intend, woman."

"Very well," she said, and she told them what they wanted to know.

She watched them journey toward the sunset, hoping that her powers would gift her with glimpses of Merlin's sufferings to come.

ix

Fiery shimmers limned the Hollow Hills. Lightning lit the western night sky. It looks, mused Merlin, as though the sun has second thoughts about setting.

His rear hurt from many hours atop his steed. His back ached. He longed for the rest his cave would provide, as he joggled in the saddle, tasting the bile of a queasy stomach at the back of his throat.

Not far now. A mile. Perhaps less. It was worth traveling through the dark of early evening to be home tonight. Worth the risk of the portending storm rolling with the thunderheads above. Sensing the coming rain, Mornpacer shivered beneath Merlin's legs and increased her speed, clopping along the dirt and stone and grass.

The week at Hector's fort had not gone well. Artorius had hardly listened to a scrap of the wisdom Merlin had in abundance for him. His attention was absent during the session. Lost, no doubt, in anticipation of his hunts with Amlodd, or his games with the fellow, or his evening drinking. Merlin could not help but resent the roughened, boisterous man.

But like everything else in Artorius' life, Merlin knew that Amlodd would serve his purpose. Fate's weave was clever in the life of Artorius, son of Uther Pendragon. Merlin needed no magic to sense that. A drop of rain plopped on Merlin's uncovered head. Wet. Cold. He spurred the horse on, not wishing to arrive sopping at his cave.

The lightning of the far distance soon became streaks of jagged light-tongues issued from moiling clouds. The sky belched thunder like a sated troll.

Not far now. Not far.

Merlin noted landmarks. Shapes of rock peculiar to the Hollow Hills.

Even in the darkness, he knew that his cave was just up the slope before him.

Riding up the path, a sudden tingle of dread grew in his spine. Something waited for him. Up ahead. But his mind drew rein on his fear.

So it would be so soon. Well and good; this could not happen at a better time.

The raindrops had increased. They struck Merlin's mount now. Mornpacer twitched her pointed ears in vexation.

The wind screamed past Merlin's ears, fluttering his cape away from his grasp. It was difficult to contain the fear. Bleakly Merlin wondered if he was truly prepared for the ordeal that waited.

But it was too late now.

Too late.

For as he topped a rise, a ragged course of lightning touched the distant mountain peak . . . backlighting figures of riders, not fifty yards before him.

Men on horses. Waiting. The lightning glimmered on war helmets and drawn swords.

Merlin's horse whinnied at the sight.

His mind echoed the cry. These would be fearful times.

The briefly lit landscape dipped back to black. But there could be no mistake. The riders had seen him.

Someone barked an order. Horse hoofs clattered on rock.

Another rash of lightning on the heels of booming thunder. The light made mad-eyed devils of the riders.

Capes belled. Frightful cries ripped the air. Merlin almost panicked, almost bolted. Feeling the approaching doom, his horse tried to turn and run. But Merlin controlled her still, would not permit such action.

No. Best to wait. Just wait.

Merlin drew his sword. These scum would learn that a hand in the fire means burned fingers before a coal is pulled out. They would not have him without a price.

Rainwater dripped down his face, into his mouth.

It tasted like blood.

The front riders crashed past him, like a cresting sea breaker. It would be their duty to cover the possibility of his escape to the rear. Merlin's sword lashed out. The warrior to his left wailed. Blood spurted and mixed with the rain. The man tumbled off his horse and lay still on the ground, neck slashed.

A cry full of bloodlust above the tumult. Merlin could hear the *woosh* of a sword heading for him. He held his sword in defense and was almost knocked from his saddle with the clanging blow.

"No!" cried a commanding voice. "I told you. Do *not* kill him!"

Merlin smiled. It was as he had envisioned.

"In the name of Britain do not detain me!" he cried. "Wrath will follow past your death, I promise!"

The voice of the commander rose again: "Take care of the horse."

A swirling rider swooped down, sword singing in the wind. Before Merlin could do a thing, the sharpened blade cut deep into Mornpacer's neck. The beast screamed, tottered, fell. Hurling Merlin to the rocky ground. Gouts of horseblood spilling, Mornpacer shuddered out her life, eyes wide and wild.

Merlin pushed himself up, brandishing his sword.

A single word: "Larknow." And one of the men suddenly was upon him. With a swish that cut through the wind and the rain, a sword descended, catching Merlin's weapon near its hilt, tearing it from his grasp. Just as suddenly the rider sprang from his horse and jammed his feet upon the flat of the blade.

Promptly Merlin drew his dirk. But he reconsidered. Too much fight might scare them off. He did not want that. Iron hands seized his wrist and tore the weapon from his grasp.

It dropped to the slick grass. Merlin was aware of the strength of the man before him, the power of the hands detaining him. If only he could risk showing them his true might—*then* he could have given these toads a lesson they would remember all their lives—if they outlived it.

But he *had* had the opportunity to turn and flee.

That, however, was not in his plans.

The leader dismounted. Lightning flared his face. Ridged with scars. Hard as stone. In a grim voice the man said, "You will use our slain companion's horse. Your hands will be tied. Don't try to escape, or you will be draped belly-first on the horse."

"Are you sure I'm the man you want?"

The imposing figure was quiet a moment. Thunder spoke in the heavens. "You had better be, my friend. Or we will have to kill you." Mocking laughter filled the night.

"What do you want of me?" Merlin demanded as the leather thongs were being tied.

"It is not we who want you," declared the man, walking back to his steed. He mounted easily, gracefully. "A most high personage wishes to have you as his guest for a time."

"You are Picts."

"You see well in the dark, druid." He spat. "Come. Put him on the horse and let's go. We've wasted enough time contesting with this troublesome man. Huil no doubt grows restless."

Without ceremony, but with the help of two other Picts, Merlin was placed atop the dead warrior's horse. Two riders positioned themselves on his flanks. One rode behind him, another ahead.

There would be no escape anyway, Merlin thought. A feeling of calmness and victory overcame his fatigue with its froth of euphoria. *Fate. How pleasant it is when you play into my hands*, he thought.

They rode off into the storm.

x

Blast this rain, anyway, thought Garfon, huddled miserably under a yew that served scant purpose as shelter.

As though in answer to his wish, thunder racked the sky.

The sheep gathered around him bleated with alarm.

The storm had caught him dozing. One moment day filled the sky. Bright. Golden with the promise of summer. The next it seemed as though night had poured in, tugging the clouds and the rain with it.

His father had gained just enough strength to give him a good hiding, the boy brooded.

Horse hoofs clattered above the driving torrent. Many horses—coming down the slope, fast. And close.

Lightning split the sky.

The coruscation lasted long enough for Garfon to discern six horses, six riders. On the path, just up the hill from the yew.

He gasped.

One of the riders was Merlin. Bound. Guarded. His face looked pale and weary.

The light flickered and disappeared, plunging everything back into darkness.

The patter of the horse hoofs faded into the roar of the rain.

Garfon swallowed and shivered. A frightening sight—like a still-life frieze. Those other men—tall, strong. Almost all had red or blond hair. All wore armor. It was like a strangely warped representation of a scene Father so often told him about—Christ being taken to Pontius Pilate by Roman soldiers.

The chill stabbed deeper as he realized what the tableau meant.

Somehow Merlin *had* foreseen this. . . .

He had to get back home, right away. Thunderstorm or no thunderstorm!

Filling his lungs with the air, musky with bracken, he drove the sheep and himself through the rain-streaked night toward home.

xi

The rabbit stew had been delicious.

Old Baron Hector pushed away his greasy trencher and washed down the last morsel in his mouth with a swallow of cellar-chilled heather mead.

Cook should be congratulated.

Food was one of Hector's last pleasures. Food and, of course, drink. What else could an old man do? So Hector made certain that his current serving woman was greatly good over a cooking cauldron besides being handy with the other chores. Hector's servants didn't have to be comely anymore. That, in his sunset years, was not one of the baron's priorities.

Just as well that the servant, Emmorlia, was neither young nor particularly attractive. If she were either, his nephew Amlodd would have ruined her. The sparkle of adventure that glittered in the big man gave him away. The fellow reveled in sport, wild or otherwise.

There he was now, mopping up the last bit of gravy with his bread, sopping up another jar's worth of brew with a single swallow. Damn, if the man couldn't drink more than any other Hector had ever encountered. Except maybe for himself, in younger days.

In between bouts of eating and drinking Amlodd was embarked on one of his more fanciful tales. Plates of savory meat, carrots, and potatoes lay half forgotten under the noses of Kay and Artorius as they listened, entranced.

Most likely the tale wasn't true. Or it was an exaggeration. Baron Hector was of two minds about Amlodd. All the years he had known his dead brother's son he had been so. Oh, Amlodd was a likable enough lad, full of hearty bluster and *bonhomie*. And there was none better to hunt or fish or sport with. Hector couldn't think of a man he'd rather have on his side in a brawl.

Hector shrugged. No harm in him. Amlodd amused the lads, taught them much of swordplay and of the woods—things beyond Baron Hector in his present age. But he wouldn't be here that long. It was obvious that, even now, the man was growing restless. Another week or two of sloth and drink, sport and play, and Amlodd would be out again, looking for fortune and a fight.

It was just as well he had come, Hector supposed. Certainly Amlodd had loosened dead-serious Artorius up. Such a pleasure to watch the youngster laugh so much! Merlin did not seem to take such pleasure in the changed Bear. But damn the druid anyway. Amlodd was a good man. Although he obviously favored Artorius, he devoted fully half his attentions to Kay, ever needful of such. Growing up with a boy so superior in all ways is no easy thing. Although Kay loved Artorius as much as anyone, there were now occasional shreds of hurt and rivalry showing in his eyes.

Too, he could see why Artorius and Kay liked the man so much. He was hearty, friendly—all in all, a good companion. Full of mirth. Most of all he exuded the sense that he enjoyed life . . . that he relished their company more than he could possibly say. A jolly, reckless rogue he was, who savored each moment of his prime. No coward, he was a good fighter—obviously loyal to his friends.

But then, he was something less than selfless. He did not hide the fact that Amlodd's best friend and idol was Amlodd. Cheerfully self-involved and self-serving, he was an independent soul who needed other people only to assure himself what a fine, worthwhile fellow he was.

He hadn't done a speck of work, despite Hector's gentle hints that such would be more than welcome during his stay.

In short, he seemed a lovable rogue. So Hector couldn't blame the boys for being so fascinated with him. He was teaching them how to be fascinated with themselves.

But enough of these somber thoughts. Baron Hector leaned back deep in his chair. He enjoyed the warmth of the mead slipping through his veins. He felt comfortable with the scent of burning tallow candles in his nostrils and Amlodd's boisterous, unlikely tale in his ear.

A clamor at the door. Knocking. Hector found himself roused from his semistupor. "Well, don't just sit there, Kay! Answer it."

Kay hopped from his seat and unlatched the door. Standing there was Gwynnoc, a worker and guard for Hector's farm. He jerked a stubby thumb to someone behind him. "Found him banging at the gate. Looks harmless enough. Wants to give something to the Bear."

"Thank you, Gwynnoc," said Kay, looking past the rough-hewn man. "You there. Come in. What's your name?"

"Garfon." A boy entered. He appeared nervous: he fidgeted. He seemed weary. "I have a message from Merlin for Artorius. And from myself."

"You look as though you've traveled the breadth of Britain," called Amlodd. "Sit. Eat something. Drink."

"If you please, my message first." His eyes darted to Artorius. "*You* are the one I seek?"

"I am Artorius. What is it that Merlin has to say to me that he didn't say three days ago?"

Garfon licked cracked lips. "I'm from around the Hollow Hills, if you please. And I'm here to say that Merlin—a kind and good friend to myself and my father, humble shepherds—has been kidnapped!"

Artorius had been sitting slack in his chair, unconcerned. But with these words he stood so quickly that the chair fell back and banged onto the floor. "What?"

"By whom?" demanded Hector, incredulous. "And how do you know this?"

"By huge, red-haired giants on horseback, sir. I was concealed under a tree, and I saw them pass. Headed north, sir." Fright widened the boy's eyes. "Please, sirs. I only bring you a message. It is not my fault."

Sternly Artorius said, "No one's blaming you. Please. Sit. Warm yourself. Tell us all."

The boy sat in the proffered chair and told them of the storm and what he had seen illuminated by lightning. "And the odd thing is that not two weeks ago Merlin told me that if anything should happen to him I should bear this message to you." He pulled a rolled piece of parchment from his tunic's sleeve and handed it to Artorius.

Quickly Artorius untied it, unfurled it, and read. He gazed at Hector. "I must have a horse. Immediately. There is no time to waste." His eyes were bright with resolve.

"What? Here, let me see that!" Hector wobbled from his seat and grabbed the paper with his only hand. It was in Latin.

> Artorius, son of Pendragon,
>
> Should you read these words, then my vision has come true.
>
> I saw a group of Pictish warriors from Fortren, far north, their leader one, Huil, son of Caw, descend upon me and carry me back to their land. For what reasons I do not know.
>
> If you read these words, provisions I have made against this capture have failed. I am now their prisoner. Take care of little Garfon, the faithful lad who bears this message.
>
> I ask for succor. I in the name of Britain. My uses with this world are not yet done. My purpose unfulfilled. Artorius, I have asked for nothing else

from you in this life. Rescue me from these barbarians.

Your servant,
Merlin

"It's the druid's fancy handwriting all right," announced Hector. "If the Picts have got him, he's for it."

"Picts, eh?" murmured Amlodd, sniffing. "What would they want a druid for? We have little enough use for them. What's the letter say?"

"He wants Artorius to rescue him," Hector said. "If I were twenty years younger, I would. Pictland's no place for a youngster like Bear."

"I'm leaving right away," Artorius announced. "Kay—help me prepare."

"Not on your life!" bellowed Hector. A sudden vision of Kay impaled on a Pictish javelin, bleeding, made his heart ache. "I've no control over this ruffian," he pointed his chin at Bear. "But you—you're my flesh and blood. You're going *nowhere.* Too young." He cast his rheumy eyes toward Amlodd, nose in drink. Pointed. "There's the man who will help."

Amlodd choked. Brew and froth spewed out over his beard.

"Me?" he cried. "I want nothing to do with the likes of druids *or* Picts. Besides I've obligations."

"What?" demanded Hector, moving his face close to Amlodd's hairy countenance.

"Well, er—friends, down south. Awful Saxon problem you know. I'm to help fortify their settlement. Just remembered that I'd better leave tomorrow."

"Company or no," declared Artorius, striding for his room, "I'm going. Tonight."

"Not tonight!" said Hector. "You'll need a horse. I'll not give you a horse until tomorrow morning. You need a rest before you set out."

Angry, Artorius kicked over a stool and stomped out

of the room. Kay, frustrated, was fuming. "Why can't I go, Father?"

"No argument from you, boy." Hector flushed. "You do as your father says!"

"Well, I can help Bear pack, can't I?"

"Just don't pack yourself!"

Kay huffed and stalked away.

"Crises, crises!" Hector sighed, slouching back into his chair. "Can't any part of this life be free of trouble?"

Amlodd did not reply. He was studying the last of his mead.

Hector smiled.

"Amlodd?"

"Uhm?" Amlodd quickly quaffed the last of his mead and filled his jar again from the pitcher. The hearth fire cracked and spat. How warm it was in here, thought Hector. "Dear, nephew, I forgot to mention one fact of interest regarding Merlin the druid."

"What's that?"

"He will be very grateful for outside aid in his rescue. I know for a fact he is a rich man. Very rich, indeed."

The brawny man looked over to his uncle. Interest sparked in his eyes . . . or was that a trick of the candle . . . the firelight?

"And I might add, he is exceedingly generous when he is grateful. Yes, bountifully."

Amlodd scratched his beard. His brow furrowed in thought.

"And I might add that I have been known to reward people bonuses now and then. I, too, have a healthy supply of gold."

The big, hairy man watched Garfon dispatching a plate of stew set before him by heavy-hipped Emmorlia.

He turned his head to Hector and showed teeth in a roguish smile. "How much?"

xii

The Picts were poorly trained riders.

In that, and that only, could Merlin identify with them.

The air filled with groans and complaints as the horsemen progressed across the hills and dales, the plains and valleys that comprised Britain's north country. Their backs hurt. Their legs pained. The sun was too hot in the south. The horses frothed and fretted.

All these things the druid could agree with, wholeheartedly.

But he stayed mute, impassionate. Rocking in his saddle, hands tied. Speaking only in answer to a question.

His moans he kept to himself.

"You're a strange one, magic man." The round-featured leader, Brys, was interminably talkative. By simply listening to the man, who stayed by his side most of the time, Merlin learned a good deal of the purpose for this kidnapping. Also of the Pictish life, which seemed all bleakness and savagery.

Such was the way the Celts used to be.

And some *still* were.

And Merlin learned more of this Huil, son of Caw.

"He came from the Western Island," Brys had explained. "Evidently those of his race there—the Scots—expelled him. Too dangerous perhaps? But now he is uniting the Pictish peoples, finally. As much as I dislike the man he is doing a rough service for my people, bringing them together, if only through the cohesion of his leadership and personality. He fairly throbs with power, magician. You will see. But he needs a higher power of the supernatural sort to speed up his mission in our country.

"If *I* had the power to do what he is doing, I certainly would. I do not like a foreigner leading my people. But I will serve him as long as it is in the interest of my race and myself. In the meantime, I will do my best for him. It was at my insistence that he sent me to fetch you.

"But *you* are a creature of few words," Brys continued. "Why is this?"

Merlin remained silent a moment, flecked eyes surveying the sun-swathed greens and browns of this hilly country. The air was sweet. Fresh. To the east, Merlin knew, were many lakes. A wild, beautiful country . . . edged by the brooding bleakness of moors and reedy bog. Plants and flowers abounded: bilberry, liverwort, even dandelions, springing from the acidic peat. Faint cheeps of pipits floated in the air, like ghostly birdsong. Sour was laced with sweet here. Death with life. "Too many words," Merlin answered finally, "allow the soul to seep out. Dissipate."

"Huil has your soul now, druid. Make no mistake about that." Brys wiped a lock of greasy hair back out of his eyes. "Words will pass the time. What think you of your situation?"

"I merely hope that my meager magic is enough to satisfy the wants of this Scot you call lord. From the sounds of him your head will be on a pike along with my own if I fail to satisfy."

Brys' muscles tightened. His jaw grew taut. Merlin could tell that he had struck a sensitive subject in the man. . . .

Without warning, Brys' fist swung. Merlin was struck hard in the chest. The impact flung him off his horse.

He landed painfully on a clump of grass.

Face immobile, eyes fierce, Brys reined his steed about, hovering over the fallen druid. The other riders stopped. They seemed as still as death.

"You had *better* satisfy, magician," muttered Brys. A drop of sweat dripped from his nose. His armor was hot. "There are worse things than death for such as you." With utter contempt, the tawny man spat on Merlin. "Pick him up," he commanded. "Get him back on his horse. No time to waste."

The others silently obeyed. It was all Merlin could do to halt himself from further provoking the man who had struck him.

Back upon the horse, the frightening pain subsiding, Merlin chastised himself.

For Artorius to save him, it was important that he stay in one piece.

He would have to be more discreet with future statements.

CHAPTER 3

The Marauders

A campfire.

A bower, shaded by leafy elm.

Two figures squatted amongst blankets, chewing pieces of a squirrel roasted on the fire before them.

"An uneventful trip so far," mused Artorius. He listened to the sad song of a night breeze whistling through the trees, with clacking twigs and branches as accompaniment. "All the same, I'm glad you decided that Merlin was more important than your friends in the South, Amlodd. It is good to have you along." He threw his bone away. The meat was almost too gamey for him.

Amlodd was dour. Their wineskins, after a two days' ride, were already depleted. "Well, I've been meaning to take a journey north sometime. See what's up there. Now's as good a time as any. I just hope we get to a settlement soon, so we can buy supplies."

"Do you think this quest will be successful?" Artorius asked, half afraid of the answer.

Shrugging, Amlodd replied, "Who knows. But the morrow will go better if we get some rest. You take first watch. Never can tell what's afoot in this part of the country. Best to be prepared."

Without further word Amlodd draped his bulky form

in blankets. Soon, his heavy sleep sounds rivaled the wind.

Artorius stared into the flames bleakly. The excitement and recklessness of the first day had long since disappeared. Fear and foreboding had taken their place.

Before, he had been perfectly confident of his prowess. Of his competence. All his life had been one long lesson, it seemed, and he was spoiling for some experience. But he'd had no inkling of how the uncertainty of reality undermined self-confidence.

An indifferent night hung over all. A black ceiling, speckled with stars. Concealing what? Hordes of savages? Pain, death, misery? All of these and more, Artorius knew, lurked there, waiting. Merlin had educated him for that well enough.

What bothered him most was the mystery. The not knowing. The sun might set on his exposed entrails tomorrow evening. The sun might not set at all. Who could tell? How could you take comfort in anything?

He was grateful for the presence of the slow-breathing bulk that was Amlodd, sleeping. It would have been bad alone.

What gods truly ruled all this otherness that wrapped the world? Any at all? Could a man control his destiny, or was that simply a matter beyond him entirely?

There were no answers in the drifting clouds, nor on the curling wind, scented with moss.

A rattling.

Footsteps? Horse hoofs? Branches and dead leaves crunched and snapped in the near distance.

Fear stiffened Artorius. His eyes sought a change in the shadows. Nothing moved but the swaying branches.

His throat dry, he crept over and put a hand on Amlodd's shoulder. Shook him.

"Hmm?" Awake, the man turned over. "What's wrong?"

Artorius positioned a forefinger over his own lips. "There's something *out* there," he whispered.

"How do you know?" Amlodd stood. The sight of his massiveness eased Artorius' trepidation.

"Footsteps. Sounds." He pointed. "That way."

Grabbing up his knife, Amlodd said, "Let's have a look."

Seeing the blade shine in the firelight made Arthur remember that he had one by his side. He unsheathed it and set off after Amlodd, skulking soundlessly through the bushes, between trees, bent almost double.

More sounds crackled the air.

Amlodd halted. Cocked his head, listened. "You're right," he breathed. "And I see something moving up there. Something big. Stay behind me, Bear."

They advanced.

At the edge of a treeless glade, Amlodd stopped. Artorius peered over his shoulder.

Lit only by starlight, two figures moved across the greensward. A horse. And a man leading it by the reins. They moved stealthily.

"Stay here," Amlodd whispered. "I'll sneak up from the rear. You attract his attention this way."

And before Artorius could blink, the man was swallowed by the wood. Leaving Artorius alone.

The dark figure moved forward, almost hesitantly.

Artorius tasted the bile of fear in his mouth. His grip tightened on the hilt of his knife. His palm was slick with sweat.

Attract his attention, Amlodd had said. But if he did that, wouldn't this intruder charge?

Well, there was nothing to do but trust the more experienced man.

Artorius took hold of a gorse bush. Shook it fiercely.

Immediately the man stopped. His horse whinnied, tried to back off.

With a sigh of metal against leather, a sword was drawn.

It reflected the stars.

"Who's that?" queried a voice.

Not a man's voice. A voice like his own . . . it quavered, pervaded with fear.

A familiar voice.

Artorius stood from his concealment. "Kay? Is that you, Kay?"

The voice filled with relief. "Bear! Oh, Artorius, you scared me!"

"I scared *you*?" cried Artorius. "You sounded like a whole gang of Saxons marching in full armor!" He sprang out of the forest to meet his friend. "Amlodd!" he yelled. "Amlodd, it's Kay."

A figure bulked huge at the edge of the glade. "Blast and damnation. I thought I was going to have a little fight!"

"So since Father would not let me go, I took matters into my own hands!" Kay said, sitting by the snapping fire.

Amlodd looked up from a cup of mead. "I'm glad you took these skins of drink in your hands as well. I've been parched for hours!"

"You can't go along with us, Kay," Artorius said, shaking his head. "Too dangerous."

"Oh, come on, Bear. Admit it. You can use me. You need as many as will come with you. My father's just a worry wart. At my age he would have done exactly the same thing."

"True, true," commented Amlodd. "Besides, if the lad's clever enough to sneak a horse and himself out of Hector's guarded fort, he's certain to be a help."

"Besides, you wouldn't want to make me ride all the way back home alone, would you now?" Kay smiled, eyes full of sincere hope.

Artorius grinned. "No. I suppose not. Welcome to the quest, Kay. I'll admit, it's awfully good to see you."

Amlodd heartily toasted the statement.

ii

They rode.

From before dawn to after dusk their horses were hardly spared. From Garfon's story Artorius estimated that the Picts had no more than a two-day lead. Chances were they would not overtake the savages in mid-journey. Artorius' intention was to arrive at their destination as soon after them as possible—lest a sorry fate be visited upon Merlin.

From settlements and farms hither and yon they ascertained exactly which way and how fast the Pict horsemen traveled. Generally the Celtic peoples were friendly enough to provide the information. If not, a scowl and grumble from the imposing Amlodd intimidated the information from them.

The landscape they traversed, just short of summer, burst with wildness. The explosions of green, the scent of valley flowers, the taste of open-fired meat inflamed Amlodd into a behemoth of barely checked power. Their journey quiet thus far, Artorius noticed a peculiar restiveness aborning in Amlodd. Obviously anticipating action of some sort, the man grew fidgety and skittish, like a surging river pounding at a poorly constructed dam. The spectacle of this mounting violence riding beside him lent Artorius a sense of security. With such a man how could they fail in their mission? A deep liking had grown in him for the brawny fellow. And yet the violence in Amlodd had a feral quality to it—almost without purpose or direction.

Plainly he itched for battle.

They just missed one.

Four days out from Hector's fort Kay pointed out twirling streamers of pitchy smoke rising from a distant valley. Amlodd pursed his lips, considering. Then said one word. "Saxons." He dug his heels into his mare. "Come. We may be able to help."

They strained their horses, cantering and galloping.

But they were too late.

It was a village, small, obviously poorly protected.

Or rather, it had been a village, Artorius observed, looking down into the seared, smoking ruins. The bodies of the dead lay strewn about, like reaped shafts of wheat before gathering. The stench of the burning, the malodor of death hung everywhere. It turned Artorius' stomach like nothing he had previously experienced. Senseless pillage. A mindless rape of life. Artorius found it difficult to swallow. As he surveyed the holocaust tears smarted his eyes—half from the smoke, half from emotion.

"Come on," said Amlodd grimly. "Let's have a look. There may be survivors." He guided his horse closer to the destruction.

It was even more ghastly than Artorius imagined.

Most of the bodies were mutilated. Dead animals lay about. Blood smeared everything that was not charred. The smell was beyond belief.

Artorius gagged, trying to control his gorge.

Kay lost his breakfast.

Amlodd, no doubt used to such things, remained impassive. But he took frequent drinks from his ever-present wineskin.

Somberly they paced through the twisted wreckage. Tears dripping uncontrollably down his flushed cheeks, Artorius said, "Saxons? Are you sure, Amlodd? If so, they shall pay."

"Saxons all right." Amlodd nodded to a prone helmeted warrior, eyes staring into death. The characteristic Saxon armor was clotted with gore. "Getting damned far inland. Just raids to weaken us, I suppose."

A sudden ruckus filled the air. A scream . . . a woman's scream. Artorius jerked his head about.

Both hands locked about the hilt of a sword almost as long as she was tall, a girl charged them. "Beasts! Murderers!" she wailed. The sword swiped the air. "Villains!"

She was almost upon them.

Taken aback by shock, Artorius yelled, "No! Wait!"

But the enraged girl was beyond hearing. Her eyes glazed with fury as she swung her blade.

Artorius was barely able to counter the lunge with his own spatha. The girl's sword banged away into the dirt. She fell with it but did not linger long. Hoisting herself back to her feet, she tried another stab at Artorius.

Fortunately Amlodd had speedily dismounted. With a grace that belied his girth he dove headfirst for the girl, catching her sword arm just in time to check its descent. In a flurry of arms, legs, and knotted blond hair he propelled the maddened fury to the ground, knocking her weapon from her. Pinned, she kicked and screamed, tried to gnash teeth on Amlodd's arm. "You'll not have me!" she shrilled. "I'll *die* first. Not like my mother, my poor sister, my—"

A resounding slap. Amlodd raised his coarse-palmed hand for another, but the first had done its work. The girl was stunned silent.

"No, listen," Amlodd said. "We are Celts. We are *friends*. We want to help, not harm."

Sliding off his horse, Artorius kneeled by Amlodd. "That's right. Don't be frightened." He scanned the surroundings. Totally deserted of life. "Are you the only survivor?" He gazed down upon the small, prone form. Ashes clung to her sun-yellow hair, smudged her face almost black. Her clothes were barely rags, barely decent. What they showed, revealed the body of not a girl but a young woman. Perhaps eighteen. She was damp with the perspiration of fear and grief. She began to tremble.

"No," Amlodd interrupted. "She's in no condition for explanations right now. I just pray she hasn't lost her mind." Face still without expression, Amlodd peered up at the smoldering relics of the village. "We must get her away from here. Far away." The young woman's eyes had closed. She breathed shallowly. Amlodd picked her up, held her as though she were as light as a bundle of straw. Instinctively she shrank deep into his arms. Her tiny whimpers were muffled by Amlodd's chest. "The sooner she's put this behind her, the sooner she'll recover."

They rode away, the woman on Amlodd's horse, secure in his powerful hold. Putting the horror of the village plundered by Saxons far behind them.

iii

No question about it. The young woman had spirit.

Lounging in a gully amongst foothills, their horses cropping grass on a slope nearby, Amlodd gently plied the woman with sips of numbing mead. In return the party received her story. And her name.

"Guenhumara. Daughter to Lothor. Betrothed of Mathwich." Her mouth took a bitter turn. "Both killed. Both gone." Her gray-blue eyes grew distant, searching a memory shot with pain. "The Saxons took us just before sunset yesterday. My family's house was the first struck. At the time I was below in the storage cellar tapping a barrel of drink for my father. The villains torched my house. A rafter fell, blocking the trapdoor. I could not get out. Fortunately smoke and fire rise up—and it was a damp, airy cellar. This is why I survived while all my family, all my friends were destroyed or captured for slavery. But through the sounds of the flames above me, I could hear their screams, and my imagination revealed to me what was happening vividly enough." Her voice choked.

"Here, lass. Another sip," encouraged Amlodd. "You're among friends now. No reason for fear."

"Yes. Yes, I realize that now." She shut her eyes and breathed deeply. "I'm sorry I attacked you today. I was beyond thinking, drenched in hate. Thirsting for revenge." Her opening eyes revealed a fire burning deep within her. "And I shall have that vengeance. I shall."

She lapsed into silence. Kay dabbed her high forehead and delicately molded cheekbones with a cloth he had wet in a brook nearby. Artorius shivered at her intensity. How could so much emotion be contained in such a frail-seeming vessel of femininity? The only woman that Artorius had ever known was Baron Hector's serving woman and cook—Emmorlia. And at no time in Artorius' recollection had she ever been young or beautiful like this Guenhumara. Even through the dirt and the distress. Artorius could tell that here was the sort of loveliness Amlodd had spoken of that women could achieve. It was simultaneously frightening and endearing. Accessible yet distant, like the beauty of a sky touched with dawn, fragrant with dew and morning. There for all to see, yet for no one to own.

"How did you get out of the storage pit?" asked Kay in low tones, obviously as affected as Artorius by Guenhumara.

"The wood that blocked the entrance burned away. As did the wooden hatchway. The ruins cooled. I poked my head up in time to watch the triumphant Saxons dance and parade away. I knew if I should show myself I should either be raped and killed—or raped and enslaved. The bodies of my mother and sister attested to that. So what am I to do now? All gone, all gone—I have nothing to look forward to but the agonized deaths of those who killed my people."

"Time assuages all pain, Guenhumara," said Amlodd. His eyes caressed her body, filled with appreciation. "We must put aside grief with life." He gently removed the wineskin from her fingers. "And disown all past terrors with healing drink."

He practiced his preaching, sighing with gratification. An amused light danced in his eyes. "I think, though, that you would feel more comfortable if you put new clothes on a cleansed body." He nodded to the horses. "I believe that one of the lads has a change of clothing that would fit." He raised eyes expectantly at Kay, who lost no time in repairing to his horse to obtain the requested items. "And yonder," he pointed casually, "lies an admirable clear stream. Bathe in peace. We'll camp here the night . . . and have dinner when you're finished."

Silently Guenhumara agreed and accepted Kay's fresh tunic and breeches with a faint smile of thanks. She rose and strode toward the water, disappearing over a rise.

"Well, lads." Amlodd grinned hugely. "What do you think of the new addition to our expedition?"

"You mean," Kay sputtered, "you mean she's coming along?"

"Certainly. And why not? She's handy enough with a sword. She proved that. And the hate in her will be as effective against Picts as Saxons. We need every sword we can get!"

"I agree," Artorius said, a peculiar sensation teasing him within.

"Besides, what a fine ornament for our party!" Amlodd's eyes were alive with a rakish glint.

The sensation deepened in Artorius. An uneasiness. . . .

"We should see about a campfire," Kay suggested.

"Time enough, my lad." A knowing smile crept to his lips. "For now it's time for a lesson. Yes. I think you and Bear are exactly the age for this teaching." Ponderously he pushed to his feet, gently tugged at Artorius' shirt. "This way."

He trudged in the direction that Guenhumara had gone. Kay was immediately at his heels—like a faithful hound. Bemused, Artorius stared after them, not moving.

Halting, Amlodd directed a frown at Artorius. "I said *come*, king's son. Have you so little trust for friends?"

Used to obeying the domineering man, Artorius loped to catch up. "But . . . but we can't go that way. You said Guenhumara is to have privacy. Can't you show us whatever you wish from another hilltop or ridge?"

Amlodd slapped Artorius' back merrily and chuckled quietly. "Other hilltops will not have this particular view, I think." He looped his arms under their elbows and heaved them along. His grin broadened. They climbed the slope. Just before the top, Amlodd cautioned in a whisper, "We must be very quiet, or we'll frighten the object of our attention away."

A knuckly finger directed them toward a mossy boulder at the summit. "Creep behind that, my boys. That should be close enough."

Curiosity rapidly pushed back Artorius' uneasy feeling. Along with the other two, he positioned himself behind the limestone rock. Amlodd peered around the side briefly. He snapped his head back. "Better than I thought. Have a peek, lads. Have a long peek."

Along with Kay, Artorius looked down the hill.

A stream purled and gurgled over the rocks and weeds. Shining bright. Clear as air. The westering sun hung just short of the horizon, throwing dazzles and speckles upon the mirrorlike surface. Amidst the grass and dirt smells, Artorius detected the clean scent of the water. He could almost taste it.

But with all the beauty of the stream and the verdant landscape through which it ran, the center of attention was the woman. Swallowing did not relieve the dryness of Artorius' throat. He blinked. But the incredible vision lingered on, solid. Startling.

Guenhumara stood by the lapping water, shedding her ruined clothing. The sun-dappled water limned her body in a faint coruscation as she doffed her tunic. A breeze caressed her dirty tresses as she slid off her breeches. Lithely. Smoothly. The dirt and soot that smeared her skin could not conceal its creamy loveliness. Nor the rounded forms of her figure, jiggling joyfully as she splashed into the stream.

Lucky water, thought Artorius. Unable to tear his gaze away, he gawked. Guenhumara kneeled, cupped her hands, dipped them into the stream, and ladled the sparkling liquid over her breasts. *To be able to touch such beauty so. . . .*

The water hung in jewellike drops on her shoulders. . . .

Artorius jerked away. He took a hoarse breath, realizing that he had forgotten to breathe. From his perch peering over the boulder Amlodd turned to Artorius. He winked. "Pretty nice, no? Never seen a woman without her clothes, have you, Bear?"

All agog, Kay still stared. His mouth hung open.

Artorius choked back his feelings. "It's . . . it's not *right*, Amlodd. Not right to . . . to *spy* so—"

Shrugging, Amlodd said, "No harm. After all, *we're* not the savages." But something in his aspect belied his words . . . a gleam of mindless desire at the back of his eyes.

Not responding, Artorius turned his back and slouched back to the encampment. There was firewood to be searched out. . . .

At the core of his being Artorius felt ill. It was *wrong* to gaze upon a woman in her privacy. It *felt* wrong . . . and guilt was heavy in the boy's mind.

Yet as he gathered the dry wood for the fire by the verge of a tree copse, no matter how he exerted himself, the effort, the induced weariness could not hold back the vision stamped in his mind.

Water.

A drop of water gleaming in the setting sun . . . sliding down a curved back, a rounded buttock.

Into dark mystery.

iv

It was pleasant to have the woman along.

However, as it turned out it was Guenhumara who was almost their downfall when they stumbled upon the band of roving Saxons.

Having only three horses and four people, it was necessary that Guenhumara ride with someone else. After their evening meal the day they discovered her, it had been agreed that, in the interest of the horses, the chore should be rotated. In a day's riding, a third of the time Guenhumara should sit behind Amlodd, dividing her remaining riding time between Artorius and Kay.

As it worked out the majority of the time she sat on Amlodd's saddle. The burden was no boon for Amlodd's mare. But neither Guenhumara nor Amlodd objected to the arrangements. Both Artorius and Kay were too shy to comment.

The countryside they traversed in the next few days grew wilder, as did the people who lived there. Like a trip back in the past, commented Amlodd as they skirted huddles of shabby farms and valleys of roughly hewn homes. Here, he said, were Celts hardly touched by Rome's hand. These Celts lived a way of life brought in from far-off Europe by wandering ancestors even centuries before Julius Caesar began conquering the Celtic folk.

"Yes and I dare swear we've all got a bit of Etruscan blood in our veins, thanks to the Romans," Amlodd said. He shook his head sorrowfully as he rode.

As usual Guenhumara perched behind him, hands resting on his sides for balance. Her smile of admiration when she looked upon the hairy man was not lost upon Artorius. It was time that she ride with him, he decided. A pang of jealousy moved in his breast as Amlodd and Guenhumara ignored him.

"You know of our forebears?" Guenhumara asked, sweeping a stray lock of golden hair from her eyes. "We had only legends amongst our tribe."

Artorius could not keep his eyes off her. Since that first evening of her bath, his dreams, sleeping and waking, were full of her image, her person. He ached to touch her. Yet he could hardly speak to this radiant woman without tripping over his own words.

Amlodd—that smooth, lucky rogue—seemed capable of sweeping away her attention with a single gaze. Something very peculiar was happening. Something Artorius did not comprehend. Last night Amlodd and Guenhumara laid their blankets quite close. Whereas the previous night the woman had kept a discreet distance.

Something was up, no doubt about it. For no reason he could explain a hollow pain grew in the boy.

"Ah, yes. Tribes! A few yet remain, don't they? Especially here to the north." Amlodd's eyes grew distant. "To have been born five hundred years earlier! To have lived the life of a true Celt warrior. That must have been the life. I can hear my blood singing its song from time to time. A tune of a proud people, proud and fierce in battle. A song of a race that shall have many songs derived from its heyday. How sad the song is now. It slowly becomes unrecorded memory."

"Tell us of our ancestors," Kay said, eagerness in his eyes. "We know a little, yet not as much as you seem to."

Artorius' interest perked up as well. And yet he could not rip his attention from Guenhumara. Her lustrous hair. Her upturned nose. They rode through a sunny day, through boundless majesty. The sweet-smelling grass shivered green as could be before turning blue. The hills that lay in humps and lumps ahead wore fine halos of mist that evaporated in the sun, streaming a bit of rainbow in the horizon. Grouse and curlew called. Little animals scampered unseen through the brambles and the glades and the oaks. Despite all this, Artorius only noticed Guenhumara and her strangely graceful manner of holding herself. Her guileless smile beneath those astonishing eyes. . . .

"The Celts? Well, lad," Amlodd answered after a moment's thought. "We *are* the Celts, and yet it could be argued that our hour in the sun of this world is gone. Do you know that, years past, we *ruled* Europe? We even had settlements as far into the East as hither Asia. Yes. Hard to believe but true. The Romans themselves had us knock at their city several times. We were spread across Europe like dandelion seeds upon a spring field. And we were powerful. Why? I'll tell you why.

"Any race of mankind is only as strong as each individual member. And every man and woman of the Celts were noble, proud people. Loyal only to themselves. Their family. Their tribe. In that order. And such warriors! Terrors as you'll not see today! We went into battle naked save for torques and spears, our hair limed and bristling. Ah ha! How the Romans quaked to see us in our might!"

"But if we were so strong in battle then . . . so brave and valiant," said Kay, "why then were the Romans able to defeat us so thoroughly . . . all the way to the north of Britain?"

Eyes flashing, Amlodd said bitterly, "Oh, do not ever think that the Romans had an easy time of it! But alas, with the Romans—our strengths became our weaknesses. We had no sense of racial identity. The armies of the Caesars were too large, too well controlled, despite our warriors, who gladly gave their lives in battle. Had we one influential man . . . one leader of leaders who could match those clanking generals wit for wit, instead of tribal forces, we too could have had vast armies. *Ours* would have been the empire. Antlike legions of the Mediterranean." Amlodd sighed. "But to go that way, that which we Celts prided so much would have been lost. So who is to say who won and who lost? The Celts as a people may have been defeated, overrun. However, individually they were not beaten. They lived and died the life they chose. And that is the way to live, is it not?"

Kay said, "We still bear much of the past in ourselves, do we not?"

"Yes, indeed," Amlodd affirmed. "Take pride in this. We certainly do. But the sun has set on our glory. Imagine. Once all our warriors were as big as I. And not so fat. Do you know that at one time a Celt could be fined for too much girth? Aye. And the warriors dyed their hair blond and were clean shaven. Except for bushy mustaches. Like ourselves they liked their tunics brightly colored. Even today you're not likely to find a more valiant bunch of fighters anywhere. But Roman blood and Roman ways have doused some of our fire. There was a Greek geographer named Strabo who once proclaimed, 'The Celts are madly fond of war.' But only, I should hasten to say, when it was foisted upon us by invasion. And oh, how we fought. To frighten the enemy, we cut off the heads of our victims and attached them to the necks of our horses. And if we did not have warfare to occupy ourselves, why we had plenty to do. We hunted and we gambled. We raced our horses and our chariots. There was many a mirthful brawl at our feasts. You think I drink much mead? Our ancestors consumed much larger quantities than I.

"And let it not be said that we were lax in work or industry. Why, we brought iron for tools and weapons into general use! We had a bustling civilization, a free trading method, and courts of arbitration. We introduced *soap* to the Greeks and the Romans, and they called us barbarians! Yes, and we taught them to shoe horses and to make handsaws, chisels, and files. These are but a few of the things we accomplished. And all of the Celts were free men who took vast pride in that. Free as I . . . their descendant. Free as you Bear, and you Kay, and even *you* Guenhumara. Our women had and have more rights than any other race's! May we be free till we die!"

Amlodd's face had grown red with passion.

"Free to birth babies and clean up after men," said Guenhumara drily.

"A better lot than elsewhere. Take it from someone who has been in many lands!" Amlodd proclaimed.

Artorius found himself interrupting. "All these things are very well. Our legends are rich indeed, as you say. And yet . . . did the Romans not bring civilization to our race? Writing . . . a sense of things other than selfish needs. A life to be lived in the interest of unity, and a better life for future generations? Perhaps the Romans did overcome us. But they did not kill our race. Maybe it was for the best. From the sounds of it our ancestors were almost as savage as the Picts. Human sacrifice?

Constant warfare? What a dim sort of life *that* must have been!"

Drawing rein, Amlodd whipped his steed about and trotted to Artorius. A tensed, clawlike hand shot out, gripping the boy by the front of his tunic. Anger seethed in those hazel eyes. A fury deeper than emotion. "Say such a thing again, Bear, and I'll flay your hide, king's son or no. Spit on our heritage, and you spit on me."

Alarmed, Artorius said, "I meant no offense. I was only speaking in loose terms, Amlodd."

Rage draining immediately from his face, Amlodd smiled apologetically. He released the wool and held Artorius' shoulder meaningfully. "You must excuse my tantrum, Artorius. For a moment I was being taunted by Romans again. I lost my head."

Uneasy, Artorius tried to return the smile. "I understand. But it appears that Cloud-Eyes wearies from her burden. Perhaps Guenhumara should ride with me awhile."

A twinkle in his eye, Amlodd regarded the boy he considered his protégé. "Why, of course! How thoughtless of me." He twisted about toward Guenhumara. "Well, young woman. It's down you go."

Not pleased, Guenhumara slid nimbly off the saddle. Just as athletically, she bounded upon Artorius' with awkward help from the boy. Slender fingers gripped his side. Her nearness was intoxicating . . . her smell, the softness rubbing against him.

"Off we go! A day's ride, by my reckoning, before we glimpse Hadrian's Wall!" With a shake of Cloud-Eyes' mane as the big man's heels dug into her flanks, Amlodd trotted ahead. Kay kept pace, all questions about ancient Celtic life. Artorius and Guenhumara brought up the rear, Chestnut plodding with the added weight.

"So then," blurted Artorius after a strained silence. "Are you feeling better?"

"From what?" asked Guenhumara.

"Uhmm . . . you know. You weren't in the best of moods. . . ."

"Can you blame me?"

"I mean, you tried to *gore* me!"

"You had a sword. A fair fight." A smile lit her voice. "Sorry, all the same."

"I've never fought with a woman before," stated Artorius, eyes straight ahead, watching the swishes of the horses' tails. The sun was directly overhead. It was not uncomfortably hot, though. Yet Artorius felt stiff, ill at ease. A film of sweat grew on him.

"What? No mother? No sisters?" Guenhumara's fingers pressed in. A jest . . . her tone was warm. Amused.

"Actually, no. The only woman about Baron Hector's fort is an old serving woman who doubles as cook. I've—er—not—had much experience with women."

"You're a candid one, Artorius. How old are you."

"Fifteen . . . er, before long I'll *be* fifteen, that is. You?"

"Eighteen in the fall."

"What will you do . . . once this journey is over?" Artorius asked, feeling better with the young woman's friendliness.

"Does this Baron Hector need another servant woman?"

Artorius laughed, surprised at how fast the tenseness was fleeing. How peculiar. Just listening to Guenhumara, just sensing her, feeling her behind him told of her beauty. "I don't think that Emmorlia would appreciate competition. I suppose we can find out, afterward."

"Amlodd mentioned that if we rescue this druid friend of yours we may well get a reward. I could use the money. I have nothing."

"Reward?" A troubled feeling flowed through Artorius. His brow furrowed. "Yes. I suppose there may be. And I'm sure you'll have a part of it." So *that* was why Amlodd had so speedily changed his mind. Artorius tried hard to be shocked and angry but found it impossible. This was entirely within the rogue's character. Artorius realized that he liked him not one bit less for it.

"All the same, that's not the main reason I'm going."

"Revenge?" asked Artorius.

"Of course. My people meant much to me. But I also find your friend Amlodd quite interesting. Tell me. Is it true that he has no mate?"

"As far as I know." Disappointment welled in his heart. "But with Amlodd it's hard to say what's the truth. He may have five wives in as many lands. He may have none."

"If he had twenty, it would be much the same, I suppose."

Artorius nodded. "He has taught me much. He risks his life to go after my friend, Merlin. I really could not do without him."

"Your other friend. Kay. He seems frightened of me. As you do at times, Bear. Why is this?"

That was easy. "We are both simply overcome with your fairness, Guenhumara. And the fact that you are a different sort of person than we are accustomed to."

For the first time the young woman laughed, unrestrained. Artorius, close, could feel the vibrations of her mirth. "So *that's* it, is it? What strange creatures men are. You worship the way we look and feel. Yet you treat us like slaves sometimes."

"Not I!" Artorius exclaimed. "Why, *I* would treat you fairly and with utter equality. I know nothing of what my fellowmen do. I only intend to do what seems right to me. I refuse to be yoked to tradition and ignorance!"

"Ho ho! You'd best not let hair-face over there get within earshot of that statement. He might think you're blaspheming our beloved great-grandfathers, stomping off naked to battle! And what's this about treating me fairly? I'm not your servant yet."

A blush covered Artorius' face and neck. He changed

the subject. "Tell me, Guenhumara. I've never lived amongst the people of this country. What is it like?"

"Tell you what? It's just living."

"No. Of your ways. Your hopes and needs. Your fears."

"Well, one of our fears was our eventual end. The Saxons, of course, Bear. Why are you so interested in the rest."

"Perhaps, one day I can see that this sort of horror does not descend upon British villages like yours."

The woman laughed sourly. "So what are you going to do? Stand sentry?"

Artorius flustered. "Of course not. One day I may be high king!"

"Well, excuse *me*, your majesty!" Her tone was ironic. Mocking. "But for all the good our other high kings have done we Celts would still *own* this island."

Artorius grew upset. "You will not make fun of my father!"

"Who? Pendragon? Oh, that's right. Amlodd told me. You're his bastard." Another person Artorius would have flung off the horse. But from Guenhumara the words had a gentleness that rendered them less harsh.

"I am *not* a bastard. I will be proved legal heir one day, Merlin tells me. And if I choose, I will ascend my father's throne when he's gone."

"The barons really won't care much. They do pretty much what they please. Or so Amlodd claims. Living apart from most other Celts, I'm not very well informed. But I learn fast. Anyway, you have to find Merlin first."

"Please do tell me about your village. My question was quite sincere."

"Questions generally are. It's the answers you have to beware of." They laughed together, and as the sun dipped down from its zenith, lengthening shadows, burnishing the countryside with brilliance, Guenhumara spoke of the way of life that now lay cleaved by Saxon war-axes, torched by barbarity. "What's to say? Like most people, we ate, slept, worked. Breathed and loved and died. But it's the way you do this that counts, isn't it? To do all these things without meaning would be ridiculous. I realize *that* . . . now that it's gone. Strange how we take the people around us for granted, as though they are part of the furniture of life. Until they're gone. That's when we appreciate them. When they're not part of our lives." Her voice was wistful, melancholy. Artorius wished he could turn around and hold her.

As the hours passed she talked of her life before the Saxon raid.

Of simple things. Of how her father liked his leek soup. And of her sister's fondness for dolls. In her lovely voice all came alive in Artorius' mind. It was as though he knew these people as well . . . had lived with them as Guenhumara had. And when she finished, her voice barely a whisper, he too felt her pain . . . or an inkling of it, at least.

Her story ended in a sob. Artorius reached around and held her hand. He was suddenly aware that he was not anxious at all to grow up. Not in any hurry to have these awful burdens that life heaped upon folk.

"You have been hurt much, Guenhumara. Please forgive me."

"For what? Don't get all formal with me, Bear. I loathe tradition almost as much as you do."

When the sun, partly obscured by puffy clouds, sat just above the trees of a nearby forest, they still traveled through rolling hills. They topped a rise. Eyes filling with alarm, Amlodd held up a hand. Artorius reined Chestnut to a halt. Kay, he saw, stared down the other side of the hill with startled fascination.

"Quiet!" Amlodd whispered. "Noises! In the valley!"

"Stay here," Artorius ordered Guenhumara as he dismounted, sword in hand. Speedily he strode to where Amlodd and Kay had halted. Following Amlodd's directing forefinger, he immediately saw the enemy. Very close indeed. . . .

A party of six Saxon warriors, on foot. They marched haphazardly by the foot of the hill. The sun gleamed on their armbands and link-mail.

"Stay still," Amlodd commanded. "Let the vermin pass. We've other things to attend to. Stay back. Out of sight."

"Do you think they're the ones who razed Guenhumara's home?" Kay asked, an inherited hatred showing.

"Hard to say, lad. Hard—"

A sudden *swish* sailed past their ears. Abruptly one of the Saxons staggered. Artorius saw with astonishment that the stricken Saxon clutched at an arrow piercing his neck. The warrior fell to his knees, squealing shrilly . . . then keeled over, kicking.

"Jove!" swore Amlodd, swinging his head. "Put that down, woman!"

Stunned, Artorius turned. Holding his bow, Guenhumara sat upright in Chestnut's saddle. Her face was a mask of fury. Her hand reached down for another arrow.

"Imbecile!" cried Amlodd. "Bear, why'd you leave her alone?"

Already a swarm of shouts arose from the valley. Artorius looked down again, saw the warriors pointing up.

Unsurprisingly they had been spotted.

V

Bellowing with rage, axes and swords brandished, the five Saxons climbed the hill.

They were less than a hundred yards away.

"Damn!" Amlodd said, bringing his horse about. "Why'd you have to try your target practice here, woman?"

"Only *five* of them!" snarled Guenhumara, fire-eyed. She raised her bow, let another shaft go. It arced down the hill. Skewered the foremost Saxon in the stomach. The wounded warrior pitched down the hill, a cry gurgling in his throat. "*Four* now, Amlodd. I thought you were so fierce in battle. So brave. Your ancestors would not be pleased."

Amlodd snorted. "I am brave when it befits me. But I am *not* stupid. Do you think those sea wolves down there travel alone? Most likely there's a whole *army* somewhere about. With riders as vanguard! Bear, get back on that horse, and let's fly! I don't want—"

An arrow whizzed barely a foot in front of his nose. He whipped his horse, proceeding to retreat. "Follow me!" he cried.

Vaulting onto his horse, Artorius grabbed the bow from Guenhumara's hands. "We'd better do what he says." Reins in one hand, he kicked Chestnut, guiding her around to run hard on the heels of Kay's horse, keeping pace with Amlodd.

In a flurry of speed and clattering hoofs that drowned out the war cries of the pursuers, Amlodd led them down to one valley and up another slope.

Excitement charged Artorius' body as the wind slapped his long hair back. Guenhumara clung to his waist, hard-pressed to maintain her balance at this joggling gait, ripping pell-mell for safety.

The horses' breaths strained. Their noses flared. They crested the hill and were about to descend when a horrified cry broke from Amlodd's lips: "Stop!"

The man did not have to explain to Artorius why they should halt. At least two hundred warriors swarmed in the valley below, all of them Saxons. Astonished . . . but at once they were reaching for swords and axes. A leader, on horseback, was already screaming orders, sword gleaming in the sun as it pointed up the hill toward the new quarry.

"If they catch us, we're dead!" Amlodd yelled. "Back down! Better to face four than a whole army of the pig-spawn!"

Yanking on his reins, he pulled his nickering steed around and urged it back down the hill. Numbly Kay followed suit. Artorius twisted his own reins about, pulling Chestnut's head toward the others.

Confused, Chestnut bucked.

By clinging close to the rank, perspiring horse, Artorius managed to stay in his seat.

But Guenhumara spilled backward, tumbling to the ground. Inwardly thanking Baron Hector for providing excellent horse training, Artorius soon regained control of Chestnut.

"Guenhumara!" Swinging about he saw her sitting on the tufts of grass, stunned from the fall.

Artorius jumped from his saddle, ran to her.

He pulled her up and slapped her. "Come on! Hurry!"

The blow stung the woman back to her senses. She tried to take a defensive swing at Artorius. He caught her arm and yanked her up, pointing at the Saxons below. Already they had reached the base of the long slope. Some readied arrows.

Guenhumara understood. Deep fear showed in her face. She dashed back to Chestnut before Artorius.

In the saddle again they soon galloped downhill.

Halfway down, Amlodd and Kay had struck out at an angle that gave wide berth to the four Saxons below, just about to ascend the hill.

Artorius lit out after them, urging Chestnut aspeed.

One of the four stopped. Fitted an arrow to bow. But the shot whistled wide. By the time the warrior had another shaft to drawstring his fellows were between him and his intended targets: Amlodd and Kay.

The Saxon foursome noticed the laggers. Another barbed missile slashed through the air, this time closer to its intended destination. Short of spitting her neck by a foot, the shaft whizzed by Guenhumara. Artorius could feel her grip him tighter. Fear trembled through her. *How fast flees boldness*, he thought, *when death looms*.

Aware that the others were beyond their reach, the four sea wolves turned all their attention upon Chestnut and her riders. The Saxons' cries were gleeful. The muscles that corded their sleek, trained bodies grew taut as they leaped ahead to intercept. Artorius dug heels into his mount's flanks, slanting over to pour encouragement into its ear.

His salt sweat dripped over his lips. A chill wind swirled about. But despite his zigzags, his maneuverings, and Chestnut's incredible pace under the circumstances, the Saxons drew abreast of their path. Crossed it moments before they would have passed them by.

Amlodd and Kay were far distant.

Choking back his terror, Artorius drew his spatha.

He felt Guenhumara unsheathing the dirk from his side.

Grimly he smiled. He had never killed before, but Merlin had warned him often to be prepared to take a man's life in this savage land.

Artorius rode straight toward the axe-wielding Saxons, speed undiminished.

vi

A cloying mist cloaked the evening as night fell upon the Highlands.

Merlin was bone-tired.

Beneath his filthy robes he could feel the saddle sores on his buttocks and legs. His vision seemed as blurry as the fog in the valley.

Oh, come soon, Artorius, the wearied man thought, drooping over his bonded hands like an old oak bent by wind. *I don't know how much more of this I can withstand.*

Brys, at the forefront of the travel-worn party, raised an arm and commanded a halt. He trotted to Merlin. "Well, magician. The journey is ended." A broken-nailed finger shot out toward the valley, below a ridge. "Here is the home of Huil."

Merlin peered down. Hard to see anything with this waving mist, these darkened shadows. The sun had just sunk behind a heather-smudged peak beyond.

But . . . ah, yes. A glimmer of fire. Forms moving in the dusky bleakness.

And solid shadows: huts, houses.

Homes.

Merlin found it difficult to envision the Picts with homes and hearths. The druid vaguely imagined them almost as wild beasts of the field. Like wolves or ferrets, slinking through forest and fell, ever hungry for bloody prey.

Hard to accept that below stood a harkening-back to the past of his own people, before the advent of the Romans.

Well. Perhaps the Celts had not lived in such a grimy clime or such dim circumstances, anyway. . . .

"Onward," said Brys stolidly, obviously holding exhaustion at bay himself by only an arm's length. "You will want some rest before you show our leader your talents. He will want a look at you, all the same, before you sleep."

Unwilling to expend energy in response, Merlin continued to stare down into the valley wrapped in mist. Brys grumbled a curse, then ordered the march to resume.

They traveled downward to the Pict village.

Merlin swayed as they descended, barely clinging to consciousness.

Sights, smells, and sounds swept past, mingling.

A mother crouched by a cooking fire, clutching a wretchedly dirty baby.

Scents of burned meat and unburied sewage permeated the dampness of the fog.

Raucous baby wailings, warrior mumbles. Scoldings from women.

Merlin closed his senses to all, focused his inner reserves on maintaining his strength.

If things went wrong or if Artorius was late, he would have to extricate himself from this country, and that would take all of his power.

He wished his crystal ball and dreamroot had been more specific about the future.

vii

The Saxons were so close Artorius could see their yellowed teeth.

Their scars reddened with exertion.

The blades of their axes and swords were nicked. . . .

. . . but freshly enough sharpened.

A howl escaped Artorius as he swung his spatha down. So strong was the blow that it split the wood of the axe coming up to meet it and cleaved straight down into skull and brains. Guenhumara's dirk dived hard . . . came up bloody and adrip. Swooped down again.

A death yelp split the air.

Swords and axes jockeyed for hacking distance. . . .

Chestnut barreled past the Saxons, somehow escaping unscathed. But an axe caught the hilt of Artorius' sword. Unable to release his weapon in time, the boy was pulled cleanly from the saddle. As the horse thundered past, Guenhumara still atop it, Artorius thumped to the ground. He barely rolled away in time to avoid an axe blow, which sank deep in the sod.

Springing to his feet, he brought up his sword.

One of the enemy lay dead just beyond him. Another two faced him, grinning like vultures expectant of a meaty feast. As one tugged his axe from the ground, the other leaped toward Artorius, sword flashing in the last rays of sunlight. Artorius parried the blow easily, but he then had the axeman to contend with. Warding off a blow of that double-headed instrument of death, he was just in time to clang away another stab from the swordsman. He saw his opening and immediately availed himself. The point of his spatha gored the swordsman's chest. The Saxon writhed and slumped to the grass, a death glaze fast filming his eyes. Artorius, nose twitching with the awful smell of death, tore his spatha away, sensing the approach of the axe-holder. He brought the iron sword to bear just in time to stop the blow's brunt—but the force of it knocked the flat of the spatha against his cheek and temple, propelling him to the ground. Dazing him.

The grass tasted bitter in his mouth.

Rolling, he caught a glimpse of an axe. Raised high, in arms knotted with tension, it began its downward plunge. The Saxon face below it—plaited hair disheveled—leered with triumph.

A flash of metal. The grinning head suddenly jumped from its shoulders in a spray of blood. The unguided hands released the axe, which fell harmless to the ground as the body, fountaining blood, toppled.

Artorius was suddenly aware of a looming hulk. Of clattering hoofs and a Celtic victory whoop. His vision clearing, he watched as Amlodd, brandishing a bloodied spatha, reined his horse and reached down to pull Artorius up.

Past the snorting nostrils, Artorius saw the Saxon with a bow, kneeling twenty yards distant, aiming.

"Amlodd!" he cried. "Behind you."

The burly man turned just in time to see the archer swerve his aim toward him. Immediately the arrow was released. Amlodd's arm jerked. With a thunk the barbed shaft was caught in Amlodd's full wineskin, held aloft. Amber mead spurted over Amlodd's face. "Oh, damn," he cursed.

Without hesitation the archer drew another quarrel. But before he could even fit it to his bow an arrow feathered red and yellow quivered in his chest. The man crumpled without a sound.

Power returned to his limbs, Artorius leaped to his feet. Behind him, on Chestnut, was Guenhumara. "You didn't think we'd leave you, did you?"

A warm feeling coursed in Artorius.

Amlodd drew up to his side, reached down a sticky hand. "Up we go. I don't think we'll be able to handle that bunch up there. So we'd better pound some turf, eh? I need to find some more mead."

Swinging onto the back of Amlodd's horse, Artorius looked back and saw the meaning of Amlodd's words. Saxons boiled over the hilltop above.

Arrows began to rain.

Kicking Cloud-Eyes' side, Amlodd was soon off with jingling rowels and creaking leather. Mead still dripped down his face.

The horses of the Saxons were runty beasts and soon fell behind the superior breed of Celtic mounts. Breathless, Artorius shut his eyes and clung tightly, praying that a lucky arrow would not find his back.

Several twisting valleys traversed, they soon spotted a dense forest. Amlodd gestured toward the trees and cried above the wind and the thundering horse hoofs. "We'll hide in there."

They sped for this shelter and soon found themselves threading through lush vegetation. Amlodd guided them through glade and bower, a virtual maze of pathways, until he indicated it safe to slow their pace.

The sun set. The woods were full of shadow.

"Just a bit farther in!" Amlodd said lowly. "We'll dismount and make camp. No fire tonight."

"You think the Saxons will search us out?" quavered Kay.

"What for?"

"We killed six of their men."

"Lives of their own people are nothing to them. They won't detain themselves from their pillaging fun to waylay a scrawny company like ours. Nevertheless, we should take precautions. Which is why I've brought us to this forest."

Artorius breathed easier. "Thank you, Amlodd. You certainly kept my body in one piece."

Amlodd's chuckle broke the frightened atmosphere. "It all equals out, lad. If we thanked everyone we should, we'd spend our lives in the task!"

"Yes," Artorius responded, "but—"

They rode under a gnarled oak filled with branches. From the leaves forms dropped suddenly upon them.

It happened so quickly Artorius barely felt the blow that knocked him into unconsciousness.

viii

No root. No ball of crystal.

But visions nevertheless.

Faces.

Faces of men, women. Old and young. Crowns upon their heads.

Scepters in their hands. They looked down upon him in his terrible state, and they said as one, "We shall remember you, Merlin," said these kings, these queens. "We shall keep you near our hearts, and your name shall delight the hearts of our children in our legends and our dreams."

An emotion welled . . . beyond vision . . . price . . . a great empire of Britishmen smiling upon him with their souls.

"But I'm not dead yet," Merlin murmured, slipping in and out of sleep. "Not dead!"

"You shall never really die, Merlin," they said. "Never."

Dully the druid started, half-awake.

Immediately he was aware of the stench and the lingering exhaustion. He lay in a bed of itchy straw. Darkness filled the hut, save for the tremor of a candle in its center. By this stood the bulky figure of a man staring at him. Scarred of face, keen and clever of eye. "This is the creature, then."

A voice from a shadow nearby: "Yes, Huil. This is the man I spoke of."

The other grunted. "He has the air of the other world. You have done well, Brys. Let us hope that this Merlin has the magic we need."

The image blurred. Merlin could not check his descent back into slumber.

No. Not dead. Not dead, he thought.

Not yet.

ix

Something cold and wet splashed into his face.

He awoke, not knowing where he was. Barely remembering *who* he was.

Tight straps bit into his wrists. His ankles.

Darkness hung all about, and fear of the unknown suffused Artorius. He remembered the last images his eyes had seen: the trees, the falling dark figures. . . .

But this was certainly not the forest . . . it was close and musky. Damp. No, he was in some sort of enclosure.

But where?

A grumble. A moan of pain, deep, resonant.

"Amlodd." Artorius strained hard to discern the husky form in the rank darkness. A foxy smell it was, rife with peat.

"Bear!" The mumble was coarse and groggy.

"Over here! Tied securely!"

"As am I."

"Amlodd. Saxons?"

A moment of silence, then: "Na. Na, Saxons would have slit our throats long before. Besides, why would Saxons own a hut—and a big one, if it has individual rooms such as this. But here . . . where are Guenhumara and Kay? If we're alive, surely they must be as well."

Extending his bound legs, tapping here and there on the floor, Artorius soon found a human form. He struck it too hard. "Aow!" it replied. Guenhumara's voice. "Get your boot out of my face! Why is it so dark and smelly? Damn! I'm all tied up!"

Her shrill complaint roused Kay, who tried to jerk up and tumbled onto Artorius. Apologizing, he rolled off.

With the confusion dying down, Amlodd commented: "Well, we're all here and alive. There's a blessing to consider."

Mulling this over, Artorius brooded. What sort of help would they be to Merlin trussed up like this? And who were their captors?

The question was soon answered.

Hides curtaining a door were thrown aside. A candle shown in. Firelight flickered in the room beyond. Another candle. And yet one more, until there was as much light in the chamber as shadow. The bearers of these candles, at first sight, seemed as young and immature in height as Artorius or Kay. Yet Artorius saw that they had the faces of mature folk . . . dark hair tumbling loosely alongside narrow faces. Huge eyes, filled with mystery. They wore only plaid loincloths or beaver skins about their waists.

"Please have no fear," intoned one, in a voice evidently not used to the Celtic tongue. "We intend you no harm. You are tied merely for our own safety. Your legs will be untied, and you will come with us. Explanations will follow."

The candlelight reflected amusement in their eyes.

"What of our horses?" boomed Amlodd. "What gives you the right to assail us? You could have killed one of my lesser companions with your blows."

"It is not our place to respond," replied the one who appeared to be the leader. "The Old One asked that the task be his alone."

Tapered knives glinted in the candlelight.

CHAPTER 4

The Dark People

"We are the People of the Hills."

The old man spoke in a singsong voice. He squatted before the peat fire, immobile as a statue. He stared into the hissing fire with watery eyes. His ruddy face seemed to have five wrinkles for each of his myriad years.

"What were you doing in the forest then?" Amlodd interrupted. His face cringed with the bitter, sour taste of the unnamed drink they had been served. Strong even to Amlodd's taste, noted Artorius, sitting between Kay and Guenhumara, holding a porcelain cup of the fiery, black stuff.

The old man turned his head slowly, glaring at Amlodd. "We have watched your journey much of its course. We did not wish to see it ended by the sea wolves. There was no time for explanations in the forest. We stopped you, and we have brought you to our hill, where you will be safe."

"But we were safe in the—" Amlodd interjected.

The old man's hand waved in a motion indicating silence was desired. "There are things to be said, and there is rest to be had by you before you proceed upon your journey. The talk should be mine—not yours. Drink. Heed my words." His stare slowly was directed to Artorius and there it stayed. They were dark eyes, and they seemed to bore through Artorius' soul. He sipped at the astringent mead . . . nasty, but warming.

Around them stood at least ten dark warriors. Weapons were hung on the walls. A precaution stationed no doubt against the unpredictability they sensed in Amlodd. Artorius noticed how short their orange-feathered arrows were.

Not long after the thongs about their legs were cut, their arm ties were removed as well. They had been marched into this big room, given a hasty meal of roast goat and tuber roots in silence. The atmosphere of the place, thought Artorius, was decidedly portentous. Chilling.

Definitely eerie.

And the weird old man—the focus of the sensation that floated over everything—grew more intense as he spoke:

"Our numbers have grown sparse these past centuries. But our people have been on this island a long, long time . . . so long that we are one with it." The man—a tribal witchperson, Artorius assumed—wore a robe of furs of stoat and rabbit, rat and beaver—all the furred animals of Britain seemed represented, sewn into that robe. . . .

"This earth was full of our dust long before those of your race trod upon it. From the jutting peninsula into the dark deep of the South, to the dip of the lake-filled north, the swamps, the fens, the forests, this island was ours—and we belonged to it. Our gods slumber in its caves, one in mind with this island . . . and they dream brave dreams. They dream of peace and prosperity blanketing these climes . . . they dream of the best of the races of this land merging into one people . . . a people to mount a light for all the world to see. They dream loving visions of this perfect sea-girt land, moated round with stormy ocean, becoming of one mind as we are—cohering, growing with the pastures, tilling the fields, sowing happiness. Their dream spans time . . . and has started long ago. . . .

"We of the Hills are servants of these god-dreams. The Wild-Folk have mixed enough of their blood with this soil. We wish them not destroyed—but absorbed into the island. Cut off from their barbarous origins so that growth might occur in their hearts.

"And so we, with our unseen eyes all over, have knowledge of the confused events of the past years . . . we know of the struggle which rages." The eyes glistened bright. "We know of you, Artorius Pendragon, and of your druid, Merlin. We know what he means to make of you. So our eyes and ears have been on your birth and growth with interest and concern. Yet till now we have not made ourselves known. We deemed a change necessary under the circumstances of today."

"Sounds fine to me," Amlodd interrupted, having managed to swallow his stiff brew and obviously feeling its effects. "Now if you'd provide us with a reasonably numbered army to rescue this druid of such importance, *that* would be of some use."

The old man nodded at the attendants. "Fill our friend's cup. He asks for too much—that which we do not have."

"But Amlodd has a point!" said Artorius. "Allies in this endeavor would certainly be welcome!"

"Does the earth rise up in favor of its people in battle? No. The course of destiny, to be of value, must be bought in blood and agony. Sacrifice and endeavor. We can only aid you in small ways, friend Artorius. Our numbers are too few to be of brute-force value. But we will watch. Know, then, that this island is your throne. If you earn it. Know that thousands of happy lives rest upon your shoulders. A nation waits aborning in your loins . . . know this, Artorius of Britain, and take your fate in hand, and decide. This is all I have to say to you."

The old man seemed to drift into a trance. The assembly slumped into a tense silence.

Broken by one of their number, who came forth and announced: "Your sleeping quarters are prepared. Come, rest, and be refreshed."

Amlodd staggered out with them, smiling broadly. The drink had been strong indeed.

ii

Merlin woke.

His joints needed limbering. His whole frame felt as though he had taken rot drink the night before.

But his utter exhaustion was gone. And his apathy.

Hearing birdsong through the thatched walls, his spirit rose.

So there was yet a cheery note to fill the gloom. And sunlight to fall on the earth, he noted, as he saw the hides part at the doorway, letting sun stream in.

"Ah," said the new arrival, Brys. "You are awake finally. I was ordered not to disturb your rest. But now that you are awake, we must strengthen you with food, and then bring you before Huil, who grows impatient."

The memory of the vision he had viewed the night before floated in Merlin's head. He did not relish this impending event.

Pulling back the curtains, Brys called out in his own crude tongue.

Moments later, a young, cross-eyed wench, too plump by half for Merlin's taste, brought roast fowl and a bowl of new-drawn milk for his breakfast.

Despite his lack of hurry to meet his appointment with the Pict leader, Merlin wolfed the food ravenously. He had not owned such an appetite in years! But even the underdone bird and the faintly soured milk tasted like ambrosia and nectar to his hunger.

Brys watched without expression. When Merlin was finished he said, "Come. We will see to your ablutions. Then we will repair to your audience."

He cocked his head with curiosity. "Last night, magician, I could not sleep well. The thought entered my head: surely, here, a man of magic—and therefore surely money—heading uncomfortably toward a destination he did not relish. . . . Why did he not attempt to offer ample coins to his obviously poor captors for his release?"

Merlin turned to Brys, eyebrows lifted with inquiry: "Bribes, my Pict? Why did you not ask me for such? Too stupid?"

Face flushed, Brys spat: "Bribes would not have worked, Celt. Roman-minted gold is of no value to me. . . ."

"Ambitious, eh?"

Brys ignored this. "No. What troubles me is why you did not try to bribe us. Nor escape. Also, I've been watching you. You are much stronger of body and of will than you pretend to be. You could have escaped. Tell me."

For the first time in days Merlin found himself smiling. "The answer is on its way, Brys . . . that I will promise you." A sense of confidence filled him. "The answer is on its way!"

iii

Awe overwhelming him, Artorius looked upon Hadrian's Wall. A vast enterprise.

The stone structure snaked away to both sides of the horizon, through hill, field, and forest . . . to both sides of this thin neck of Britain, to lapping seas this mass of rock and wood and mortar stretched, Amlodd said.

Atop a weedy knoll, the party of four lingered upon horseback, silently viewing this Roman relic, this work of man.

Below this bluish vault of sky, puffed with clouds amidst the natural beauty of the north, this battlement-topped wall looked entirely in place . . . a man-made part of nature. But then, was the human persona not nature's creation. . . . How could the works of man be unnatural?

His lungs full of air scented with heather, Artorius felt a deepening love for this land, the growing, *becoming* home of Britons.

What a glorious place to live!

"Down there," stated Amlodd, pointing. Preparations completed, he moved to stow the baked-clay flask of the Hill-People brew into a saddlebag. "There's a break in the wall we can go through. Lots of those these days with no Romans to keep the thing in repair. Let's move. According to the dwarf, old Huil is certainly not going to wait for us if he finds Merlin no use to him. What use the old druid is to anybody, Jove knows!"

At dawn, the Dark People had awakened them and had provisioned them with supplies. The old man himself had instructed them in the way they must go; the places they must avoid to survive the increasingly savage country. He even knew the exact location of the center of Huil's chiefdom . . . and had provided Artorius with the welcomed information that Merlin was as well as could be expected. . . .

They threaded downward through blooming bush and brushing leaves . . . gorse and elm, sprinkled with outcroppings of wild bluebells, cowslips, and pimpernels. They gnawed bits of dried mutton for their midday meal as they rode, and Amlodd spoke expansively of the Roman structure they approached.

"Eighty Roman miles, this wall is . . . from Segedunum on the river Tyne to Bosness on the river Solway. It sort of just grew."

According to Amlodd, the wall was put up in several stages. At first it consisted principally of watch forts, observing possible invasions from the north by the barbaric tribes that lived there. Finally the wall, when finished, consisted of the actual stone structure, interspersed by mile castles and turrets for a patroling garrison. Forts for fighting men were built along the wall until there was an efficient system for preventing a much-feared, large-scale attack.

Twice this wall had been destroyed by northern tribes, when the garrison was withdrawn to deal with civil war. Then later again, it fell by attack from land and sea.

It had been abandoned, claimed Amlodd, for over a hundred years.

"We could certainly use it now, couldn't we?" Amlodd noted grimly. "All the way 'round our coasts!"

A forest swallowed them and, after a time of riding, disgorged them back onto greensward. Coarse and prickly weed waved from there up to the weathered stone abutments of the cracked and ancient wall. Amlodd had guided them well: before them the wall was parted. A spill of jumbled rock, mounds of dust, and rotted wood framed a view of the countryside beyond. Hints of black storm clouds threatened to the north.

Amlodd nodded solemnly toward the land beyond. "Now we discover what the Romans built this wall to contain!"

iv

Into the long house strode Huil, son of Caw, matted with clotting blood.

Merlin and Brys sat by the smoldering fire, drinking particularly bitter bracken brew. Caught by surprise, Brys stood awkwardly at the coming of his leader, whom they had been awaiting. Merlin remained seated, but his eyes, sharpened by his repose, scanned his nemesis.

So. This was Huil, son of Caw.

Merlin possessed capabilities of perception long trained through his life. He could sense the almost hypnotic power this man's eyes had. His presence had an uncontrolled, almost magnetic quality—intensified, of course, by the deep piercing black pupils of eyes, which looked like twin wells into nothingness and desire.

The build of the man was impressive. Strong, sinewy legs boosted up the heavyset torso—every inch of it dominated by dense muscle, no doubt. Settled on top was a harshly handsome face that could have been carved from stone for all its hardness. From the looks of him Merlin estimated that he was in his prime.

Every part of him seemed aware of his surroundings, questing for power constantly. Power over everything.

Yes. Merlin could see now why people followed this man. He had the necessary qualities. And Merlin could also see that he had underestimated his opponent. Before, Huil had only been a tool. An instrument to tug Artorius Pendragon into a character-shaping experience. But now the druid knew that the man was a threat—not merely to this bleak country, but to the light kept alive in Britain.

Had he been foolish, or had some wisdom other than his set up these circumstances?

Against this man, Merlin felt, he would need to call on his arts and wits even more than he had ever known before.

The shaggy Scot tossed a brace of tied rabbits to the floor. "Good hunting today. Only a sample of my kill," he boasted. "Ah, druid. Welcome to Fortren. I trust you have your bag of tricks."

"I need no bag of tricks for magic," said Merlin in a monotone. "That talent is within me. But to work, it need inquire what it is wanted for."

Huil hunkered down, eagerness showing on his crafty face. "To obtain a handsome reward for your services, sorcerer. That is what it is wanted for. Women, horses . . . I even have a hoard of treasure awaiting you, if you cooperate. I sense that you indeed have the power I crave."

"Let me rephrase. To what ends is this power of mine to be used? Who *are* you, Huil of the Picts?"

The man grinned. "I? I am the dark and the fog. I am the wind and the rain, the storm and the lightning. I *want* this land of the Picts to be under my sway, druid."

"And the South? You want your raindrops and your mist clinging there as well?"

"Your land?" Huil could not prevent an evil grimace. "What would such as I do with *all* of this island, druid? I am not greedy!"

"Nor are you stupid," commented Merlin. "Your captain has done you well. I am your man."

Huil's crusted eyes widened, revealing glimmers of the ambition he had disavowed. "You can lend me your power that I might humble the other chieftains, bring their tribes under my command alone?"

"All that and more, Scot. My power is beyond bounds, and if you spare my life and give me the treasure that you mentioned, then this magic of mine is at your disposal!"

Standing, quaking with anticipation, Huil said, "Immediately, then. My hunger demands to be fed!"

Merlin shook his bearded head. "Would that I could oblige, great leader."

"What!" Honest confusion crossed the chieftain's face.

"Alas, the time for the quickening of my great sorcery—magic that can kill your enemies in a wink, enslave nations in a gasp, I might add—cannot be practiced with full force until the final darkening of the moon."

"But . . . but . . ." stammered the Scot, frustrated. "This is *days* away!"

"Days away, true. But have you not waited weeks, months, years? Can you not abide four more days, great chieftain? In return I promise magic greater than your mind can imagine . . . vaster than any single thought can encompass."

Huil sulked. "I've killed for less an offense to my face."

Merlin shrugged. "Kill me then. We shall both be the losers, and your dream shall die on the tip of your own sword. But I can see that you are a smarter man than that, oh, Huil. I can *tell* that you have the intelligence to realize that if you have but a little patience then all that you desire can be yours. Am I correct?"

Brooding, Huil stared at Brys. "What say you, captain? Can we wait? Is this stalling trickery?"

Brys said, "He will be just as dead in four days if he lies as he will be this evening."

And so, thought Merlin, amused, *would be a certain Pictish captain.*

Huil nodded. "Very well then. So be it." He turned back to Brys. "See that he is well fed and looked after. Guarded without violence, but guarded nonetheless." He grunted. "When the moon has slivered down to almost nothing, we will see if the magician can do what he claims."

V

Artorius regarded the moon. Amongst a bountiful harvest of stars, it had narrowed down to a silvery scythe of the sky, cushioned on a bed of black.

The campfire spat and snapped, cooking a hare that Kay had shot not two hours before. Imagine that, pondered Artorius. Kay actually *hitting* something. The notion amused him.

The night was quiet, its air clear and cool. Artorius was warm, comfortably ensconced in a blanket of skins.

Life could be so good.

And yet so bittersweet.

The irony of the situation was thrust upon him by Amlodd and Guenhumara, sharing a blanket, openly snuggling in the firelight.

The two had seemed to cool over the past two days, renewing the hope in Artorius' breast that Guenhumara might take more notice of him.

But, alas, they were at it again, all smacking kisses and playful hugs. Coos and tickles. Amlodd was on the wrong side of sobriety.

"What do you think, lads?" crowed Amlodd, bringing the flask of Dark People brew to his lips . . . which he had learned to quite enjoy by now . . . and eyeing the roasting meat hungrily.

Kay, tending the spit, prodded the hare with a stick. Juice squeezed out and sizzled in the coals. "A minute more. Then a while to cool."

"Cool? Cool?" blared Amlodd. "I could eat the fire itself I'm so famished. What about you, sweet child?"

Guenhumara opened her mouth to reply but was interrupted by a faint vibration, a gurgle from the pit of her stomach.

Amlodd roared. "Answer enough! Answer enough! Saucy lass!"

Kay and Artorius joined in, as did Guenhumara.

In a trice the hare was declared fully cooked. It was speedily consumed, with much lip-and-finger smacking, much rowdy mirth-making.

Picked clean, the carcass was thrown into the foliage for the ants to gnaw, and Kay leaned back, saying, "But truly, Amlodd. You've made fun enough of this quest, which is, after all, quite important. It is what Bear and I are living for now. What is it that you value?"

The bluff man thought a moment, then responded, "Why, times such as these, young Kay! The moon and stars in place and showing themselves through a rainless sky. Good food, good drink, and good friends. Yes, and a dear and loyal woman to hold!" He winked at Guenhumara, who slapped him playfully on the shoulder.

Staring into darkness that seemed to wall them in, Artorius considered this awhile. Insects buzzed in the forest. The camp was full of the odor of the smoky fire, the roasted hare. He looked upon Guenhumara's lovely face, and something hurt within him, a hurt to be cherished, for it opened up new worlds. "I can't deny the importance of emotion . . . and yet, should there not be a balance? The roaster of the Head, and the mistress of the Heart, in equal places of the kingdom of the whole?"

"Bah." Amlodd dismissed him with a wave of his

hand. "Men grow old sitting about talking philosophy. By the time they decide how to live their lives they are too old for it. Old age is for sitting and brooding. Youth is for acting and living."

These words ended the discussion, and more frivolous matters were brought up. Soon, however, it was time to bed down if they were to get an early start for the next morning.

Kay was dubbed first watch. Guenhumara and Amlodd, arms draped about one another, made their mutual bed far from the firelight from which eventually arose rustlings, moans, and sighs.

Artorius lay awake, sensing the night about him. Inside, he ached.

vi

Someone was shaking him. Hard.

"Bear! Bear, I hear someone out there!"

Abruptly Artorius realized that he had been asleep. His eyes shot open, taking in the sight of Kay leaning over him. The fire now was merely a rubble of glowing coals.

"Out there," continued Kay, frightened, pointing into the darkness. "Sounds."

"Probably just Amlodd stirring about." Artorius groaned and turned over. "Let me sleep. I've next watch in a while."

"No, Bear, I don't think. . . ."

War cries tore through the silence of the night.

Forms parted from the shadows, starlight glimmering on raised blades. The camp was hurled into a confusion of cries, darting bodies, flashing knives. Artorius sprang to his feet, clutching up the spatha he kept by his side. "Amlodd!" he screamed. "Guenhumara!"

A foot kicked the fire coals. Flame and sparks fanned across the ground. Artorius caught a pitted dagger on the blade of his spatha. The sound of metal on metal pealed as the force of his blow tore the weapon from the invader's grip. With one swipe the spatha tore limb and life from the shadow form and was ready to spill more blood.

It had its fill of that as more figures danced into thin moonlight. So fast and furious was the fighting, so hard pressed was Artorius to keep the swords and knives away from his throat, he lost track of time. It was a madness of flashing metal, death screams, and the odor of death as he fought to hold onto his own life.

Three men dead at his feet, two more pressed in. He could no more answer Kay's cry for help than he could take a break for a restful nap. A sword cut at him. Metal clanged . . . and another sword dove toward his vitals from the left. He dodged and kicked the leading man in the face, feeling teeth and bone give way beneath the blow. Gagging on his own blood, the man tottered and fell. Artorius fended off another blow from his attacker. Another, and another, and then he began to rain his own blows, as Amlodd had taught him. "Speed is all, Bear! Speed and quick judgment. Destroy the defense with an unswerving offense, and you'll have him!"

Heaving in strained breaths, Artorius struck a well-aimed blow, slicing through the man's arm. Yowling, the man dropped the weapon. Artorius banged him across the temple with the flat of his sword, spilling him into unconsciousness.

As he looked up he saw, amongst the dying fire coals, Kay's fallen sword.

No sign of his friend, alive or dead.

Emotion welling in his throat, he screamed out: "Kay! Kay!"

In answer Amlodd's voice bellowed: "Bear! Over here!"

Artorius jumped the bodies he had felled and tore through the bushes. He bumped into a massive form and was about to give battle, when the man said, "Hold, man. It's me. Amlodd. We've driven them off! God help us, we've beaten them off."

Artorius could barely see him. There was only the feel of him and the harsh sound of heavy breathing. "They've got Kay! We *must* go after them!"

"He'll keep awhile. If they've kept him alive, they must want him to stay alive. Come over here, Bear. Know you anything from your druid of how to keep life in a stricken body?"

"Amlodd? Are you hurt?" His voice was fearful.

"Na. Na, I've a scratch or two, but nothing to fret about. For every cut on me, I delivered five to the three or so of 'em that I killed. It's Guenhumara. They tried to carry her off . . . and must have gotten confused about where they were sticking their blades."

"Guen . . . where is she? Where is she hurt?"

"In this darkness I can't tell. Just over here. . . ."

"A candle, Amlodd. Get me a candle—light it from one of the coals and fetch me my saddlebags!" Artorius crept along the ground, feeling. A hand caught his up, squeezed it. "Artorius?" The voice was filled with agony.

Amlodd lumbered off to follow his instructions.

"Guenhumara?" Artorius put comforting arms around the woman. "Are you all right?"

"I . . . I'm not *sure*, Artorius. It . . . it *hurts*. So much!"

"Where Guenhumara? Where?" She smelled of fear and blood. She sprawled out on the ground like a fallen doll.

"In my belly. Ohhh . . . don't touch it. It stings."

Artorius' hand came up, slick with blood. He swallowed, full of helpless fear beyond definition. When he had been young he had found a baby rabbit in the woods. It had a broken leg, and it shivered like a leaf in a gale. The youngster had held it close, dashing madly for the long house, helplessly hoping that Hector had some magic balm to heal this tragic little creature. It had shaken so . . . and when he reached the fort, it lay dead and stiff in his hands.

Guenhumara was shaking now. Shaking and holding

him. "Oh, Bear, it hurts so much. Help me, please. Tell me I'll be all right."

"It's . . . it's nothing, Guenhumara," lied Artorius, voice choking. "Just be still, and we'll make you well."

"Yes. Yes . . . I will." She let herself relax . . . her breathing grew less taxed. "Bear, I don't want to die. I'm too young . . . I have children to bear . . . I have hopes and dreams to live. Help me, Bear. Help."

"I love you, Guenhumara," said Artorius, tears dripping down his cheeks. "We'll do all we can. You'll be better, just as Amlodd brings a light and some bandages. . . ."

The woman's clench to his hand tightened. She grew delirious.

She shuddered, spasmed, and her breathing gasped away, a torch sputtering out under a torrent of rain.

She was still and dead, yet warm. Artorius held her and wept more tears than he knew he owned.

Amlodd came, a tallow candle flickering before him. "I brought what you needed. And my flask of drink. She might. . . ."

"You drink it," Artorius said. "She'll never drink again." Face a mask of hatred, Artorius rose and held the hilt of his sword hard. "They've got Kay, these people. And they have a debt to pay."

In the guttering candle flame his face grew hard as stone.

vii

"That way, I think," Amlodd muttered. "Yes, definitely. That way." Underneath his sun-browned skin the burly man's face wore an unearthly, ashen pallor.

Atop their horses, they led Kay's steed along behind them by its reins, deeper into the forest. They had tossed some stones and dirt over Guenhumara's body, as though that would keep the scavengers away, thought Artorius glumly.

Amlodd was raging. Every other utterance from him

was a demonic curse. Artorius was happy to be on the friendly side of the big man's sword.

They traveled aways in silence, shadow, and starlight. Vengeful ghosts slinking through bower and valley. Before long the trail of the marauders was easy enough to follow. Broken branches. Bent bushes. A scrap of clothing, a bit of blood smeared on stone. To Amlodd, these and other signs were as telltale as torches marking the barbarians' pathway.

The arc-shaped moon sank. Milky clouds floated under the stars. Time passed.

Before long loud chants penetrated the quiet. Fires glimmered through breaks in tree branches. Amlodd turned his horse's snout toward these, and Artorius followed. The chantings grew louder. Amlodd dismounted, tied his horse's reins to a tree. Beckoned Artorius to follow suit.

On feet quiet as whispers they crept toward the clearing from which the sounds and the light emerged. A grassy glade opened before them, a dip in the ground, surrounded by thick foliage forest. Amlodd halted, well within the concealment provided by a thicket of bush.

Artorius peered down into the glade. He gasped.

Bordered by cairns of rugged stone, spotted by wood posts topped by leering human skulls, a ceremony transpired. Lit weirdly by a roaring bonfire, two naked women, skins adorned with elaborate bluish tattoos, capered in the flame-glow. One held a squawking goose, feathers full of blood. The other held a goblet. They danced through a crowd of frenzied men and women who made a ring of bodies about a long flat-topped stone.

Stretched upon this stone, hands and feet tied, was Kay.

The crackling bonfire reflected terror in his eyes. At the end of this makeshift altar stood a druid, cowled in black. In knuckly fists the man held a broad ceremonial killing knife.

"Here," Artorius muttered bitterly, "is our heritage."

"And a druid in action," countered Amlodd. "You still wish to rescue a man of this creature's ilk?"

"We should not throw barbs. If this is indeed a Celtic tribe, then it has been cut off from civilizing influence for years . . . centuries . . . to indulge in such barbaric rites."

"I agree. We can argue later. Right now we must rescue Kay, who is dearer to me than a dozen druids." Contemplating, he sucked a lip. "As to exactly *how* I'm hard pressed to say. Any ideas? We'd better hurry. They seem working up to a frenzy that will end with that blade stuck in poor Kay."

"A sacrifice," said Artorius. "But to what?"

"Hard to say. Celts are a superstitious lot."

"Would a distraction help?"

Amlodd scowled. "Yes. And I believe I know what we're going to have to do. And do *quickly*."

A crazy plan.

Insane. Foolhardy.

And yet Artorius had to admit that it was working . . . so far, anyway.

Amongst the crush of zealous worshippers, Artorius was anonymous.

"After all," Amlodd had said, "we *are* Celts. We ought to blend in well enough. . . ."

So Artorius had hunched down into the crowd, knife tucked in his tunic, to join in the ceremony and hopefully to spirit Kay away once Amlodd created the planned disturbance.

Artorius had never felt the like of this experience before. Amongst the dancing, swaying, chanting tribe, a religious fervor buzzed through the air. Melting into the jabbing elbows, the rolling eyes, Artorius could not help but be tugged into the emotional excitation as well. The beat of the song seemed the beat of some rhythm deeper and more basic than his own heart. Sweaty smells, berry-dye scents reeked in the heated air.

Through the crowd, unnoticed, he cut toward the dais that held his friend Kay down so harshly.

He had to be there at just the right moment. . . .

His right hand gripped the hilt of his knife inside his tunic . . . his teeth were clenched with tension, and his breathing was ragged and hard . . . but nothing compared with the gasps and cries that assailed his ears from the barbaric Celts in this ancient rite. Dodging hands and colliding bodies, he plowed through the brush and suddenly found himself as close to the altar as the ceremony seemed to allow. The circled area, a perimeter marked in pitted stones, was a sacred place, trod on only by the sacrificial victim and the wielder of the killing knife.

Rigid in a fearful daze, Kay lay immobile upon the slab—which bore gutters cut out in the edges to carry off the blood. Above him, eyes bloodshot and ringed with black, the druid issued words and dripping spittle from his mouth . . . like the froth of an insane beast. Veins bulged on his forehead and on the taut hand that gripped the hovering knife. Artorius had heard tales of this sort of thing . . . legends of Celtic tribe-kings being stabbed in such ceremonies for not siring children. Their writhings and the gush of their split abdomens were studied carefully by the druids, sure that they could tell the future in this manner. But it had all been legend before: myths, fireside tales to arouse a delicious shiver.

This, now, was reality, and it sickened him in a way that the Saxons, the Scots, or the Picts did not. It made him ill because these were *his* blood-people . . . his own kind that had done this. *Were* still doing it in little-known regions of Britain.

He positioned himself just behind the druid.

Amlodd, he thought. As though the fellow could hear his thoughts. *I am ready*.

He tensed himself for the leap, the plunge.

And Amlodd's ploy began.

A bellowing voice rang out above the din, seemingly from the forest.

"Behold the voice of the Earth God! Cease this farce

immediately. The offering displeases me. Release him lest you feel my terrible wrath upon your sinful heads!"

The words petrified the celebrants. Eyes staring, shivering. As though a heart-chilling cold had descended upon them, the dancers stopped dancing, the singers singing, the chanters chanting.

"Do you not heed your god?" The voice was recognizably Amlodd's—but somehow rendered deeper, more resonant. If Artorius did not already know whose it was, he too would have been startled. "Obey me at once!"

The druid had lowered his knife, removed his cowl. Inflamed eyes peered hard into the darkness. Doubt twisted his features. "A hoax!" he announced. The language of these people was scarcely recognizable to Artorius. Celtic, yet an older version. The knife sang as he brought it up, directing its point toward the voice. "How could a god's voice have a direction? Our ceremony is interrupted by a profaner. Silence the villain immediately, before our true gods are angered. Quickly!"

The crowd now wielded into one mind . . . a mob . . . all immediately tumbled over one another, a mad rush of clawed hands and bared teeth, into the surrounding forest to ferret out Amlodd. Leaving only the druid and a few stragglers. . . .

Amlodd would have to fend for himself. . . .

As would he, thought Artorius.

He lunged for the druid. His attack caught the man by surprise. Artorius tried to knock the sacrificial knife from the robed man's hand . . . but his grip was too firm. Eyes wide with surprise, the druid wheeled into the man's rib cage.

The man grunted and the knife dropped, clattering away on the stones, reflecting torchlight. Wobbling, oblivious to Artorius, he wrenched off the blade and tried to run, but stumbled. He pitched down and was still, his blood soaking the grass.

Wary of further interference, Artorius slit the leather bonds tying Kay down to stone.

"Bear!" Kay said, hope seeping into his eyes. "I'm so glad. . . ." Right hand, left hand, snick, slash. Artorius moved down to the feet . . . and something caught his eyes just beyond the farthest ring of torches by a collection of huts . . . a coagulation of stark nothingness that seemed to suck any light into itself, killing it. At the depths of his being Artorius felt a fear of such tremendous power that he could barely move.

It was like staring down into a tar-black pit . . . that had no bottom. *Some sort of god?* Artorius thought fearfully. No . . . his instincts told him immediately. Nothing like a god. A not-god, just as death was a not-being. A mindless force focusing over this barbaric rite that worshipped it.

And it was growing. . . .

Sheer necessity drove him out of his reverie . . . he parted the thongs from Kay's right leg. Then he freed the left leg.

Kay did not see the thing. "Bear!" he cried out. "Watch out! Behind you. . . ."

Artorius swiveled. A charging swordsman was almost on top of him, weapon arching down for a sure kill.

But the man stumbled, dropped face flat. Sticking up from his back was an arrow. . . .

. . . an arrow with a short shaft. . . .

. . . feathered orange. . . .

Kay laughed a bit hysterically. "Our friends the Dark People? . . . watching over us?"

"Come," Artorius urged as he spied others headed toward the altar. "Hurry."

But it was not these fierce, manic warriors that the boy feared. It was that hole of darkness gathering atop the trees. The darkness that seemed to grow. . . .

In the confusion a torch had toppled upon a long house. Fire licked along the thatched roof. Smoke waved over the clearing. Screams of alarm sounded, and suddenly the tribe members were less interested in catching Amlodd or regaining their victim than in preserving their homes.

Through the stench of burning, the clatter and commotion, Artorius and Kay raced. At the edge of the field, short of the brushy wood, Artorius spared one more glance back. The tribe had been thrown into a frenzy to save their homes . . . and the ball of darkness still hovered, like a scavenging raven waiting to light on the remains.

At the core of his being Artorius was sick.

This was the enemy, he realized.

Not Saxons. Not Picts, nor Scots, nor anything that lived. . . .

. . . the enemy was the darkness in them all . . . the sucking, consuming nothingness that bordered on life, waiting to demolish . . . the blackness in other people . . . the darkness in his *own* soul. . . .

That, he knew, was what he had to fight his whole life. The realization was of such galvanizing power that Artorius suddenly felt infused with meaning, and a fiery joy.

Damn you Darkness and Death! You'll not have *me* without a fight. A fight that humankind could remember and take heart in throughout the centuries. . . .

Somehow feeling as though he had grown years in a single evening, the boy led the stumbling Kay to where they had left their horses. They were to meet Amlodd there, if he survived. . . .

Artorius' heart lightened immensely as he saw the disheveled, bulky form of his heavyset friend atop his steed, beckoning in the glimmers from the burning Celt village . . . eyes reflecting back the light. . . .

Emotion stirred in Artorius' breast.

"Good job, lad," whispered Amlodd, bringing the other horse 'round for his companions.

Fire and inner light flecked his spirited eyes.

Artorius felt a deep warmth for the man. It was Amlodd's intelligence that had wrested Kay from this situation. When it came to a question of light versus darkness, for all self-interest, Amlodd was the first to light a torch.

Springing on Chestnut's back, he clapped Amlodd on his shoulder in a gesture of bonhomie.

They struck out toward the morrow's dawn.

viii

The night held a new moon amongst its cloud-smeared darkness, freckled with stars.

The moon in its final phase, like a mournful blind man's eye, moved slowly in its course, urged by a silent, celestial wind.

An earthly breeze ruffled Merlin's beard.

"Your night has come, druid," Huil said, anticipation shining with reflected torchlight in his eyes. He marched up to where Merlin stood on the brow of the high hill. "Your instructions have been followed as well as possible," Huil continued, nodding down to his clan's village below and gesturing toward the twelve warriors who stood with them. "We are well away from interference of the mass of human spirits which may thwart your magic. Only my personal bodyguard is here. You have the tools of your magic you requested. The types of soil and water, as many of the powders and potions as we could find. The roots, berries, leaves, and flowers. All here. Now let us see what you can do!" He pulled his hide-cloak closer against the unusual cold that had been carried into the highlands by a wave of mist.

Merlin raised his eyebrows inquisitively. "Very well, Huil. You have kept your word. I will endeavor to keep mine. But before I begin a display of my power . . . could you give me some hard specifics about what it is you want immediately done with my magic?" Merlin felt strong and confident; yet a sense of uneasiness prevailed. He had not reckoned with the fierceness of this Huil . . . if this show went askew for some reason, if Huil was displeased, there was nothing to stop him from simply putting the druid to death. His magic might help him . . . but his flesh was still flesh, susceptible to sharp metal.

If only Artorius would hurry!

"What would I like done?" Huil's penetrating eyes flashed darkly with his mirth. "Even you, with this magic you claim to have, could not satiate my full hunger, Merlin. Just as I eat and drink every day and want more the next, so it is with my lusts. I want all that is to be had, and each taste of life's offering I have continues to sharpen the pang of my hunger."

His hand swept about, taking in all the horizon. "This is all I want, now. To take this, there are men who must die. Three men. Perhaps with power you give me, eh? These men are Jagoth, Morag, and Myfan. But we shall speak of them later. Now I want a taste of magic. My eyes demand a proof, a sample of your powers."

"Indeed. Now let me be. I will examine the materials you have provided and see what influences I can conjure up. Patience, Huil, and do not interfere."

"When I am dead then I will be patient, Merlin. Proceed and remember. Your life hangs in the balance, should you fail." Merlin turned to regard the chieftain. Their glances met. Cold, flecked hate collided with fiery, volcanic rage. Their eyes bored into each other's like torches. Wordlessly Merlin returned to his tasks.

On a short table the Picts had set the things Merlin had requested. This included a poorly fashioned mortar and a knobby pestle carved, it seemed, from a short branch of pine.

What would he do first? Something showy, certainly. Bright lights. Thunder. Wind. A summoning of the elementals. With this stuff before him he could throw up more than a few dazzles to brighten this dark place.

But despite the fact that he knew Huil would be swayed, there remained a perverse humor—a sensation of bias, a propensity to something askew.

Shrugging off the nameless feeling, Merlin rooted

through the various things before him, selected and mixed a few berries, powders, and bits of dirt. After grinding the mixture in the mortar he dumped it in the palm of his hand, muttered a few spells over it, then said, "A preliminary, Huil. Behold."

He cast the stuff far into the sky with a powerful throw. Waving his arms, in graceful arabesques, he cried out the proper commands.

Each speck of the stuff, falling, flared up into a snowflake of cold, sparking fire that dashed brilliance across the hilltop. The Picts gasped and shielded their eyes.

Merlin clapped his hands sharply, then directed a finger in a circular motion, whispering an ancient tongue. Immediately the specks of dazzle in the air began to twirl about windmill fashion. Merlin weaved his finger, and the dazzling stuff weaved in the pattern dictated. Then with a loud cry he threw his arms up, and the stuff, like stardust, fountained into the night sky, fading to black.

A sigh of wonder, then a great shout went up from the watchers at the foot of the hill.

The air was rent with cheers.

Merlin lowered his arms, turned to confront the powerful leader. The big man stood silent, clasping the shank of his sword between restless fingers. Cold, dispassionate, a masklike face. Yet his eyes glittered through narrowed lids.

Merlin, erect, unyielding, regarded him impassively.

Again there was a flash of their eyes meeting.

In that flicker an explosive contest of power, a surging test of adamant wills.

Suddenly Huil spoke: "Interesting. But how can puffs and sprinkles of dirty ashes defeat my three powerful enemies with armies of hundreds of warriors spreading death and destruction? Answer me that?"

"You have just seen preliminaries. You asked for a show, proof of my magic, did you not?"

The Pict leader brushed the remark aside. "Trifles! Trifles and nonsense," he grated. "Tricks for children and fools. I want magic that can shake and destroy. . . ."

"Yes, great magic," Merlin interrupted. "Spells and powers the equal of the Fire-flingers of the Final Mysteries. You want potent forces of earth and sky let loose like roaring bulls and screaming eagles! And you shall have them—by the Great Immortals of the Most High—now you shall have them, Huil, great leader."

The druid magician raised his arms to sweep the firmament. He seemed to swell and grow as he strode toward Huil. He leveled a forefinger.

"You invoke the awesome powers of the air," he proclaimed. "Pict, choose to tread dangerous ways, and you walk with death!"

Huil fell back, momentarily silenced.

A thought spread through Merlin's consciousness. He had cowed the stormy, ravening Scotman. He had the *upper hand*!

O Artorius . . . the time is near, so near at hand. Come, lad, haste, haste . . . do not tarry!

It took but a moment for Huil to recover. The barbarian, recognizing his default before Merlin's ploy, lurched forward, a savage look in his eyes, seized the magician's tunic. Muscles bunched and writhed as he lifted Merlin half off his feet.

"I think you are lying to me!" said Huil, maddened. Metal swished from leather, and Merlin felt sharpened, nicked iron against his throat. "No one tricks Huil and lives to laugh. I have heard of Roman candles, and this is all you have shown us so far, trickster! I want something special now, immediately, or your death will commence slowly and leisurely."

He raised his dagger, eyes glowering.

Merlin pushed up through his muscles and his will to survive. In the man's grip he was powerless. He felt as though paralyzed by the brute strength of the man, his demonic, insensate energy. His brain danced . . . consciousness . . . life was being squeezed inexorably out of his body.

A last effort. Come, Merlin . . . close on his eyes . . . tame the wildness.

He riveted Huil's attention. The spasm. The convulsion of wills.

"Huil!" A rasping, stertorous sound. "Huil," Merlin commanded, "put me down!"

The dagger glinted in the torchlight. Merlin, released, sank to his knees.

ix

A bleak land.

A country of misty lakes, craggy mountains.

Hillsides covered with heather bushes and bracken.

It was a wild land, this land of the Picts, with the salt breath of the sea ever near, the taste of the north in its weather.

And it was haunted land . . . as though it were some ghost of a dead country, half remembered . . . its true realities glimpsed in the corner of the eye. And then fleeting away.

Yet this was a land of such splenderous beauty that on his trek through it the sights it offered sometimes separated Artorius' mind from his brooding. Tore them away sailing over the rocky fields, the oceans of mist, with the island peaks of mountaintops breaking through, green, with a faint frost of white.

Night had come, and yet they still traveled. For three days after Guenhumara's death they had ridden, and still their destination had not been reached.

"Gods! Let's have some rest! Let's have some fire!" exclaimed Amlodd. "This air is seeping down to my very soul and giving it chilblains!" He shivered as he spoke and nursed the last of his supply of drink.

Artorius twisted in his saddle. He regarded the slumped man solemnly. "No. We must go on tonight. I feel . . . I have the sensation in me that if we stop we lose everything."

Kay, rings under his eyes from lack of sleep, nodded. "We'll have plenty of time to rest after we get Merlin away from this awful country."

"Yes," roared Amlodd. "Rest in our graves. I tell you: we try anything physical in our present conditions and we fail. You don't attack when your resources are at low ebb, Bear. Haven't I taught you that?"

"We will if the situation calls for it," Artorius responded, staring ahead, remembering the directions that the Dark People had bestowed on them. "Besides, who says that we will attack? Three against an entire tribe? That would be foolhardy. Any success we gain from this will be from stealth and cunning." Feeling cold and desolate, he tried to brace his words with encouragement. "And we will. I swear by all that is holy and right, we will!"

Amlodd shook his head wearily. "I swear, the holiest things to me now seem a safe place to sleep, a sizzling partridge on the fire, and a jug of wine. Ye gods! Have I still feet? They feel like they dropped off leagues ago."

They journeyed on. In a wooded area, just when Artorius himself was about to surrender to fatigue, a diminutive man stepped out before them, strangely childlike of visage but somehow inexplicably mature. One of the Dark People. Arms crossed over chest, he wore a frown.

"You're going the wrong way, Celts."

Amlodd growled. "Well, then. Why didn't you just send along one of your people as a guide. We've followed directions to the letter."

The frown on the delicately formed, high-cheeked face slid up into a smile. "You have done well enough." A thin finger shot out, pointing. "Fortren is that way. There is your druid. And from reports of our seers, it is well that you've made it this far. It appears that he is in trouble."

Artorius felt simultaneously relieved and troubled.

"But at least he is still alive. How long . . . how long do we have? Are they going to put him to death?"

"That is hard to say."

Amlodd leaned forward heavily in his saddle. "Tell me, short one, can you bring a few of your archers to bear? You were a great help in our tussle with that tribe three days ago."

The small man bowed. He indicated a small bow. "I did it myself."

"Just you? Very good . . . your numbers *are* small," Amlodd said. "Can't get fewer than one." His brow furrowed, his glance darkened. "But tell me, if you were watching over us, why did you not warn us of the first attack. You know, the woman was killed. The loss was heavy to all of us."

The little man shrugged sadly. "Alas, even I have to sleep. The woman was beautiful. A waste. I wept. But today is not yesterday. You must alter your path. The Old One has ordered that you get no help in the final battle. The heaviest part of this task must be yours. This is the command of the Old One, and the Old One is as wise as the hills."

"Thank you anyway, friend," said Kay, bringing his horse about, his locks swaying. "And farewell."

As he stepped back into the darkness of the glade the little man nodded—and then drifted away from them under the moon and starlight like a vapor.

Artorius stared hard at Amlodd. "What's wrong, my friend. You look as though you've second thoughts."

"Damnit," said Amlodd, not looking at Artorius or Kay, but at the back of his mount's head. "It's suicide to ride into the Pict camp, the way the little one describes it, all by ourselves. Especially as weary as we are."

"Amlodd," stated Artorius sternly. "After coming all this way, you would desert the cause? You are no coward. I know that. But know this—and at once. Kay and I are going ahead. If you wish to stay, then stay and rest. Or," Artorius continued harshly, "go back the way we came. But if you choose to go back, where will it be? Through a thousand dangers worse than this last ahead. And to what purpose? To what end?"

Artorius paused. A fleeting look of ineffable sadness possessed his face. "But when you pass the cairn of the beautiful Guenhumara, our comrade-at-arms, raise your voice to that incomparable child-woman of woe and grief. . . ." His voice choked. ". . . ask where she would be in this hour of need?

"Oh Amlodd," he cried. "When you shed tears for the loyal Guenhumara the night she died were they for the girl—or only for yourself?"

Amlodd's head jerked up. His eyes held a stricken, confused look. All at once the tension, the resilient, elastic vigor seemed to drain away from him. Ashen faced he trembled uncontrollably. Breathing heavily he sought to suppress the ruinous warfare of emotions that raged in his breast. With a supreme effort he came together, tautly.

"I'll have no more of this maundering!" he grated wildly. Vehemently he leaped astride his steed, whipped the beast into a lurching gallop. He was soon swallowed up by the night.

"Why did you do that?" said Kay. "You drove him too hard. We'll never make it by ourselves. We're just *boys*!"

"If the man has lost his fiber, what can I do about it?" muttered Artorius, steely faced. "Come on. There's work to be done."

Suddenly a horsed figure sprinted from the shadows, and Amlodd reined up beside them, wearing a wry smile. He appeared to be more at ease. "Excuse me, Artorius, but suddenly I felt the need of a little refreshment. Do you suppose you could hand up my wine-skin?" He cocked his head and winked.

Surprised and delighted, Artorius said, "I'm not sure there's enough here to satisfy *your* thirst!" He laughed as he hefted up the skin.

Amlodd guffawed heartily. "Well, then, methinks

there's a Pict place close by which can supply all our needs for a long time to come—including a victory celebration! Come on, lads, let's get to this wizard of yours, and get out of that place." He looked at Artorius, a renewed strength in him. As though he had tapped some reserved resource. Saved for such circumstances. "Let's show those Picts how *true* Britons can fight!"

They turned their horses and rode with purpose firing their eyes, and with Amlodd in the lead, grinning lustily.

X

Sneering, Huil drove his dagger into Merlin's forearm.

Pain lanced up.

But the wound was purposefully not deep. Only a sharp warning. "Get up, druid, and do your work!" The Pict leader was determined to even the score.

Merlin clenched his teeth and grimly rose to his feet. Had he the power of equal combat, he almost certainly would have paid the barbarous bully back in kind. No—ahead there was a battle with something greater than Huil. This strife with the Pict leader was a warning of the dangers to come. He had to reserve his energy for the darkness that lay ahead.

He felt the wound grating on his flesh like a saw. Bringing his hand up, he felt rich blood pour through his fingers and knew the nauseating feeling that one's precious oozing fluid could induce. Merlin spoke in a voice barely a whisper: "I understand, Huil. You have been impatient to learn the secrets of our ancient ways. Now I willingly show you my crafts which will bring the Lord of Whirlwind and the Rain of Fire upon your stubborn head! Let me to my work and enough of talk."

A deathly silence had fallen. A pewter moon, old and worn, glowed dully orange in the southern sky. Fog, like a stealthy cat, crept along the bottoms. Higher, spears of lacy growths punctured the dark. Spruce, hemlock, aspen.

The multitude of Picts spread like a stain below the shallow foothill, into the rock-strewn path. Here and there flickering torchlight cast ambient, writhing shadows on the ground. Faintly, in the sky, came the shrill, remote cries of whirling, dipping nighthawks.

On the top of the knoll, grimacing and fretful, Huil had thumped down in a sling chair, surrounded by his guards. The shallow plateau was roughly circular, interrupted at the rear by the rise of an enormous rock, an ancient, lichened sarsen, rising vertically into the night. Central to all this stood Merlin; his robes caught by some errant breeze, lit by flaming tapers, he seemed a prophet of doom. Next to him stood a rude table covered with earthenware. Jars and vessels. And more. Herbs, spices, dried berries, and molds. And in shallow bowls, colored sands, pebbles; and evil, ghostly white, bright-yellow earths and powders.

Huil, in his sling, scowled and muttered. Slid his blade in and out of its scabbard with increasing impatience. He turned to Brys, rasped in an undertone: "If this spell fails, don't let him draw a second breath. I want him dead at my feet."

"Hold!" cried Merlin. "Not another sound. The time has come . . . instruments, my instruments!"

Vexed and furious, Huil choked back his rage. For some unexplainable reason, he thought, the spirit of this spellmaker would not knuckle down!

In the lambent air, the familiar acrid, bitter, and sweet smells of the earths, the powders, the leaves, and the berries wafted across the plateau. From vessel and jar and bowl, to mortar and grinding dish, Merlin poured and mixed, whispering strong Latin incantations and ancient crooning sounds over the whole.

Now in another, deeper vessel, he put together a handful of ashen powder. Mixed with yellowish, clinging stuff, sharp to the nostrils.

"The stuff of hellfire," mused Merlin as he softly

chanted and sang over the stirring. But not with a pestle. No, that would not do. Softly, gently. A flexible stirring reed to caress the mixture, ever so gently.

And now charcoal, ground and pulverized to a fine grain. The wizard eased the umbrageous spell stuff together with fingers of his left hand. Weaving this way and that, he spit into it.

Then he made a small plaquette of the witch-matter, bonded in stones and bound with straw.

On the table he made a mound of the yellow-gray matter, patting it together just so in the largest earthen bowl. And over this, but ever so carefully, a stone of goodly size. Yet finally . . . he muttered a binding spell, intoning a chant of humility, praise, and discipline to the tutelary spirits of the Power of the Air.

All was ready.

He peered up. There was moisture in the air, yes, but it seemed dry enough. His gaze went higher. Ah . . . it could have gone wrong. The table. The table must be moved. Just *right* of center.

"Huil!" he called. "I want four of your guard to move this table. . . ." He paced out three short steps, carefully. ". . . just here!"

Huil had changed. The procedure had caught his interest, his fascination. With an unconscious, urgent gesture, he commanded: "Quickly, do as he says."

Immediately four warriors leaped to carry out the order as Merlin had demanded.

The table in its place, Merlin picked up the plaquette, gently cradled it in his arms, and confronted the Pict leader.

"Great Chieftain of the Picts," he addressed the hairy barbarian. His voice was calm, serene. The antagonism, the menace had left it. Inwardly Merlin had come to terms with himself. It seemed to him, by all his intuition, his inner calculations, the time was long past for Artorius to arrive. His dream, his glorious vision was faulted. The crystal had erred. His life, dedicated to the coming of a new world, was not to be realized. His work with the boy Artorius would have to end, would come to naught, here, in this place. There would be no boy-king of the new Britons-Land. It had all been a figment of his imagining.

Artorius . . . child of Pendragon the Celt . . . you who bear a Roman name, it shall never be my task to remove from you that title of a vanished world. No one will ever know how it might have been, that you could have borne the true Briton's name of Arthur, the true namesake of Uther—King Arthur of Britain. Lad, ah, laddie . . . child of my hopes. Child of my ashes.

Merlin shook himself from his reverie. It had taken but a moment, but it seemed an age. So it is, he mused to himself, when truth will not die.

"Huil," he declared. "I am ready with my magic. I have promised you the Whirlwind. I have said the sky will darken and the earth will shake, and so it shall.

"The moment has arrived. There is one more step to prepare, and it is done." Merlin stepped back.

"It will work?" Huil asked. The air seemed charged with nameless portents. "So be it," breathed the great leader. "Show me the spell that will bring down the power of my enemies!"

The next moment Merlin quickly moved to the rear of the plateau. Disappeared behind the towering sarsen stone.

His voice came as from a distance. Echoes rebounded from the walls of rock and stone, seeming to be carried by demons.

"The time has come!" Merlin's cry rang out. "Bear witness!"

xi

From behind a massive, concealing boulder Artorius peered up at the distant figures upon the hilltop.

Chestnut nickered. The poor horse was exhausted. Artorius patted him. "Quiet. There's a long night ahead, horse. No time to rest yet." His gaze found Kay and Amlodd, slumped against stone, their horses cropping the grass that ringed the great rock. "Yes, there. And Merlin is the figure by the table! I *know* it. I can *feel* it."

"By all that's holy, I wish," breathed Amlodd, "that this rescue could wait till we did some figuring. It's risky."

Frantically Artorius tried to communicate the sense of urgency that welled within him. "Didn't you listen to the Old One of the Dark People? They wanted him for his *magic*. No magic, and they'll *kill* him. Why else would they be in such a ceremonial position—and why else would Merlin station himself upon a hill, unless to make sure he sees us if we come? An act of desperation! It's a signal to us."

"Yes, yes," Amlodd said, not moving. "But have you ever tried to storm a hilltop, warriors perched upon that height? Like trying to take a fort with a sling!"

"There are only, by my count, twelve others there. *None* have horses."

"But you can bet they're armed!" spat Amlodd. "It would be suicide. Hold your temper or we'll all be undone by your rashness."

"But Merlin's all alone up there," countered Artorius, grasping Amlodd by the arm. "I've had enough of waiting. I say attack!"

Amlodd snorted. "Poor armor against all those swords. And on a height to boot!"

Kay sprang away from the wall. "There's nothing left to us but daring, Artorius." He strode to his friend and stared him in the eye. "I've been nothing but a hindrance most of this journey."

Surprised, Artorius met Kay's gaze in the dimness and suddenly saw a different person. More mature, impassioned.

"You know what I'm talking about!" Kay grasped Artorius' arm tightly. "All my life, my friend, I have been in your shadow. What I do well, you do better.

Where I think, you act. I have to prove myself, Artorius. That I am worthy of carrying out this mission. That I am capable of doing my share." His expression was imploring. "Give me this chance. And if I die in the doing, so be it. Then I shall have had one supreme moment of conquering, in my dying, an entire life lived in self-doubt!"

"You would do this, Kay?" Emotion grew in Artorius, choking his voice. "At the risk of everything?"

"For you, for Merlin, for Amlodd. But mostly for myself. I have no head for strategy, Artorius. Tell me what is to be done."

Artorius placed his arms around his friend and hugged him close. He felt tears filling his eyes.

He said, "Yes, Kay. I do have a plan. It is the only possible thing to do."

"Then tell me, Artorius," said Kay. "There's no time to wait."

xii

Kay braced himself. His lips were dry as he sat tensely in the saddle.

His mind sped back. Not even when he was bound and helpless as a sacrificial victim with the maniacal priest standing over him with the killing knife had he felt so tense and anxious.

Ah, but there he was helpless. His fate was in other hands. Now his destiny was in his *own* control. If he survived, it would be only because of himself. Of courage, skill, and luck.

As the night wind pressed on his face, cold and wild, he let his horse, Moonstream, trot from behind the boulder. Gently reining her in, he targeted the horse toward the slowly rising, mist-swept slope. At the top, barely breaking through the translucent vapors, was the summit. There Merlin was. Surrounded by Picts.

Tilting forward, Kay whispered in his mount's ear:

"All right, good friend. Hurry this night and I promise you green fields and plenty of grazing for the rest of your life!"

Moonstream's ears dipped, rose again. Almost as though she were nodding assent.

Feeling a strange thrill of elation charge his veins, Kay kicked the steed's sides. She shot off like an arrow from a bow.

The wind pulled Kay's hair and cape back. He could almost taste the triumph he craved as he rode, all atingle, for the hilltop.

"Come up from the south," Artorius had said. "As far as I can tell, they're facing north. Just a simple confusing tactic that is sure to send at least some of them off after you. Dash through them, create some havoc, and then get out."

The damp, swirling mist parting before him, he laughed silently. The invigorating wind cold on his face. He swallowed back his fear and charged the hillside, pretending he was some naked Celt warrior of ancient times, storming a Roman battlement.

CHAPTER 5

Artorius, The Bear

Like the ghost of a forgotten river haunting its abandoned riverbed, mist crept through the valleys, making this hill's summit an island.

As Merlin moved to the rear of the plateau toward the sarsen stone he gazed down upon the fog banks. He sensed something down there. . . .

The slow-moving mist eddied in one spot. The vapory stuff formed a temporary whirlpool. A portion of ground was revealed, wreathed in streaming mist. . . .

A horse and rider. Moving toward the slope in desperate haste. Hoofbeats muffled by the swarthing vapors.

The druid's heart leaped. Artorius . . . could it be? Had Artorius arrived?

The mist engulfed the sight.

Merlin knew that if this attempt were to succeed his captors' attention must be diverted. Already he had placed the plaquette, with the spell-stuff of hellfire bound inside, at the rearward base of the enormous monolith. Tight against a crack in the granite. It would take but a blow from a heavy stone. . . .

"The spell is ready! Hold your places . . . let no one move!"

All assembled upon the hill jerked to attention. The

fidgeting warriors froze. Brys appeared agitated lest his fate be similar to Merlin's if the druid failed in this moment of sorcery. Huil, like some barbaric Caesar, leaned forward in his creaking seat.

"What is it we are to see?"

Merlin answered: "You will first hear a sound like a volley of horse hoofs." Then he cried out, "I call upon the Lord of Whirlwind to ride from the sky!"

In a weird voice he commenced a Latin chant.

Suddenly from the south, from under a dim, lurid moon came the faint sound of hoofbeats.

All eyes strained toward the valley. A soft gasp came from the onlookers. Bloodshot eyes widened to catch every scintilla of this coming miracle.

Merlin tensed.

Behind the rock, he wondered. Who was the rider? Artorius? Alone, simply come to swoop down upon him and spirit him away?

That would be foolhardy.

Besides, Merlin had seen *three* riders in his recent vision.

Why only one now?

Like sudden lightning the rider speared up from the swirling mists through the assembly, straight into the ring of flickering torches. Not halting, nor even slowing, he plowed through, spatha sweeping a trail that slashed through a Pict's head and bit into another's arm.

A multivoiced cry arose as the stunned warriors regained their senses. The fearful rider was yet in their midst, sword streaking like gleaming death.

As though he suspected something of what this meant Huil leaped from his seat, screaming commands.

Astonished, Merlin watched as the man approached, horse panting. The druid realized it was Kay, alone.

Barely checking his horse, all coal-black hoofs and screaming mane and straining muscles, Kay reached the incline of the hill and started up in a furious dash.

A war-axe zoomed off after him but fell short of its mark.

Merlin had to act now, or it would be over in a trice. Once the savage guard on the hill brought their swords, axes, and spears against the charging Kay, he would be meat for scavengers.

At once the druid picked up a heavy stone. With a faltering heave, he lifted it over his head. It was heavier than he had guessed.

Above the din he heard Huil raging: "Half of you . . . after him. Don't let him get away. Bring me his head!"

The closest of the warriors, inflamed with fury, dove down the slope swinging their weapons and wailing.

Merlin took two tottering steps, balancing his upraised stone. He realized then what the plan had been. He had been sent as a diversion. And the Pict was fooled. Hope filled the druid. It was now or never to call up the spirits to bring him aid.

Intoning a whispered prayer, he raised the stone high over his head. With a thrust he plunged it down upon the plaquette wedged into the sarsen's base.

There was a momentary spark, an eruption of smoke. Then an explosion heaved up. A violent scattering of sharp stones like chaff rattled the stones around. The ground rippled, rumbled. Merlin the druid was thrown backward against the rock wall of the plateau.

Now on the hill shouts of consternation. Across the boulder-strewn plain a fearsome gasp arose from the multitude. Awe. Wonder. Terror.

On the hill, high above the sloping valley, curling white smoke swathed the base of the monolith. The looming mass began to shiver and weave on its base. Wails and lamentations. Cries of grief assailed the heavens. The enormous upright stone, like an avenging, monstrous troll, came unbalanced. And slowly began its dizzy descent.

ii

In the torchlight they came.

Merlin saw them.

Through curling mists and confusion and terror . . . they came.

Exultation filling them, like vengeful berserkers they dashed, on lithe, powerful steeds.

A husky, hairy man, the grim delight of battle on his face, whirled his spatha. Parted a man's neck from his torso and life from his body. . . .

And behind him the most glorious vision Merlin had ever hoped to see. Glorious because it was flesh and blood and noble spirit. . . .

Artorius, *heir to the throne of Britain* . . . shining like a hero in the hissing torchlight.

Anger flowed through Artorius.

Anger of a kind he had never experienced.

He swept his dripping spatha up from a slash across the face of an astonished Pict.

He dug his heels into his mount in a furious burst of speed. Up the slope toward the hill. His eyes caught a glimpse of the form of Merlin, fallen, bloodied.

Artorius shrieked a bloodcurdling cry as he swept toward the summit.

Before he reached the top of the plateau, his eyes met a sight that froze his blood.

It seemed the hill, the rocks had come apart. A great shaft of rock—over forty feet high—a black-looming bulk of enormous size, wrenched, shivered, and descended with a hideous, quaking crash on the table of the hill. Squarely on top of Merlin's witch-matter.

A fiery burst flared up. Flame spurted to the sky in geysers of dust and debris. Great chunks and shards of rock sped through the rumbling night sky. The plateau was rent with earthquake force, heaving and tossing in a welter of terrible destruction. Smoke roiled and billowed, white, black, glowing dull-red and orange. A demonic blossoming of hellfire deep from the innermost bowels of Vulcan's Forge!

Merlin's spell had been well made. The sorcery had done its work.

Against a hollow of the rock wall into which he had been hurled by the final blast, Merlin stirred. His tunic and cape were torn and seared. Blood smeared his face. And he could feel painful contusions on his limbs and body. He tested here and there for broken bones.

No, except for some wry twinges, nothing broken.

His face creased painfully into a grim smile of ghastly humor.

Well, Huil, great leader, he thought. *It was your idea to play with fire. Play with these results . . . for a spell! I have the humors, sure.* He cackled a wheezing laugh as blood oozed from a shaky tooth.

All around him he could hear cries and moaning. Whimpering. Agony. Wretchedness. Desolation everywhere. Like broken dolls, bodies in grotesque positions, strewn across a dreadful playground by the demon spawn. Summoned from Merlin's concoction.

A sulphurous, noxious stench hovered . . . wafted lazily . . . poisonous tendrils of the aftermath mixing with fog.

Suddenly a voice erupted on the plateau: "Find me the magician!" Huil shouted hoarsely. A wild-maned madman, tattered and powerful, burst through the mist and confronted the druid. Glowering. Threatening. Holding a dagger. "My warriors. My Picts . . . my army!"

Huil lunged at Merlin with a scream of revenge. "Assassin!"

Merlin rolled away with all the strength he had. Pain raged in his body as he staggered up, but he consciously ignored it. He dodged the slashing blow aimed at him. A narrow miss. The Scot lifted his dagger for another lunge, but the screams of a warrior guard alerted him to his danger. He whirled about, dropping his knife, and reached for the sword that swung at his belt.

Artorius had crested the top of the hill. Spurred his mount to a prodigious lurch over fallen rock, rose in the saddle, shrieked an infuriated cry as he spied Merlin's peril.

He dove from his horse onto the man.

But his irrational dive had not reckoned with this wild creature's strength. Artorius found himself suddenly hurled back, propelled by the man's feet and arms. Hitting forcefully upon the ground, it was hard to keep his breath. Almost instantly the ragged man was on his feet, sword in hand, swinging.

Artorius held up his own spatha.

The raging, powerful warrior's sword struck slantwise, sliding down in a slicing motion. Only to be caught upon the hilt-guard. Sparks glittered down.

Artorius, newly aware that his adversary was no common fighter, twisted away, rolling to put as much space between them for the moment as possible.

He bent into a crouch, warily eyeing the advancing wild-haired man.

Saliva dripped from his opponent's bared teeth, a seeming behemoth of cunning and might.

Chestnut lingered close, breathing hard, eyes wide.

Artorius espied Merlin out of the corner of his eye.

"Merlin!" he cried. "Get on my horse! Hurry! Run!"

But Merlin, though he tried, seemed unable to raise his wracked body into the saddle.

A glimpse of the taxed man's bloody wounds and painful struggle drove Artorius into a fury of renewed action.

The Pict leader faced the weaving sword of the hard-bodied youth.

Halted a moment, scraps of his torn hides swaying.

"I do not know who you are, intruder, but I am Huil, son of Caw, and my adversaries seldom hold onto life for long! Prepare to die!"

That said, the berserker swished his sword up and screamed, charging.

As though Amlodd were whispering in his ear, Artorius heard the big man's instructions: "Listen, lad. Anger and fury are all to the good. But don't let them control you. You control *them* with cunning. And your sword will seem to have more than just two sharp sides!"

Metal glinting in the smoking torchlight, Artorius hoisted his sword to defend his position. Even as Huil swung his massive blade, the boy dodged hard to the left. Impetus propelled Huil past him, allowing Artorius time to deliver a slash against the man's thigh.

Huil howled and lumbered to a halt, swiveling about, something beyond madness inflaming his bloodshot eyes. Tongue protruded with effort, he stepped forward and let go such an explosive hack that had there been a tree in its way that trunk would surely have been cleft in twain.

Artorius barely stepped away in time. The sword tip whizzed just short of his neck, like an angry wasp. But Huil's swing once more was all force and no calculation. While he checked his backward motion to swipe once more downward at his quarry, Artorius darted in, ran the sword edge on the man's side, and sliced backward. A long trail of blood seeped from the wound. Huil stared down, astounded.

Then, uttering an ear-wracking cry, he stormed once more, blade arcing and hacking with incredible blows.

Artorius retreated, sword in one hand, toward a post topped with his unabated slashings.

Extending his weapon to meet one of the hacks, Huil's flashing sword bore down upon its smaller counterpart, knocking it away from Artorius' grasp. Artorius' arm felt as though it had been struck by a hammer.

With a cry of exultation the barbarian leader advanced on his disarmed adversary. He raised his sword with slow deliberation, moving in for the kill.

In that moment Artorius twisted, desperately reached

up and behind, leaped to seize the flaming taper from the post.

In a wide, powerful arc, the great spatha whistled toward the target. Huil's fiery eyes and flying hair were a frenzied vision of victory.

iii

Off to one side, Merlin's face bore a wrenching look of agony. The perilous swordplay between the Pict chieftain and his beloved Artorius was about to come to a bloody and terrible end.

From below the hill he could hear the sounds of another battle. In the dim light he caught sight of Amlodd swinging his sword, striving to prevail against a force of savage warriors. All about him, in the bloody melee, was strewn a trail of Pict bodies. Aching and muscle weary, the brawny Celt flailed and hacked. But where one enemy went down, another sprang to take his place. Spittle flecking his parched lips, Amlodd slowly gave ground. "Bear . . . Kay . . ." he whispered.

But Kay had his own problems, leading the enemy down the valley, striking from his horse, spreading consternation and confusion throughout the Pict encampment.

On the height Merlin grimly came to a realization.

The four of them—Artorius, Amlodd, Kay, and Merlin, himself—separated, forced into isolated battle, were doomed. Was this how it was to end? Was this the end of the dream?

No, it must not be!

Shaping action to thought, he crept low along the rim of the plateau. There, a fallen dagger. He seized it. In a firm grip.

Huil, you loathsome barbarian, he thought, *this day if it be our last . . . you die, too!* He shuffled forward.

"Artorius! Hold, boy! I come!"

iv

Huil's muscles writhed with the ultimate exertion of the blow he knew would cleave his enemy from head to toe.

The tough, chunky figure before him weaved and danced, waving the gluttering, flaming torch. Axelike, the flashing sword bore down.

With a quick step Artorius swerved, lunged under the outthrust arms, and plunged the fiery weapon into the chieftain's unprotected face.

With a terrible sound the barbarian screamed, lost hold of his sword. He lurched back, beating at his face with his hands. Already his hair was on fire.

"Brys! Brys!" Huil shrieked, stumbled, tottered into the shadows.

"Merlin!" yelled Artorius. The youth was in command now. "Don't let him get away!"

A welter of angry flames was beginning to grow, lighting up the rear.

Merlin stepped in, cloak raised, shielding his beard. There was a mixed look of anger, disgust, and ineffable sadness in his eyes.

He raised the blade. Gleaming in the orange light. He punched it quickly, once, twice. Deep into the chest of the searing mass.

He stepped back, unnerved. Weaponless. Tears in his eyes.

The body of Huil, son of Caw, fell heavily . . . shaking the ground like a fallen oak.

The druid turned away.

Artorius flung away his torch. He came forward to Merlin. Reached up, took the older man by the shoulders . . . and gently cradled him in his arms. Wordlessly he clasped his old teacher to his breast and stroked the tangled hair.

He led Merlin across the hilltop.

There . . . just at the brow of the downward slope . . . Chestnut, his horse.

"Come, good friend, up you go." He helped the injured druid to mount the saddle.

Suddenly a cry came to them, an urgent voice, faint, through the persistent din.

"Bear! Bear! Damnit, give me some sword!"

"Amlodd!"

The voice that had always held such boisterous life. Now it sounded frightened.

Far down the hill, Artorius could discern a tangled, struggling mass.

"Bear! Help! There are too many of them!"

Artorius spoke urgently to Merlin: "Go, now! Make a run for it. North by east. We'll meet when this is finished. Look for the blazed ash trees."

"No, Artorius . . . don't go . . . you can't be sure!" pleaded Merlin.

". . . sure that he needs my help?" Artorius cried. "Man, are you daft? By thunder *you* would look me in the eye with naught but *contempt* if ever I walked away from a friend in sore need, now wouldn't you, Druid Merlin!"

"Go, lad," answered Merlin softly. "Do what is in your heart."

"Godspeed!" The youth whacked Chestnut a hard smack on her flanks, sending her off at a plunging, rattling gallop. With a wave at Merlin he picked up his sword and sprinted pell-mell down the hill.

v

At the verge of the torches' outer light stood Amlodd. The flickering light shone on the rivers of sweat on his face, forearms, and hands.

Blood-grimed fingers wrapped about his streaming sword, the hulking Celt flailed like an insane windmill. The felled Picts in every direction attested to the man's prowess in battle.

But moving up the battle's vortex were the warriors Kay had diverted, obviously aware that the action had been a ruse. They darted forward to give aid to their fellows.

And Amlodd alone held them at bay.

In the uneven light, out of the corner of his eye, he could just make out the form of a horseman. Streaking downhill, tattered robes billowing, beard streaming. Merlin! Merlin on Chestnut . . . the horse of Artorius! Great thunder and lightning! The lad had done it . . . Artorius had gotten the druid away!

With a harsh laugh and renewed zeal Amlodd fell to, ever bolder. It would not be long before . . . before . . . they could all . . . get away.

Hard pressed. Dogged and desperate. Amlodd fended off the raining assaults.

Sword brandished before him, leaping over rocks and boulders, Artorius surged into the fray.

"Amlodd!" he shouted. "I am here!"

"Artorius . . . good lad! Stay to. Now back to back. We'll show them how true Britons fight Pictish barbarians!"

The savage battle seemed unceasing. From the mist a light rain was falling as sinews strained, metal clanked and squealed against metal, blood spilled on muddy ground.

Enemies dead at their feet, more coming up from the rear, the two men-at-arms stood, sheathed in crimson, pulsing from a dozen cuts. Artorius took the brunt of the greater number as his fresh, stout body, and young powerful arms dealt blows in every direction.

Even as a battle cry came to Artorius' lips he saw a thickset figure, vibrant with strength, plunge into the battle against Amlodd.

The man called Brys struck with his sword against the weary Celt.

Ah, thought Amlodd, *this fellow knows swordplay.* Against the clashing metal Amlodd could feel the quick, expert flick of wrist, the twist of blade in unexpected trajectory. This would take some handling!

The swords slashed again, whirling gleams of light. Cut. Drive. Thrust.

Feinted. Brushed away perspiration, blinking. Brys' spatha, a streak of light, swirled high . . . just out of sight . . . drove for Amlodd's body.

The Celt eased weight. Weaved. Deftly his gore-streaked blade cut deep into Brys' upper arm. Blood one!

The Pict's eyes widened. Only death could end this contest, he knew.

Grimly the blades returned to their work. Gyrating. Slashing.

Artorius could barely keep his eyes on his enemies as he felt the relentless, inexorable duel behind his back.

Suddenly he heard a sigh . . . a soft, ever-so-quiet ripping sound. An exhalation.

His heart seemed to stop. Did not dare to turn around.

But he knew!

Somehow, back of his mind, he saw the spatha, ever so keen . . . flick in and slide out like a silver serpent. In and out of Amlodd's body.

The hairy head swayed.

Turning slightly, the spatha slipped out of Amlodd's hand.

He gave Artorius a dazed smile, lids partly closed. In the end he simply settled down like a child at rest.

The last of the light in the eyes focused on Artorius, and they bore an awareness and peace.

vi

A wave of grief wracked Artorius' body such as he had never known. He breathed in great, pain-filled gasps, heaving and strangling against the compression in his lungs.

He howled and wailed like a stricken animal.

Wild-eyed. A demonic, furious rage possessed him.

With insensate, uncontrollable power he whirled

around. Lashed out at the astonished Pict captain with an onslaught that threw Brys off balance. With one monstrous, fearsome cry his arms raised the weapon high, brought it down with devastating force. And cleaved the man asunder. Brys' life departed before he struck ground.

Now he turned against the balance of his foe.

The Picts fell back from the menacing blade.

Momentarily the action abated.

Tears, uncontrolled, welled from the eyes of the agonized youth.

In the early dawn light, rain and mist, a wafting corpse-color of ashen-yellow, spread over the valley. There was the acrid stench of smoke and the damp, hissing torches, wreckage, carnage, mud, and rot. Everywhere.

The grief in Artorius subsided. The smell of his own blood and sweat was in his nose. His eyes roved over the endless, desolate landscape. It looked like a tapestry of death.

He saw the faces of the bewildered Picts; leaderless, they were enemies without a cause.

He reached down to retrieve Amlodd's bloody sword. For a last time he looked into his friend's face. Pushed back the tousled hair. Gently closed the half-lidded eyes against the light of the disordered day.

Artorius stood up. He cast aside his own weapon. Now armed with Amlodd's heavy blade he raised the spatha in attack position.

Silent words formed on his lips. "Amlodd, noble friend. Let the strength of my arms carry this true blade in the last cause of your unconquerable spirit!"

Artorius advanced, weapon outthrust.

"Come, Picts," he said. "Let the valiant come forward. This is a good day for dying."

But before the attack could begin . . . a galloping rash of horse hoofs split the air.

"Artorius!" a voice cried harshly. A voice that stung like boiling water. Merlin!

"Hurry! There's no time to lose!" The druid wheeled in on Chestnut, the reins of Cloud-Eyes, Amlodd's horse, in his other hand. A strength of spirit was shining from his mentor.

"To horse! Artorius . . . Amlodd . . . at once!"

With a running leap, spatha held high, Artorius gained the saddle.

Seizing the reins, he spurred the powerful horse to a gallop.

"Wait! Where's Amlodd? Artorius!" Merlin called after the racing youth.

"Amlodd's dead. . . ." The voice echoed from the walls of rock and the farther hills.

Kicking the flanks of the steed, Artorius tore across the plain in the whipping breeze, Merlin in his wake.

Farther down in the valley he could see Kay riding toward them. The sight lightened the load upon his heart.

The three riders pulled together. Scrambled with clattering hoofs up the incline. Crested the hill.

Artorius paused. Took a long look backward, where part of his youth lay dead in the distant valley.

Then the riders raced away into the leaden day.

vii

The ground leaked mist, which rose into the dawn like the damp ghost of night giving way to day.

Wraith-curls streamed along the lake, their wet scent pleasant to Merlin, seated by the shore. His wound's pain had died to a steady throb, and he felt better. He could slowly feel his strength and his resources returning to him.

By the lake a canopy of yew trees leaned out over the smooth surface of water. Reeds waved softly from a barely discernible current of air.

The sun, as it rose over the highlands, felt good. Gentle. Friendly.

To feel warm again, thought Merlin. After all this cold. . . .

The horses stood asleep nearby, tied to bushes. Kay still lay near Merlin's feet, mouth moving as he continued his breathless dream ride.

At the water's edge Artorius stood ankle deep, trying to wash the blood off his clothes, face, and hands.

Well away from the Pict tribe now, they could rest in safety. They had ridden hard through the night, Artorius at their forefront, face twisted with exertion. As though expended energy would expiate torturing guilt. . . .

Watching him now, Merlin felt a sudden wave of empathy. A boy caught between youth and manhood. Such a terrible experience to bear. *How ruthless and unfeeling of himself*, thought Merlin, *to put the youth through such unnatural tasks.*

Artorius *had* loved Amlodd, for all the rogue's ungovernable character and worse habits. And wasn't that like Artorius—to take a friend at face value, the all with the all. He had the stuff of a king in him. A king for a world to follow and emulate.

And yet something had happened up there on that hill. Something so terrible and beautiful that even Merlin, for all his perception, could not grasp its importance. It was more than Merlin could have asked for. It made the druid's heart ache to see the ravages it wreaked upon the boy.

Artorius stepped out of the water. He turned to Merlin. Water dripped down his face like a cascade of jewellike tears. But the face was impassive. The eyes empty, revealing nothing. . . .

Artorius held up his hand, almost imploringly, to the druid. "It won't come off," he muttered in a lifeless voice. "The blood won't come off, Merlin."

The lifted hands were worn and calloused. But there was no blood there. No blood that showed.

"One morning you will wake up," murmured Merlin, "and it will be like a bad dream, that blood."

Artorius nodded absently. He plodded heavily to where Merlin sat. Without a word he put his arms around the druid's neck. He gave Merlin a quick hug that asked for no response, and then he lay by Kay at the druid's feet, in the springy grass, curled up, eyes open and staring. Haunted eyes now. Eyes that looked into more than one could see.

Merlin sighed, and he sat down close beside the boy. He knew there was nothing to be said. No balm for this wound. No sorcerer's salve.

He placed a firm, strong hand on the boy's back. Something caught in his throat.

I am not worthy of you, son of my design, he thought. *And yet we bear a burden now of our own choosing.*

Dear Bear.

And Merlin remembered something he had read in Latin. A text upon the growing of wine grapes. Upon vines. For the best maturing, the finest vintage, selected branches of a vine had to be pruned. Cut off. Sacrificed so the fruit that that vine bore would be of the highest quality. This cutting was placed in the judgment of the grower.

How cruel life is, the old man thought, his arm beginning to ache again. *How cruel* I *was to put the pruning shears in the hands of this noble vine beside me, to cut his* own *branches.*

And yet how remarkable will be the vintage when it is pressed and aged.

How cruel and savage life is, he mused.

And wise.

viii

Less than a year later there was battle to do again. One day, whilst Kay and Artorius were out riding, fearful shrieks erupted near them in the rain-drenched gray of the forest. Artorius reined in his horse, as did Kay a moment later.

A half-dozen paint-daubed men with fierce beards, shields, and spears came charging at them on foot from a hiding place. Artorius reached across to his left thigh and unsheathed his nicked but sturdy Roman sword.

"Your shield, Kay!" he shouted. But his companion was too slow. The first of the Saxon ambushers flung his spear at Kay's unprotected chest.

In an instant Artorius leaned far out to the side, clutching his mount's mane with one hand while he slashed downward with the other—halving the spear shaft in midair. Deflected, the head of the spear bounced harmlessly off Kay's shoulder.

"Turn and charge!" Artorius yelled, wheeling his mount. Kay collected himself and followed.

The Saxons had crossed a small brook that the boys had forded earlier. There the enemy crouched ferocious and growling. The Saxons launched spears at the pair of riders, who came thundering at them through the gray murk, galloping flank to flank.

Kay's sword was held in his right hand, so Artorius tossed his into his left. The great blades arced and chopped. The Saxons held their places, then suddenly scattered at the last instant. The mounted boys cut and hacked as they rode between the barbarians. Artorius' downstroke opened a neck. Blood spattered the flank of his horse as the two thundered over the creek, then wheeled and came charging back. One Saxon lay headless. A second moaned and floundered in the creek, clutching the forearm Kay had laid open—

The huge, powerful horses rolled their eyes and plumed steam from their nostrils. Artorius and Kay bent low while spears raked the air above them. When they reached the creek Kay cleaved downward again as the Saxons tried to encircle them. A bearded man howled in agony as Kay's blade bit into the bone of his skull—

With three down the other three fled like wraiths. Artorius clambered to the ground, dragged the wounded

Saxon to his feet. Kay ran up, panting, his arm drawn back:

"Let me finish him, Bear!"

Artorius checked his friend's hand. "There's no need—and no honor gained from making a corpse of a beaten man."

"You've listened too much to Father prattling about saintly grace!" Kay growled.

"I've also listened to him about the advantages horsemen enjoy against foot troops." Uncomprehending, the Saxon stared at Artorius, his bloodied sword. "Today we saw the proof. Two against six—and because we were on horses we're alive and they are fled. Even my own father has never learned *that* lesson," he concluded, giving the Saxon a shove.

"Go." He gestured. "Follow your brothers and let them look after your wound—if they will."

But Artorius couldn't make the Saxon understand until he pantomimed running. The bearded man gaped at him—then staggered off into the misted trees.

Kay stared at his friend. "That first spear would have taken me, Bear."

"Oh, you'd have dodged it—"

Kay shook his head, dismissing Artorius' light reply. "You are always the quicker one. A man could do far worse than follow a captain of such skill."

Again Artorius started to laugh. But Kay rushed on:

"You *will* be a captain, Artorius, and a famous one. I've known that a long time. You understand this business of using horses—so simple a lesson, but so few pay it any mind—" He wiped his mouth, something almost awestruck in his eyes. "You saved my life a few minutes ago, Bear—no, listen to me. I give you mine in return. To follow and serve you all your days."

Artorius gazed at his friend, then suddenly gave him a soldier's handclasp.

"I take the pledge with thanks, my friend. I do mean to raise a troop of horse soldiers one day and take to the countryside against the Saxons. I'll welcome a sword as swift and brave as yours."

Artorius was thinking of the druid's prophecy about the high throne. Somehow he had never fully believed it—until this moment. With youthful passion Kay dropped to one knee and bent his head to signify obedience to the power he felt in his friend.

Artorius might have joked about that excess of emotion, too. But he didn't. When he saw Kay kneel an emotion both exciting and fearful touched his deepest being. And there in the murky woodland, with ugly Saxon corpses lying about, he came to believe at last what Merlin had told him.

He clapped Kay on the shoulder. "Let's whistle up the horses. I can't stand this dank, lightless place—"

ix

Weary, Uther Pendragon extended his hands toward the fire in the solar's hearth. A head bandage dressed a new wound. Across the roof the winter blizzard sang like a mourning voice.

"And how many did you lose this time?" Merlin asked. He sat in the shadows, only his eyes visible, fire lit and huge.

"Forty, fifty—but we routed them."

"Each time the price is higher. More men dead. And fewer barons and kings follow your standard every day. They say—"

Uther spun, shouting, "I have heard what they say! They say that another king should be chosen because the Saxons have steadily whittled away our ground. They say Pendragon is losing the island—"

"And will lose the high throne soon. One of those jealous men will seize it."

Almost pathetic in his grimness, Uther said, "I have tried begetting an heir! I've tried more times than I can remember. What has made her barren?"

"I don't know," Merlin answered. "But I knew long ago that she would be."

"And you never spoke?"

"Would you have believed me?"

Uther sank down, round-shouldered and spent. "My enemies are grown beyond counting. Any day I expect the local kings and barons to agree on a successor—"

"You have a successor—if you'll only name him."

Uther's head jerked up. "The bastard that Hector's keeping secretly?"

Merlin nodded. "Most have forgotten he even exists—" The druid rose. "It's time to remind them."

Perplexed, Uther began, "No one would acknowledge him—"

"Some would—if you name him your heir and the naming was—" Merlin's eyes seemed to become pinpoints "—properly arranged. Your only other choice is to leave the high throne empty after you die."

"I thought there would surely be another son—" Uther said in an empty voice.

"You have the only son you need. When I bring him to you, that will be plain." In a colder tone: "Of course the choice is yours."

Uther grimaced. "Oh, no! Somehow, I think you made it for me, my friend. Years ago."

"Do you want to see the boy?"

After a long silence Uther whispered, "Yes."

"While I'm fetching him, you must call in your smithy. The high king needs a new sword."

"Are you mad?" Uther slapped his thigh. "I have my brother's sword—" He unbuckled the sheath and shook it in the firelight. "It's worn, but it has served me well."

"This is to be no ordinary sword," Merlin told him. "It will be forged in the hottest fires the smithy can stoke—with special tempering powders that I will provide before I leave. It will bear the device of Pendragon in its pommelstone—and an inscription on its blade. And it will have a name, just as all good swords do. 'Cutter of steel.' In the old tongue—"

Merlin paused, then whispered one more word:

"Excalibur."

CHAPTER 6

Pendragon

The night was clear. The vast, flat plain lay empty in the last translucent light from the western horizon. Suddenly two figures appeared on the horizon, tiny against the expanse of long grass unbroken by so much as a single farm. The figures—horsemen—grew larger. A mantle billowed behind one rider. The white hair of the other shone in the first starlight. Across his thighs, the second rider clutched a long, narrow bundle wrapped in hides.

As the darkness deepened the two riders reined in near a circle of huge, upright stones. There was something almost forbidding about the stones. The mantled rider, Pendragon, shuddered as he gazed at them.

"There's not a cottager for miles because of these ruins. It's no wonder."

Amused, Merlin said, "And only the most courageous who travel on the high road dare to stop and peer in at the altar. After this night's work, however, that will change."

Merlin dismounted, the bundle under his arm. Uther said:

"I—I would prefer that you go in alone. This is not a Christian place—"

The druid halted under the mighty stone lintel of one

of the natural doorways. "It is God's place, majesty—no matter what name you call Him. There's nothing to fear. After all," he joked, "am I not supposed to have moved all these stones to this plain myself? All the way across the sea from the Green Isle—?"

Still smiling, he limped into the middle of the ring and laid the bundle on the rectangular altar of porous stone.

The altar was worn smooth by weather. But at certain places on its surface, dark ugly veins were visible. Blood? Uther wondered. Other, brighter veins seemed to glow with a faint phosphorescence.

"I was a fool to approve your schemes," the king grumbled. "Mummery will never put the boy on the throne."

Angered, Merlin said, "This is not mummery. The old gods have yielded to the new, but never doubt the existence of either—or their power to shape a great change in the world when evil is in the ascendancy."

Rapidly the druid unfastened the thongs around the bundle. He folded back the layers of hide to reveal a long beautiful sword whose bright blade reflected the stars.

Patterned after the spathas of the long-departed Romans, the sword still had its own unique quality. A translucent pommelstone imprisoned a tiny ruby dragon, its foreclaws poised, its sapphire eye aflame—

Merlin lifted the sword in one hand and swept the hides away. The sword clinked gently as he laid it down again.

"Now," he whispered to Uther. "Pick it up."

Uther's eyes showed his fear. Merlin repeated, "Pick it up as I taught you! Then stand still as these stones until I say to do otherwise. Do not fear anything you see or feel—and do not fear for your own life. The power in this place will use us for its instruments. There will be no danger."

The sheen of Uther's eyeballs showed that he doubted the druid's reassurance. Yet he managed to nod, his forehead glistening with sweat despite the cool evening air. Not a sound disturbed the silence of the plain.

"Pick up Excalibur, Uther Pendragon!" Merlin commanded.

Slowly Uther walked to the altar and laid hands on the great hilt. As he lifted the sword the tip struck the altar's edge and rang with a sweet, piercing note.

The king withdrew the required three paces, thick fingers clasped around the hilt and point held toward the ground. Along one surface of the blade a faint patterning of darkness indicated characters engraved in the metal.

Merlin tilted his head back, closed his eyes. Through the soles of his sandals he felt the strength and solidity of the earth. His hands seemed remarkably light as he brought them up, palms toward the sky, supplicating—

Uther raised the sword at the same time.

Then Merlin began to chant, strange, rhythmic words the king did not understand. Some of it he thought was the old tongue still spoken by the Celtic monks. But much of it was queer and polysyllabic, almost a crooning singsong until Merlin's voice gave it greater strength, rolling forth the incantation sonorously, louder, then louder still—

The high king trembled like a small boy when he heard the rustle of the long grass of the plain. The grass was stirred by gusts. But there had been no wind a moment ago—

Chanting, Merlin extended his arms to heaven. The stars seemed to enlarge to enormous fires that shed a flashing radiance on the sword whose cross-hilt Uther clamped in his trembling grip. The louder Merlin's voice became, the stronger the wind blew. Within moments the grass was bending and whipping in a gale—

In the sky—Uther clenched his jaw and blinked—great boiling clouds of silver and ebony were pouring out of the north. The clouds hid the stars and lit the plain as lightning flared in their rolling depths—

Merlin's beard stood out to one side of his face in the

wind. The clouds rumbled now, covering the stars directly overhead, then sweeping on to meet the horizon behind the druid and the high king. A lightning bolt came down, ripping the plain perhaps a league from the stones. Thunder exploded. Yet through the crashes of sound Uther still heard the druid's chant—

Another fork of lightning smote the earth just outside the ring of stones. Uther began to tremble violently. He knew the natural dangers of the fire from the sky. It destroyed trees, slew human beings—

Merlin's head was flung back, his face a mask of triumph. His fingertips seemed to beckon down the white fire that flickered and flamed almost continuously. Overhead, the clouds parted. Uther almost screamed as a white tongue licked straight down toward the heart of the ring—

We will die, Uther thought in that suspended moment when the blinding fire snaked downward toward the beautiful sword held high between his body and the altar. Merlin's voice was silent now, but the cataclysmic winds filled the world with a sound that resembled a chorus chanting just as the druid had—

Never in all his life had Uther Pendragon been so afraid. Yet he stood his ground. The lightning bolt struck the ground between his boots and the altar. The foundations of the world seemed to rock—

The thunder pealed, deafening. Uther tried to scream but could not. *His own forearms were bathed in the white fire of the lightning bolt that did not recede—and the sword's pommelstone was bathed in it as well—*

The glow ran down between his fingers, liquid light. It slipped across the hilt and fired the blade to a brilliance so blinding that Uther had to close his eyes—

Against his eyelids he saw that merciless radiance. Above the grinding of the earth and the chanting of the heavens he heard Merlin's anguished cry:

"Now—*plunge it in*!"

Somehow he managed to stagger forward and drive the blade down, knowing it would shatter—

Something seemed to shiver the sword. He felt it in his palms: a peculiar tingling, but no impact. The chanting, the wind, the churning earth, the blasting thunder dealt a combined blow to his senses that spilled him backward, unconscious—

ii

When he awoke the plain was as silent as before. The stars twinkled.

Merlin helped him up. Uther started to speak, then goggled at the crosslike silhouette against the light-spangled sky.

Standing in the altar stone—driven halfway to its hilt—glittered Excalibur.

Uther staggered forward, stupefied. He ran a trembling palm over the stone. It was alarmingly warm, yet unmistakably solid.

He pressed fingertips against the sword's hilt, felt the blade flex. But its imprisoned lower half gave not at all.

Full of dread he ran his palm down one side of the chilly steel, stroking the lettering engraved by the smith at Merlin's instruction. Uther knew the inscription by heart because he had puzzled over it when Merlin first spoke it aloud. By moving cautiously to a different corner of the altar Uther could read the words again.

Whosoever shall draw this sword from the stone is rightwise king of England.

Merlin laid a soothing arm across the high king's shaking shoulders. The druid seemed drained, almost sleepy. His smile was gentle:

"Come away now. Our work is over."

iii

Merlin looked exhausted. *And no wonder*, old Baron Hector thought as he studied the druid across the library.

Merlin had ridden most of the night all the way from

Uther's fort beside the river Cam. These past three months since his mysterious journey with Pendragon to the standing stones Hector had heard tales about Merlin galloping to and fro across the land to survey the inroads of the Saxons or to watch firsthand when the high king took more men into battle in what was proving a futile defense. Merlin's dislike of horses was widely known. He must indeed be a driven man to resort to that mode of transportation so often these days—

"Where's the boy?" Merlin demanded.

"In the chapel, I believe. He and my son are spending an hour in prayer for his majesty."

Merlin said nothing, limping toward the passageway that led outdoors. He crossed the fort yard in winter sunshine that did nothing to warm his aching bones. He was famished; yet he couldn't have swallowed a morsel. Spent, he knew he could not sleep.

Lines in his face had deepened. He had shivered in the saddle all night, never resting except for one short interval during which he chewed a bit of root. What he saw in his mind a few moments later confirmed the rumors pouring in from the eastern coast:

He saw the Narrow Sea still unblocked by ice and aswarm with boatload after boatload of invaders. The Saxons sensed a kill. They were closing on Uther's domain as forest wolves closed around an injured deer. Merlin awoke from his vision a frightened man.

He stepped around a sow suckling her piglets on the frozen ground. Noted some of Hector's people—a few women and children—gathered to watch a wandering fortune-teller who squatted against the wall near the barred gate. The fortune-teller, a woman, was scattering animal bones to divine the future for anyone who gave her a bit of food or a scrap of bright tinware.

The druid deemed such charlatans harmless. He would have pitied the woman if she really could have seen the coming chaos, as he had—

Merlin entered the chilly chapel from the rear. Two young men in link-mail shirts knelt before the altar, heads bowed. Above them, a cruciform window cast its sunlit pattern onto the central aisle between the stone benches. Merlin limped forward, his sandals raising echoes. The young men glanced around, hastily made the cross-sign over their breasts, and came hurrying to him.

The taller of the two clutched his arm:

"What of the king?"

"The wound he took harrying the Saxons grew poisonous. No bleeding—no balms would avail." Merlin paused a moment. "Uther is dead."

Artorius shook his head in fury. "I should have gone to him—!"

"He would never have recognized you."

"But I only saw him that once! That time you took me to the Cam fort—"

"It was enough. He was satisfied."

"He said so little—"

"He needed no words from you. He knows how I've trained you."

The druid glanced at the other boy. "Would you let us speak privately, Kay?"

Kay looked sympathetically at his friend, then slipped out of the chapel. Merlin sank down on one of the benches.

"The hour for which I have prepared you has come," Merlin began. "All of Hector's teachings—military tactics as well as the principles of Roman justice and Christian compassion—were directed at this moment. Do you remember what I said that time on the watchtower?"

"I remember," Artorius answered slowly. "I'm not sure I altogether believe it even yet."

"We will bide our time through the bad weather. The Saxons will be restricted to their camps and villages, as they are every winter. By spring a military force must be equipped and organized—an effective one or the Saxons will overwhelm the island. They hold almost half of it now."

"Am I to lead that force?" Artorius asked.

"No one else will. The barons will be altogether too busy proposing one another for the kingship, buying supporters, murdering opponents—"

"No one's pulled the sword that appeared in the altar at the standing stones?"

Merlin pierced Artorius with his flecked gaze. "No one—though many have tried. Only one man can wield Excalibur."

"Is it truly my father's sword?"

"Yes," Merlin said, "but it's also the sword of the next high king. The *last* high king, if he fails. Time has run out, and the island must be united, the Saxons driven back—"

"Did you also put the sword into the stone?"

"Until the king placed Excalibur there, no hand touched its hilt but Pendragon's. Even the smithy handled it with tongs as he forged it."

Merlin rose and limped to Artorius, who stood frowning in the cross of light on the aisle's floor.

"The burden I have asked you to bear is not an easy one, Artorius. But it's a necessary one. During the winter months I want you to think of which young men you can gather into a fighting force—"

"On horseback," Artorius emphasized. "We've lost our wars by walking to and from the battlefields. I intend to ride, swiftly, as the Romans did."

Merlin nodded, pleased. "In the spring I believe matters of succession will come to a head. At that time we will move."

Artorius' face smoothed out. There was a sad quality in his eyes, as if he finally understood the nature of the burden Merlin had described. But his shoulders lifted. His expression was confident:

"Very well."

"One more thing—a Roman name will no longer serve. When the people pronounce the name of their new leader they'll want to speak a name that's familiar. From this day hence you must begin to think of yourself not as Artorius but Arthur. Arthur Pendragon. Arthur of Britain."

iv

"Enough, I'm weary. The sight has left me."

The fortune-teller scooped up her bones, dropped them into a pouch hanging from her rope belt. A second, larger pouch stored the trinkets and bits of bread she had accumulated for her labors.

Dusting her hands on her cowled robe, she started for the barred gate. She planned to ask the men on guard whether she might speak with the baron who ruled the fort. Thus far she had been frustrated in her efforts to gain a look at the one she sought.

She had seen the hated Merlin, of course. Seen him come riding wearily in on horseback. But he had disappeared into the long house, then the chapel, and had not reappeared.

About to address one of the guards, she glanced at two figures coming around the corner of the chapel. She drew in a harsh breath. One was the hated, aging druid. The other—

Gods, how clear and startling the resemblance was! Couldn't the clods see it?

"What a handsome young man," she said pleasantly, her face still concealed by her cowl. "Is he Baron Hector's son?"

"A ward only," the guard replied. "His name's Artorius. He's called Bear."

She felt as if a knife of hatred impaled her. But she gave no sign—

For years she had been wandering and searching—and now she had seen him with her own eyes, verifying the reports of his one appearance at the Cam River fort. She had hopes that he would have fallen victim to the Saxons before the king's demise. But her sorcery had been to no avail. "I must hurry on to the next fort before dark."

Shortly she was rushing through the woods to where she had left her horse and her men-at-arms. Uther would die without a legitimate heir. The latest word from the Cam fort said the wound he had suffered was mortal. She expected her mother, whom she had not seen since that terrible night at Tintagel, to follow the high king to the grave very soon once he died. At all reports Ygrayne was no more than a recluse these days. *Repenting her sin*, the fortune-teller thought mockingly as she passed a screen of brush and saw her men waiting.

The men saluted her by clashing their spears against their griffin-painted shields. One man asked:

"Did you find what you sought, my lady?"

The fortune-teller swept back her cowl, revealing not a crone's face but the arresting features of a young woman. Her beauty was marred only by an angularity in her cheekbones and by a strange, almost fanatic quality in her large, lynxlike eyes.

"I did. Uther's bastard is still among us and must be stopped."

Uther's bastard and my half brother, she thought with icy calm.

Swiftly she doffed the fortune-teller's habit and slipped into a more elegant riding cloak held respectfully by two of the men. One tried to please her:

"No illegitimate boy could hope to draw that sword everyone's prattling about. I mean it's not possible, my lady, when noblemen of decent birth cannot do it."

"It is entirely possible," she countered. "Who do you suppose arranged for that sword to appear so mysteriously? Pendragon's druid!"

The man gaped.

Other men assisted Morgan of Cornwall into the saddle. In her mind she reviewed what she must do.

She had various means at her disposal—including some of Merlin's own methods.

And she had two great advantages:

First, the boy probably had no idea she existed. Even

if Merlin should think to tell him, the boy would probably never suspect the intensity of her hatred.

Second, she was prepared to devote her life to her twin goals of reprisal and reinstatement to power of the house of Cornwall—

Another of her men said, "It would be simple for one of us to slip into Hector's fort, my lady. Disguised as a wandering smith, let's say. The boy could be eliminated very easily—"

Morgan smiled a charming, vicious smile, remembering the infant and the druid in the woods. "No, I tried once, long ago, and afterward deemed it unsuitable. Too quick, for one thing. Let the druid give the boy a whiff of kingship if he can. When glory slips from the boy's hands, as it surely will, he'll feel the loss all the more bitterly for having experienced it. Besides, you forget I've developed skills that can be far more punishing than a common dagger—"

Her lynx eyes shone. Her men-at-arms shivered.

"Shall we ride, gentlemen?"

Like phantoms they melted into the interplay of shadow and winter sunlight.

V

When spring once again shattered winter's death-grip and unlocked loamy smells from the earth and bursts of green from bare limbs and hillsides, Merlin saw grim sights in the great sphere in his cave.

As he'd feared, Uther's death had plunged the island kingdom into convulsions. The barons and petty kings fought and wrangled over succession. All that prevented any one of them from seizing the high throne was the great sword Uther had implanted in the altar. The import of Excalibur's engraved legend had now been carried from the old Roman defense wall in the north to the remotest shire in the south, and so the campaign of each claimant routinely included a stop at the feared place on the plain. His hands on the sphere's curve and his tongue tasting faintly of the mysterious dreamroot, Merlin never smiled at the sweats and heaves and grunts of the lords who pulled and hauled on Excalibur's hilt, always failing to dislodge it. Sometimes a would-be monarch lost his grip and landed on his pretentious fundament. Even then Merlin didn't smile. He had seen too many other things in the sphere and in the clarified vastness of his mind:

He saw horizons pricked with fire and blurred with smoke—not all of it the result of the steady advance of the Saxons. In the North a vain, preening king named Lot of Orkney descended with foot soldiers upon the hill fort at neighboring Lothian. Lot slew Lothian's lord because Lot believed the king of Lothian presented a threat to his own ambitions to the throne.

Heedless of the havoc his ambition was causing, Lot ordered Lothian's fields torched and many of Lothian's folk butchered. When Merlin saw such images—women being raped, babies being swung by their heels, then dashed headfirst against a stone wall—there was no room in his heart for laughter.

Finally when full spring came Merlin went to old Hector and told him what must be done.

Because of his age and the honors that had come to him from as far back as the time of Ambrosius, Hector's word was heeded when he declared that the true enemy was the barbarian and that the kings and barons only wasted their precious energy and fighting men when they quarreled among themselves. A parlay was needed, Hector said. With all contenders represented.

The extremely ambitious, such as Lot of Orkney and Lothian, balked at first. But a sufficient number of wise heads heeded Hector, and thus the contentious barons and kings agreed to a meeting to settle the matter of succession. Lot had no choice but to attend, raising his pavilion and his pennants alongside the others that splashed color on the empty plain around the standing stones. Even as the great meeting commenced, plumes of smoke on the northeast horizon—the Saxons, burning—reminded all those present of the lateness of the hour.

vi

Lot, his sons, and their retinue rode through their homeland.

As he swayed quietly in his saddle, backside feeling chafed from the long ride, Lot scanned his northern home country.

He found it good.

The land to the southeast of the untenanted mile towers and turrets of Hadrian's Wall was rough, wind scored. Gales from the North Sea beat its shores and countryside, carving the hills and mountains over the centuries into craggy juts of rock, capped only by stubborn gorse and heather scrub.

Winter was harsh here. Almost cruel. But the land wore a ragged, cutting beauty, its colors deep and well defined between the predominant buff gray, blacks, and whites.

Lot thought upon the history of this northern land, wrapping his cloak tighter about himself against the faint chill in the air.

The Romans had been able to go only this far north in their domination of the island Britain . . . and then only to assure that the Celtic tribes of the area and the fearsome Picts to the North were kept away from the fertile and kinder lands to the south, which the Romans valued much more.

So great was the threat of the savage northern peoples that the Romans thought to drive them even farther away from the choice prizes of the southern lands. They troubled Hadrian's Wall constantly. If they broke through, there was no telling what havoc would be wreaked. Most bothersome were the Brigantes. The legions pushed these tribes back to a more logical boundary . . . a place where Britain was narrowest from ocean to ocean: the narrow piece of land between the Clyde and the Forth.

Here was built the Antoine Wall. This construction was thirty-seven miles wide. Nineteen forts were strung like beads along its length.

With this wall the Romans thought to make upper Britain a safe province.

It was quite different from the Wall of Hadrian in that instead of stone it was made of turf or clay. No rearward vallum or mile castles or turrets were situated upon it. For a while Rome's northern legions were concentrated around it.

But in the year 155 a serious rebellion brought the troops back to their former position, and once more the tribes of the Scots and Picts swarmed over the lowlands, stopped only by Hadrian's Wall.

Thus the north of Britain had always been primarily a military land to the Romans, thought Lot of Orkney, returning from Eburacum. Not so Latinized. The people here were of truer descent from the wilder Celts.

Thus he had usurped their former king's place with no real trouble.

Osri had been a relative. Lot had tired of Orkney and had moved south to become a king. It suited his disposition very nicely, he thought, guiding his horse and retinue of twenty companions along the old Roman highway, back to his fort at Caerwent.

Eburacum had proved a limited success. Only a few other kings had thrown their allegiance toward him at the council meeting. Minor kings, at that, no doubt eager for their share of the glory.

A throne stood empty.

The throne of Pendragon.

With Uther's death the way was open to Lot, and he felt destiny heavily on his side.

He would be high king of Britain, no matter what bodies had to be ground beneath his heels.

The squabbling had already begun. Arthur really was no threat. Arthur! Such a jest! As though by changing his name from Artorius, Merlin thought to make him worthy of the high throne. As if a bear could be transformed into a king. Ha!

Lot sneered to himself at the very thought. With the right applications of force and ambition there might only be a few battles ahead of him to squash those who objected to his claim upon the throne.

Yes, and *he* had heirs to take the throne afterward. Sons. Strong, healthy lads. He took much pleasure in them—almost as much as he'd gotten in siring them.

They rode beside him now through the blooming countryside. Gareth to his left. On his right Gawain.

Gawain, the oldest, said, "I hope we reach home before sundown. Even though spring has come the nights are still cold."

Gareth laughed. "Can't take a little chill, brother?"

"Your sibling grows saddle sore, I think," joked Lot. He himself was an excellent rider. Firm upon the saddle, his thin, well-appointed frame had a regal poise that suited the riding of horses. His narrow features, casually framed in a cluster of dark curls, bent into a smile.

Gawain did not take offense. An easygoing lad, slow to anger, he had the smooth facial lines of his mother beneath his new, sparse, and downy beard. His wealth of brown hair shook with his mirth. "Not as sore as your feelings after being snubbed by so many nobles."

Lot's expression grew dour. "They shall pay for that. Soon their contempt shall be put to the sword."

Gareth, the quicker of the two brothers, said, "Really, Father. I don't know why you bother yourself in this squabble over unenviable power. You'd think we didn't have enough trouble here with Picts vaulting the wall and Saxons raiding the shores. You want to deal with that problem all *over* Britain? You'd have to face up to that, you realize. By the time you and the other kings look up from your kickings and bitings of one another's butts you'll be hemmed in on all sides. Then what will you do with your precious throne? Sell it for scrap metal and firewood?" He had the sharpness of feature of his father—and the sharpest of wit.

Lot was stung. "I know how to deal with the invaders. All this I do, I do for you, my sons!"

Gareth's clean-shaven face broke into a smile. "Don't try to make us believe *that*, Father. You do it for yourself. You just want to lord it over everybody!" He shook his hair and scratched his long narrow nose. "Father, don't you realize you can't deal with savages by bargaining with them? I say that the best thing to do is to throw in together with the rest of the land and protect ourselves as one nation. Not as a bunch of squawking idiots more interested in cutting one another's throats than in saving our country from the torch."

"I will not argue with you, son," said Lot. "You will do what your father says. That is your duty. You will soon find that I am right. *I* alone am able to bring Britain together. I alone can save it and its people."

Gareth sighed and shrugged, shooting a glance to his brother, who echoed his exasperation.

Past primrosed hillock and stands of ash they rode on. Through mists of bogs and sweet smells of the plains. The moors of the North usually were strange and murky. It was good to see them touched now with spring. The blooming of the hawthorn gave the bleak dreariness a bit more color.

Lot smiled to himself grimly, knowing that he was a reflection of this resolute and unyielding countryside.

The sun was drawing on toward setting, kicking up hues of purple and red on the horizon, when they were set upon by a band of perhaps thirty warriors.

They emerged from behind a large overhanging jumble of rocks, swords drawn, intent grim upon their twisted visages.

"To arms!" cried Lot, drawing his spatha, even as he retreated slightly behind the cover of his other men. He was no idiot. Better to give a little and so live to fight tomorrow! If there was any lesson of conflict he had learned during the squabble for Pendragon's throne, this was it.

No banners waved in the wind. No telling who it was that comprised the ambush. Certainly not Picts or Saxons, though. None of the telltale spiraled paint, wild hair, or screams.

No, this was an attack of cold calculation.

Someone wanted rid of this pretender to the throne.

Even as he ducked a thrown javelin tore the air by Lot's ear. The spear buried itself in the leathered shoulder armor of one of Lot's riders, Diarmid. The stocky man paused long enough to grunt, pluck the weapon from its bloody hole. Then sword raised, he hurled himself, maddened, into the fray.

Since they had been in the forefront with their father, Gareth and Gawain bore the brunt of the frenzied onslaught.

Mighty thews bent with strain. Swords rang. An arrow thunked into an invader's chest. He burbled blood and dropped as though slammed by a giant fist.

Lot slashed the fallen man's neck open to be sure he was dead. The smell of kicked up dust and fresh blood clotted his nose.

Amidst the melee a contingent of four armed men speared through, intent upon one target: Lot.

Gareth's sword arced.

A head tumbled.

With a scream of outrage, Gawain hurled himself from the saddle, drawn sword impaling another through the back. The two warriors tumbled to the ground.

But two of the men fought free. They bore down upon Lot, swords up and reflecting the dying sun.

"By the old gods," cursed Lot. "You'll not have me!"

He reined his horse around and galloped down the road. Almost instinctively, hair prickling about his neck, he averted his head.

A sword swished where he had been seconds before.

Frightened, Lot pulled on his reins. His horse

screeched, pawing the air with its front hoofs. Lot tumbled off.

He regained his feet swiftly, sword out and ready.

Damned animal. The steed was supposed to have executed a swift left turn. Instead, Lot found himself in the dreadful position of being on the ground at the forefront of the other's charge.

"Who sent you devils!" he cried, voice quaking slightly. "Begone with your lives. I will see that your families—"

A sword swiped down. Above, a skull-like face grinned.

Reflexively Lot held up his sword, firming his grip. The sword rang away. The force of the blow numbed Lot's hands. In the time it took for the other, blunt-faced warrior to ready another blow, Lot scrambled away to higher ground, amongst a pile of boulders.

He ducked below one just in time to avoid the blow of the other attacker. It chopped a bit of shale away from the boulder, raining it down on Lot's caped back. He slipped in a puddle, muddying his fancy breeches. Angered, he flailed with his sword. The lucky blow caught the nearing man in the arm. With a cry the man fell from his steed, disarmed.

A cry of victory filling his throat, Lot pounced. His sword point caught the fallen man just below the chin and drove upward. The spearing motion muffled the man's death wail.

But Lot had neglected an attacker. Yanking his sword out of the dead man's head, he turned just in time to see the other closing in. Fruitlessly he tried to raise his bloodied sword to fend off the powerful hack.

A horse thundered by. So fast its rider blurred. The sword he bore whipped out like the tongue of snake. The sword of Lot's attacker was deflected. The other sword turned its flight in toward the man.

Gutted him.

In a spray of blood the man tumbled from his horse, rolled to the ground, moaning.

The moaning quieted.

Lot's savior dismounted. "Father. Are you all right?"

"Yes, yes, Gawain. I think so!"

"Father, they were after *you*!" Rivulets of sweat poured down Gawain's big face.

Lot glanced back to the scene of conflict. Bodies sprawled all about. His men. The attackers.

In the distance a cloud of dust plumed, hazing the sight of belled capes and horse tails: the ambushers, driven away.

"Yes," said Lot. "I knew that immediately."

Another voice joined the conversation. "You run very fast, Father," said Gareth. Ripped clothing shredded down his legs. He held a bloody arm. He was not smiling.

"Er, it was the only thing I could do," said Lot, standing his ground. "How did we fare?"

"Five dead. Ten wounded by my count. We drove them off, killing maybe ten. But we paid a price," said Gareth.

"They will pay the price in the end," snarled Lot, shaking a fist at the retreating band. "Blood will be spilled in reparation."

Grimacing, Gareth looked down at his wound, then shook his head wearily.

vii

The land was full of spring.

The sun rode high, bright, and warm. The wind waved the high grasses and the elm boughs as though in gestures of welcome. Flower scents laced the air.

So, thought Arthur of Britain. *This is Gaul.*

The youth rode his brown and white mare, Landsong, well and confidently. He remembered his friend Amlodd's words on horses.

"A horse makes you a giant, lad," the hairy man had pronounced between cups of wine. "In Rome they have tales of creatures half man and half horse. Called centaurs. Learn to use a horse, Bear, learn to control it properly, and *you* will become a centaur when you ride. It is the captain who knows horses who wins battles!"

Arthur had taken those words to heart. Days passed when he had ridden all day just to learn the ways of horses. And he learned the value of good breeding in a horse. He realized that strong, swift, nimble steeds were needed to help British warriors stem the encroaching barbarian tide.

The best horses were here in Gaul. Owned by the king of Benwick, whose son, Lancelot, had already earned fame across the channel for his riding and his fighting.

Gold pieces stuffed the purse on Arthur's leather belt. When jiggled they clinked. It was hard to realize that part of Britain's future could be held in one small pouch.

The thought of Amlodd caused a dull pang somewhere deep inside Arthur. He yearned for the company of the boistering rogue. Yet as the back and forth, up and down motions of the horse lulled him into deeper contemplation, he realized that if the huge Celt were indeed his constant companion he would not have to rely on himself. If there was one thing he had learned in these formative years, it was the importance of self-reliance.

The trip was meant to be a testing of that.

Merlin had wanted him to bring a whole troop of soldiers along. As Arthur grew older the druid worried more and more. But Arthur had promptly brushed off the notion. It was but the work of a moment to convince his teacher that to travel alone, cloaked by anonymity, would be far safer than to lumber along with clunking followers.

Rather than risk Saxon capture by crossing the channel at Dover, he had taken the longer boat trip from the Cornish coast, landing in Normandy. Skirting the more populous centers, such as Paris and Tours, he kept to the countryside. An interesting land. Brighter, hotter than Britain, and quite beautiful in a way. Yet even as he traveled Arthur yearned for the dark greens and rich hues of his homeland. Its tastes and smells and mysterious mists winding through valleys and bowers like damp spirits.

Using only a crackling map with few landmarks, he negotiated his way, his sturdy mare consuming the distance in healthy strides. According to the old map, he should be in the king of Benwick's land now. Doubtless, he would eventually have to inquire of some peasant the exact location of Benwick Castle. Whenever he could find one.

He crested a hill. Below, a shimmering river snaked. At one point the river narrowed, and here a thin bridge spanned it.

In the distance a few laborers worked fields. The castle must be near.

Arthur set Landsong's nose toward the bridge. The horse whinnied obligingly, and they descended the hill. Disturbed grouse erupted from thickets. A disappointed fox slunk away into deeper undergrowth.

As he approached Arthur noticed another rider hurriedly jouncing down a dusty trail toward the opposite end. Although he reached the bridge first Arthur paused. The simple wood and stone bridge, no railing guarding its sides, was only wide enough to allow one horse and rider to pass.

The stranger in these parts, he thought it best to allow the other man to cross first. Besides, he wanted to inquire as to the direction of Benwick castle.

Landsong, taking advantage of the rest, munched on the fresh-smelling tufts of grass growing around the bridge bed stones. Water gurgled hushingly. A dragonfly buzzed over riverside cottontails. Arthur refreshed himself with the sweet stream water in his saddle flask.

Horse hoofs clopped up to the other side of the bridge, then stopped.

The man atop the black, pure-bred steed stared at Arthur piercingly. Even at this distance—by Arthur's estimation perhaps twenty yards—it was obvious the man was no peasant. Although his basic riding clothes—simple *braccae* and leather tunic—were rough and worn from use, he wore a fine scarlet neck scarf—and a silken cap of soft black, almost perfectly matching his long freshly washed hair. A long spatha in its bejeweled sheath slapped the horse's side as the rider moved to get a better look at Arthur. He seemed about his own age, Arthur observed.

Trying to remember some of this country's language that Merlin had taught him some time back, Arthur addressed the rider: "A good day to you, sir. Please. Cross." He underlined the polite request with a gesture and a broad, friendly smile.

The rider rocked his head and then said what seemed to be: "No, sir. It is my honor to allow you, first. You are obviously of another country by your accent. I do not wish it to be said that our land is barbaric."

"I thank you greatly," replied Arthur courteously. "But since I have already been waiting a little bit a few more moments will not hurt, in the interest of good manners, you understand."

"I disagree," spoke the rider curtly, stiffening in his saddle. A strained smile showed. "It would be good manners, sir, to accept my offer."

The tone of threat rankled. Arthur flushed slightly. Who was this fellow to insult his sense of propriety so? He answered in a more abrupt voice: "We waste time. Cross, sir, and your arrogance will be forgotten."

"What!" cried the other. "I warn you. Anger me further with your insolence and your gabbling of our language and you shall raise my anger."

Arthur shouted back, "Foreign bumpkin, take advantage of British courtesy and learn what civilization means!"

"Son of a pig! Cross, I say, or I shall come over and drag you across!"

Arthur felt pure fury drive through him, reddening his face. All thoughts of safety or mission departed as

Celtic anger rose within him. "I would rather ford this river and become wet than cross your poorly made bridge."

A sword snicked from its sheath. Sunlight glistened on sharp metal as the rider raised it high. "Then be prepared, villain, to cross this bridge . . . in pieces."

Answering the challenge by drawing his own sword, Arthur spurred his horse on to the rough planks. Hoofs clattered raucously on wood as the inflamed youths charged one another, swinging their swords.

The wind of his passage threw back Arthur's locks. As the other rider loomed he struck out, even as he reined in his horse so as not to collide with the other. The other youth did so as well so that when sword clanged upon sword they were off-balance.

Frankly Arthur had not reckoned with the power behind the youth's blow.

Nor obviously had the arrogant youth reckoned with Arthur's well-trained might.

As a result they both tumbled off their horses into the river.

The wet chill drove straight through Arthur as he splashed headfirst through water. He thrashed to the surface, barely able to touch the bottom.

On the other side of the bridge a head popped from the surface, gasping and sputtering. Whipping dripped hair back, the youth stared at Arthur balefully.

Arthur, cooled off now, said, "Our pride has gotten us both wet!"

The youth stared a moment.

Arthur chuckled. Laughed. Soon the other joined in heartily. "You have a fine sword arm. I shall shake it." They sloshed their way back to the bridge and climbed back onto it. Arthur returned his sword to its sheath and offered his hand.

They shook hands heartily.

"I am Arthur of Britain."

The youth's eyes opened wide with surprise. "I am Lancelot of Benwick."

The two new friends rode in the direction in which Lancelot had been headed, intent upon that young man's mission.

"Brigands!" exclaimed Lancelot. "Thieves! They took ten of my father's best horses, several of them reserved for your order."

Squelching in his saddle as he moved, Arthur felt uncomfortable in the sopping clothes. He and Lancelot rode side by side. The river swirled beside them. "And you think to find them alone?"

Lancelot smiled recklessly. "Yes. Before. But now I have you with me, don't I?"

Blinking, Arthur said, "Yes, I suppose you do."

"Your talk of Britain fascinates me," said Lancelot as they entered a woodsy trail. "You have the same trouble with the Saxons as we do with the Franks."

Arthur nodded. "If we could but reason with them. We want only peace. They want only plunder."

"And with their ravages they bring their barbarity," concurred Lancelot. "And our peoples thought that the Romans were bad. In truth the conquering did us some good." Lancelot folded his hand into a fist. Shook it. "I'm proud to say my sword helped drive back the Franks. They bother us not, for the time being." He shrugged. "Meanwhile, I grow restless."

Arthur chuckled deep in his throat. "You and your sword are always welcome in Britain, 'gainst the Saxons."

With great sincerity and gravity Lancelot gazed with great blue eyes at Arthur. "Thank you, my new friend. I shall consider your invitation."

"I meant the statement as a jest," said Arthur, appraising this slightly younger counterpart of himself. Long hair pasted over his ears with the wet, he nonetheless retained his dignity. Lancelot sat straight as any of those well-crafted poles supporting the roof of Hector's solar. His sense of purpose showed in his poise. The handsome lines of his face showed his noble breeding. For the most part they remained still. But his piercing eyes and nostrils seemed constantly agitated with emotion when he talked. *Arresting features and character*, Arthur thought. This one would be a devil with the ladies of Britain, bored with the brutish manners of their men, their thick, hairy faces.

A moment of uneasiness assailed Arthur, something like foreboding . . . and then Lancelot spoke again with his strong, well-enunciated baritone. Lancelot spoke his language beautifully indeed. "Never speak in jest about such things, Arthur of Britain. Neither the Saxons nor the Franks—nor, I might add, women—are in my repertoire of jokes. All of them take themselves seriously and therefore should be taken on their own terms. The barbarians know little save their lusts of the moment, their dark gods, their hungers. We are little removed from them, Arthur. Our ancestors were much the same." He turned a haunted gaze upon Arthur, who felt as though his soul were being searched. "The Franks kidnapped my mother. We never saw her again, despite constant shipments of ransom. But she cries out in my dreams, Arthur. And she says, 'Lancelot. Avenge me. But not for the sake of revenge. Avenge me that this darkness might be cut from mankind.' " Fists grabbed reins and twisted them. Cords stood out in Lancelot's neck for a moment, then relaxed. "Yes, my friend. They are indeed alike, barbarians and women. From the loins of darkness civilization springs. From the wombs of women we are born. We must labor hard that both do not swallow us back up, eh?" A shadow of a smile crossed his features. "But I have disobeyed my own rule. I joke."

"You have had much experience with women, then?" said Arthur, genuinely intrigued. His work in Britain had largely been in the company of men, leaving him little time for that of women. Besides, his experience with Guenhumara had been so painful that he had learned to keep his emotions and his heart to himself. This caused a certain distance between himself and the few girls of his acquaintance. Despite his rough good looks, which attracted them, they could not pierce the armor he wore in their presence.

Yet he was torturously interested in them.

Lancelot's eyes widened at the question. His nostrils flared as he drew fingers through his fair hair. "Ha, women! Yes, I have known a good many to various degrees." His blue eyes burned with fervor. "I love them more than I love my life." He swept his arm out, alluding to the bright bloomed countryside. "They are the earth, Arthur. I think it appropriate that Nature is always feminine in legend. They nurture life and give it love and context. They hold us together. If men took lessons in the ways of women and scorned them not, I think wars would be fewer. We'd not have to worry about the likes of Saxons and Franks." He clenched his teeth in frustration. "And yet. And yet, Arthur, I know no more of women really than I do of this land, of this forest." Gesturing toward the stands of spruce and elm covering the nearby hills, he said, "You can sit among the trees and dig your hands into the rich loam. You can smell the holly and taste the nectar of wildflowers like the bee. Soon you forget the beauty of the whole. But stand beyond the forest and gaze upon it. Elusive, aching beauty. Wild mystery, life itself." He sighed. "Yes, I love women, Arthur. But for some reason that I do not understand at all, I think I hate them a little as well."

"But why, Lancelot? I think they're splendid," said Arthur, warming to the subject. "They should be adored from afar like well-grown gardens. It is my dream to make a Britain far, far away from the ways of barbarians. And proper respect for women is high on my list."

Lancelot barked a cutting laugh. "Ha. Idealist. And yet I think I am one as well. If ever I find the woman of my heart . . . ah, then I shall be happy indeed. Somewhere she exists. I shall find her, Arthur, and she will be my life."

The youth's intensity was overwhelming. Like a physical force—a spiritual presence. *This fellow*, thought Arthur, *has the stuff of greatness in him.*

Drunk with his own words, Lancelot continued: "She will be loved and adored and cared for as no woman has ever been before. She will know the duty of a son, the gentle care of a father, and the burning ardor of a love beyond telling."

"You speak most candidly to a man you've barely met!" exclaimed Arthur, impressed.

Lancelot's eyes twinkled with a dark humor. "Everyone who knows me very soon hears the same. It is my nature. This is a warm country. It brings out the emotions, my friend."

"Yes. I noticed that on the bridge."

"Yes. You wield a fine sword and a temper. We must have at each other—in play, of course—with swords when we return to my father's court. I have the feeling we both will learn much."

"Your exploits are legend in Britain."

"Are they now? I dare say they've been bloated a bit in the telling. I have had some fearsome adventures. I am too reckless in battle. Again, my emotions take hold." He smiled grimly when he looked off into the distance. "Those thieves out there will discover that very soon, I hope."

ix

With a shrieked war cry, Lancelot of Benwick bore down upon the napping men, sword flashing in the sunlight. The filthy gaggle of men—five in number—scrambled up from their sprawling reposes and grabbed their weapons. Three rose with rusty swords gripped in knobby hands. One wielded a long dagger, eyes hard and baleful above a broken nose. The biggest, a virtual mass of sores and ragged clothes supporting a bush of hair, had only a cudgel. Of them all, however, he looked the most threatening.

But Lancelot and Arthur had the advantage of surprise.

They had come upon the men by a stream. The horses were tethered to nearby trees. Obviously the men had hoped to gallop to another land and then sell the handsome specimens for a good price. According to Lancelot, they were simply a motley crew of bandits, several of them Frankish. They had stormed out of nowhere the night before and had stolen the horses from a stable.

No doubt they'd thought they'd long since outdistanced any pursuit.

They had not, however, reckoned with Lancelot of Benwick's fury.

Arthur, even as his horse thundered after Lancelot's steed, was astonished with his companion's fierceness. Lancelot's lightning sword made fast work of the nearest brigand, eluding the ugly man's awkward stab and chunking deep into his neck. Blood flew and the man toppled lifeless, hands frozen into claws.

"Such is the fate of thieves!" cried Lancelot above the din.

The man with the dagger leaped upon Arthur. The spatha fell, pommel driving into the man's yellowed teeth. But even as he fell back the man grasped the top of Arthur's breeches, jerking him off the horse.

Arthur landed atop the man and was repulsed at the foul aroma that rose up from him. But he could not bring himself to kill the man when merely knocking him senseless was possible. The youth slammed his knee into the man's dirty face. The man's head pounded back onto a rock, and the man groaned away his consciousness.

Catching a glimpse of Lancelot's attack on two men,

Arthur had just enough time to ward off the sword blow of the skinniest of the bunch. Iron clanged upon iron, filling Arthur's ears with a hurtful ringing.

They traded blows for a time, succeeding only in hurting one another's hands and tiring them. But the robber was not a trained swordsman. Soon his breaths were heavy and fatigued. Sweat dripped down his face; Arthur was soon able to disarm the man with a twisting blow that Amlodd had taught him. The sword blew away, leaving the men blinking. "Mercy, sir," the man wailed pitifully.

Arthur responded by swinging his sword. The flat struck the man's temple, knocking him down. The man lay there, moaning and clutching his bloodied head, not unconscious but somewhere very close. He would be no more problem for a time.

Swinging about, Arthur saw immediately that Lancelot was hard-pressed by sword and cudgel. Fight-maddened, the sword-bearer lunged. Lancelot immediately swung his sword to bear with a speed the attacker had not expected. The thief was impaled in the chest. With a scream he toppled—ripping the sword from Lancelot's grasp.

Immediately the huge man pressed in, swinging his hard wood with a frightening ease. Spittle slopped from his mouth as the man grinned with anticipated victory. Lithely Lancelot dodged the blow, then drove a fist into the man's round belly. The man gave an *oof*, but that was the only sign of any harm the blow had caused him.

Instead of raising the cudgel for another attempt as might have been expected, the man started the blow from down and swung up. Surprised, Lancelot attempted to escape it, but the wood caught him on the back of the head. A glancing blow, but it knocked him down into a bed of toadstools and moss.

With a gurgle of victory the big man raised the cudgel to finish the job.

But Arthur was already at him. The man spied this from the corner of his eye and diverted his weapon to strike the sword-bearer. Arthur's well-sharpened spatha hacked into the wood. Chunks and splinters flew. The grinning man nearly yanked the sword from Arthur's grasp, but the youth held firm. With a grimace he lifted the sword again, chopped down with all his might.

The blow lopped the cudgel off just inches from the giant's handle.

The man looked at his ruined weapon, stared a moment at the spatha and Arthur, and decided that retreat would be most judicious.

He turned and ran.

Arthur did not give chase. They had the horses now. And he wanted to see to Lancelot. Those were the most important things.

He knelt beside the dazed warrior, cradled his head. Blood oozed onto his hand. But not that much.

At his touch Lancelot's face went into a paroxysm of awareness. Eyelids blinked. Mouth wrenched almost comically. He lifted himself up. "My sword!" he cried.

"Don't trouble yourself," soothed Arthur. "The thieves are defeated. Two dead, two captured, one escaped. And we have the horses."

"Escaped!" cried Lancelot. "Then we must pursue."

"Not worth it," responded Arthur.

The Gaul's eyes focused full on Arthur. "The bastard knocked me out! You must have—"

"Saved your life?" Arthur shrugged. "You'd have done the same for me. It was fortunate I accompanied you."

Lancelot scrambled to his feet, then knelt on one knee, grabbed Arthur's hand, and kissed it. "No man has saved my life before!"

"I assure you, Lancelot, I would have done it for—"

"Ah, but you don't understand! I have dreams! Portending dreams!" Lancelot's eyes were wide with wonder. Blood dripped disregarded onto his tunic. "Dreams that the man who first saved my life would be the symbol of my idyllic quest! A king!"

"Well, Merlin says I'm to be king, but I really don't know. . . ."

"King of Britain!" cried Lancelot, dead serious, a frenzy in his respect. "But of course! How could I have been so stupid! You must forgive me for any previous disrespect, your highness. I truly had no idea." Lancelot bowed deeply. "I will follow you to your homeland, to serve you and your good cause. My sword should be put to a good use!"

"What nonsense, Lancelot. Save this sort of thing for when we're older and more foolish."

"But of course," said Lancelot, rising. "We have the horses now as well." He beamed. "We shall straightforward return to my father's house, and I shall order up a grand celebration tonight to welcome your arrival!"

x

Torches burned brightly, miniatures of the bonfire that roared in the courtyard. Pigs turned on spits. Their succulent aroma was offset by the tang of the best wine that Arthur had ever tippled. Numbed with the drink and good spirits of the affair, Arthur lounged by the king of Benwick and his youngest son, Lancelot. He watched the dancers.

One in particular attracted his attention. All swirling red tunic and blond hair, flashing eyes and supple movement, she danced with disciplined abandon. A gay frolic, this dance. She smiled at the men, and they smiled back, much taken with her healthy looks. Perhaps a year or two older than Arthur, her body owned a mature yet slim woman's figure that stirred Arthur's wine-shot imagination.

"You are welcome to our land," the drunk, red-nosed King Felios droned yet again, slapping his guest full upon his back. Red wine spilled over Arthur's cup brim onto his pants. He barely noticed. "Stay as long as you like."

Lancelot, to his other side, jabbed an elbow into Arthur's arm, and whispered, "I think he likes you."

"From what Lancelot says you will be a good ally and friend," continued the king, stroking a full gray beard. "A shame that we are so far apart. But we shall have a worthy emissary in our Lancelot. Just don't take the lad too seriously. He blows hot as that bonfire at the oddest times."

The eyes of King Felios grew sober, distant. "I would that I could change the past, though. To my great shame, it was my great grandfather, Aegidius, who is partly to blame for your present troubles in Britain."

"Sir?" said Arthur. "How so?"

Felios scratched his wine-stained beard ruminatively. He belched. "Years ago, after the Romans left your country, the Britons were faced with the terrible pressures of the savage Picts and Scots to the north. For centuries they had relied on Roman forces to protect them; their own armies were few. The groans of the Britains fell upon the ears of Aegidius of Gaul. They pleaded that help should be sent. My great grandfather ignored them. Vortigern of Britain had to turn to warriors of Teutonic lands, the Angles, the Saxons, and the Jutes."

"Ah, yes." Arthur leaned back in his chair. "I have heard the rest from my master, Merlin. The *superbus tyrannus* and the councillors, the *omnes consiliarii* hired these mercenary armies. They came and held back the Picts and the Scots . . . and yet it was fire against fire. Seeing the bounty of Britain, the Roman towns full of civilization's riches, they grew greedy. Soon hordes of the barbarians crossed, with no invitation. They laid waste to many towns. They sacked and burned and raped and then returned to their own dark lands. But some stayed and settled to the southeast, in Kent and Wessex. Soon more returned. They would drive us into the sea." He shook his head wearily. "And yet despite this terrible threat our factions squabble, even war amongst themselves." He folded his strong hands together. "We need to be united under this common cause." He smiled at the king. "And we need strong, swift horses. I had a friend who fought with the Romans. He convinced me of the military might of cavalry."

"Yes. The least I can do is help you in that, Arthur." Turning his attention back to the dance and his wine cup, Felios thus ended the conversation.

"You have concluded the dealings for the horses?" asked Lancelot.

"Yes," replied Arthur. "At surprisingly low prices. While you watched the dancer. It only took a few words. And the king has promised that his own men will bring them."

Lancelot smiled.

"Hold it, Lancelot," said Arthur. "You didn't have anything to do with that, did—"

"I see you've been eyeing Rosania," Lancelot interrupted.

"Who?"

Lancelot pointed out the girl who had attracted Arthur's attention.

"Oh, yes," said Arthur meekly. "Very beautiful."

"Come," said Lancelot. "I will introduce you."

xi

His vision swam before him.

Tallow candles guttered in the gust of his entrance. A bed of soft furs on a wooden dais awaited him. He stumbled to its foot, made an effort to remove his scuffed boots. The movement propelled him onto the furs. He could smell the wine fumes that surrounded him. The room spun slowly and pleasantly.

Arthur of Britain knew he'd drunk too much. Nevertheless he was pleased with himself. As he lay there on the bed he contemplated the victories of the day. He'd made a new and valuable friend who intended to accompany him back to Britain to fight the Saxons. He had acquired fine horses. Good breeding stock. Soon British soldiers would ride fleet steeds into battle. The horses could mean the difference between victory and defeat.

And finally he had met Rosania, at Lancelot's insistence. In their polite conversation he had not made a fool of himself, as was his wont with women.

No, he had been very clever. He smiled at the thought of her sitting beside him, bright eyes illuminated brilliantly by the dying bonfire. How gracefully she moved. How delightfully she spoke! She had smelled so clean and fresh when he leaned forward to catch her words in the din of celebration. The swell of her breasts beneath the dyed cloth of her long tunic moved something deep and natural within Arthur, even as he looked back on the image with his mind's eye.

Oh, how she had smiled at him! Obviously she was most taken with him. How impressed she was that he might become a king.

Mind dallying in pleasant thoughts, Arthur lazed upon the fur-covered bed. Musings gradually became dreamings, and he was back in his homeland again, gazing upon rolling hills like the ripe figure of a beautiful woman.

"Arthur!"

A whisper.

Wind through the heather of his dream?

"Arthur, dearest." Closer, more intimate than wind. A breathy mutter in his ear.

He opened his eyes. Candles, half melted now, still flamed. Quiet filled the castle. The revels had ceased.

"Arthur. Are you well?"

He blinked. He turned his blurry vision to the source of the voice.

A woman hovered over him. A long nightgown of white silk hung around her most enticingly. Her blond hair was worn long and well combed, filled with silver highlights from the candle she carried. Her lovely, pear-round face was full of care and concern.

"What?" Arthur muttered, astonishment and drink allowing no other response.

"I was passing in the hallway on my way to my chamber, back from the privy." She spoke forthrightly. "I heard you groan. Your door was ajar. I came in to make sure you were well. You drank quite a lot this evening, I fear."

"Yes," Arthur said, mildly embarrassed. "My Celtic heritage. Amlodd would have been proud of me."

"Who?" asked Rosania.

"A friend."

She glanced down his body. Was that a trace of desire in her eye? Or just a trick of the light. "You have fallen asleep in your clothing."

"Yes. My boots were giving me trouble. I decided not to bother."

She smiled. "I often help my father with his boots. May I help you before I go?"

"I think I can do it on my own." He yearned to reach out and touch her flowing hair, her flowing body. But discretion halted him.

"No!" she replied. "I insist. The least I can do for a prince I may never see again." She walked briskly to the foot of the bed, took a firm hold of Arthur's muddy boots, and pulled. The boot slipped off easily, as did the other one.

"You are very good at that," said Arthur, his mouth dry with excitement.

She was studying his bare feet. "You have very sensitive-looking extremities. I wonder. . . ." She flicked a light finger down one of his arches. Tingles shot up his leg, and he laughed involuntarily.

"A ticklish prince," pronounced Rosania. "Nice to know that rulers are human too."

As he stared at her with wide-eyed astonishment, she traveled the length of the bed and leaned toward him, supporting herself with her hands. "Please don't think me bold or forward, but I like you. May I have a kiss to remember you by? I may not see you again before you leave in the afternoon." The white silk of her gown dropped low, affording an opening that Arthur could not help but gaze upon. Rosania wore no underclothing. Her breasts hung like fruit to be plucked from a tree.

Impulse overruling propriety, Arthur lunged upward, grabbing her clumsily, mashing his lips against hers. Her mouth was tart and sweet with wine, and it greeted Arthur's with a hungry passion.

He pulled her down, mumbling awkward phrases of ardor, feeling at the full pitch of inebriation again. Suddenly his hands were all over her, as hers cradled his head delightedly.

She pulled back a bit. "I am not only expert at removing boots," she purred. She smiled at Arthur's hesitation. "Do not be concerned with catching a chill; I will keep you warm."

He nodded submissively, astonished at the simplicity of all this. Women were not merely mysterious; they were surprising.

Deftly she helped him remove his breeches and tunic, tossing them with lustful abandon onto the floor. Arthur's head buzzed with excitement and wine.

Quickly Rosania shed her gown, leaving her long hair her only covering. She slithered playfully into Arthur's arms.

Arthur found her prediction to be quite true.

No, he thought as he embraced her, clutching her smooth skin close. *He wasn't cold at all.*

After a few moments he gained some semblance of control. "I—" he said, "I would not leave you with child."

She batted her eyelashes with surprise. "I've not heard that from a man before." She gazed at him with amused suspicion. "You've not lain with a woman before, have you?"

Arthur blushed bright red. "I . . . I. . . ."

"Dear Arthur," Rosania chuckled. "You need not be embarrassed. There needs must be a first time with everyone. As for a child, let me worry about that."

She drew him close, and Arthur found in her a skillful and eager teacher in the ways of love.

They did not sleep until the light of dawn fingered the window ledge.

xii

Arthur awoke.

The chamber was filled with light.

He lay under a pile of furs. Sleeping, Rosania lay tucked against him, her slow breathing gentle memories of her night's gaspings. He recalled the lovemaking with astonishment and yet warm acceptance.

He nudged her awake. She squinted sleep-gummed eyes at him, then stretched luxuriously and sleepily, a warm smile on her face. "You are a wonderful man," she said.

"Rosania," he said, swallowing. Guilt felt heavy on his mind. "I took advantage of you last night. It—it was not right. I was full of drink. I owe you . . . something. Do you want to go back to Britain with me?"

"Well, that sounds very nice. But I think you just feel obligated. Besides, my hand has been promised to another man."

Arthur was aghast.

She laughed at his expression. "He's off to Rome now, so don't worry."

"But if you're promised, then why . . . ?"

Briefly Rosania let her head fall. "I . . . I don't know." She lifted her eyes to his. They were filled with bright intensity. "When I first saw you I just melted inside. I knew you were someone special. I wanted to be close to you . . . if only for one night. I can't help myself. I'm drawn to you, Arthur, even though it's hopeless. What more can I say? Are you sorry I'm here?"

"No," he said truthfully, feeling tender, yet downcast that he would never see her again. "No. Not at all."

"We had better get dressed," she said, and just as she

was climbing out of bed Lancelot burst in, waving a piece of paper.

Arthur cringed. But Lancelot did not even seem to notice Rosania's presence . . . as though it were as natural as a breeze.

"It's a letter brought by a messenger, practically dead with fatigue," he said. "From the druid you mentioned before. Merlin."

Arthur took the note and read the scribbled Latin.

A solemnity fell upon him. He looked up at Lancelot. "Get ready for departure. We leave immediately."

xiii

Nervous, Merlin slipped to the edge of the sun-drenched ring. He was hardly conscious of the several hundred kings, barons, captains, and squires who formed a circle within the standing stones, watching and nudging one another as each new contender wrestled unsuccessfully with Uther's imbedded sword.

Merlin limped past a baron and his retainers who were openly expressing their dislike of the next to try—tall, slim, and elegantly dressed Lot.

Lot approached the altar stone with sneering reluctance.

"I still say this is mummery, my lords," Lot began uneasily.

A baron near Merlin bawled out, "Mummery or not, you had better pull the sword if you mean to lead the people. They're convinced of the sword's authority even if you are not."

Doffing his enameled metal cap and handing it to a servant, Lot walked to the altar. At the place in the circle that Lot had left, two younger, stoutly built men exchanged dubious glances. Lot's sons, Gawain and Gareth, seemed embarrassed by their father's behavior—a not atypical situation between father and sons, Merlin had observed. Merlin slipped between two of the upright stones, which were splattered with the whitish droppings of the rooks that gathered atop them in huge numbers. Behind, Merlin heard Lot begin to grunt—then to swear. Someone laughed but the sound was abruptly cut short. No doubt Lot's men were reaching for their sword hilts.

A pavilion outside the stone ring flapped in the wind as Merlin limped by, positioning himself for a clear view of the eastern horizon.

Unbroken. No sign of riders. *What had become of Arthur?*

Had he failed to receive the message that Merlin had sent by courier? Had the courier's ship been wrecked in the Narrow Sea? Or had Arthur reached the island, only to be attacked and cut down by a marauding band of Saxons? There were scores of them abroad between the plain and the coast.

The flecked eyes kept scanning the horizon. It remained empty except for the smoke in the northeast. The courier had set out days ago! The moment the gathering was agreed upon—

A furious oath caused Merlin to spin around. As dozens laughed he peered through the stones and saw Lot collapsed on the grass near the altar, his face purple. The laughter boomed. Lot had few partisans.

"Very well!" Lot cried, scrambling up. "Let the next man try!"

"All have tried who have any claim," someone said. There was an uneasy muttering around the ring. If that was so, how would the succession be decided?

Suddenly Merlin limped forward a dozen steps. He stood on tiptoe, squinting—

Yes! Two mounted figures were on the horizon. Coming at great speed—!

As fast as he could he limped back to the circle, thrusting men out of the way. "There is one who has not tried," he announced.

Back among his followers Lot pointed a gloved hand at the druid.

"Then let him step forward! We've squandered too

many days here already. I'm of the opinion the high throne belongs to the man with the courage to seize it—"

Grumbles of opposition accompanied Merlin's sharp shake of his head.

"It belongs to the man who can pull Uther's sword. You saw that clearly on the blade, King Lot."

Lot snorted. "Words in steel. Who's to say who really put them there? Uther can't tell us from the grave." His eyes pinned the druid. "Perhaps someone other than Uther stood at the smithy's elbow—"

A hundred pairs of eyes fastened on Merlin. He didn't dignify Lot's accusation with a reply.

"I repeat—there is one who has not yet tried."

"Where is he?" Lot shouted. Other voices growled the same question.

"Coming to this very place. Listen."

The crowd fell silent. Above the clucking of the rooks perched on the stones, a distant rhythmic drumming drifted into the ring.

Merlin's body lost its tension. A sigh of relief escaped his lips. With the others he turned toward the steadily increasing sound of hoofs on the plain.

xiv

The two horsemen dismounted by the pavilions. The moment they strode between the stones, Lot of Orkney and Lothian laughed in contempt.

"You're trifling with us, druid. It's only Uther's bastard."

Young Arthur's cloak, leather chest plate, breeches, and boots were filthy with mud. A huge smear of dried blood stained the right sleeve of his link-mail shirt. He swept off his metal war cap and tossed it on the sunlit grass, his eyes neither angry nor benign, but opaque, as if he were awaiting the next insult from Lot, waiting to respond when the diatribe was over.

A rook cawed shrilly as Arthur continued to regard

King Lot. The ambitious nobleman wiped his lips with one glove and glanced at the ground.

Merlin could feel the tension building—only to be broken suddenly by the rich, boisterous voice of Arthur's companion, equally bedraggled and bloody. He stepped forward with a great clinking of silver rowels:

"This is hardly a decent welcome for two soldiers who weathered storms on the Narrow Sea, then fought through three companies of Saxons between here and the coast—"

The young man, fair-haired and handsome, turned his bold, almost arrogant smile to Lot. "I don't know your name, my lord, but I'll tell you this. In Gaul you'd be gutted for what you said. In Gaul a man's father is his father; the side of the blanket makes no difference."

Some laughed. Lot colored. But the threat of a confrontation was aborted as Arthur turned his back on the furious king and took two steps toward his mentor.

"The courier was delayed by the storms. We came instantly once he reached us."

"And encountered heavy Saxon forces as you rode here?" a baron demanded.

Arthur nodded somberly. "We'll be overrun soon—unless we make a stand. I bought three dozen fine horses in Gaul. Stallions and mares. Ships will be bringing them within a fortnight."

Lot snickered. "Are you foreswearing fighting for horse breeding?"

Calmly Arthur said, "I will breed the horses, but not for the pleasure of it, my lord. If you had ever read your Roman history, you'd remember that the great generals employed troops of cavalry to strengthen their armies. We're going to have such a troop ourselves. It's the only way we can gain an advantage over the Saxons—"

"Pretentious twaddle!" Lot exclaimed. "A stripling's wishful thinking—"

The fair-haired young man growled, "In Gaul we haven't heard that the strategies of old men like you have accomplished very much—my lord. I put store in my friend Arthur when he related his plan to my father's court, and I called it a good one. As I do now."

With a merry smile the lithe young man pulled his long Roman sword partway out of its sheath.

"Would you care to quarrel personally over my judgment—?"

Lot paled.

"Who is this upstart?" someone demanded.

Arthur smiled too, but less contentiously than his friend.

"A stout soldier whom you've surely heard about—Lancelot. The son of King Felios of Benwick, from whom I bought the horses."

A murmur ran around the assembled lords and men. Even Merlin registered a faint smile of approval. The fearsome reputation of Lancelot as a war captain had indeed come across the Narrow Sea. Arthur finished:

"Lancelot will ride with me in the horse troop company."

Long silent, old Hector thrust forward from the back of the crowd with a straight face. He asked:

"Do you honestly think this strategy will serve our cause, Arthur?"

"My lord Hector, it was you who taught it to me."

"Aye—" Hector broke his pretense, grinning. "But most of these noble gentlemen don't seem convinced."

"Then let them pursue their own schemes, and I'll pursue mine." Arthur swept the ring with a challenging glance. "But to any who would like to see something other besides continual defeat and retreat, I offer a place. And a horse."

Hector looked proud when his son Kay stepped forward.

"I'll ride, Arthur."

Arthur nodded his satisfaction. Merlin noted that a number of other captains seemed on the point of offering their services, novel though Arthur's idea was to men who had long ago given up trying to learn the lessons of history. Even Lot's sons, Gawain and Gareth, appeared tempted.

But young Lancelot, still with his sword half drawn, had another matter on his mind.

"The king yonder hasn't answered my question. Does he wish to question my judgment in pulling my sword beside that of Uther Pendragon's son?"

Lot glanced away. "We have more important business than petty quarreling." Lot's sons flushed, humiliated.

"I think not," Lancelot whispered. "I see this as a matter of honor."

He would have drawn his sword all the way had not Arthur laid a hand on his arm and said quietly:

"Save your strength for the time when it can do us good. Our enemy's the Saxon."

Glowering at Lot, the young Gaul finally gave way. He clattered the sword back in its sheath.

"Now," Arthur began, "who will ride with me in this new company—?"

Merlin intervened: "There is one other matter to be concluded first."

Arthur turned, a breeze riffling his long brown hair. "What?"

Slowly Merlin lifted a hand toward the altar stone, a hand veined with the age that was slowly creeping over him, sapping his strength, and bringing fearful dreams that he would die before his great strategy was complete—

Arthur followed the pointing finger. Other heads turned. Every eye fastened on Excalibur implanted in the altar.

"You have not tried to pull it forth, and you are Uther's son," Merlin said.

"Is there no other man who—?"

"None," Merlin interrupted. "All have tried."

"He's illegitimate! He has no right—" Lot began. Another baron cut him off:

"He has as much right as you, and more!"

Lot started to say something else, saw the hostile expressions all around the ring, shrugged:

"All right, let him try. He'll fail like the rest of us."

There was a moment of silence. Then Arthur laid his sword belt on the ground and walked toward the altar.

XV

Arthur's long, clean strides took him to within a pace of the altar stone. There he halted, turned again to look at the druid. Their eyes locked.

Merlin watched the young man's expression change—a flicker of fear appeared, as if Arthur realized the momentous nature of what was about to take place. But the fear was quickly gone. Though still unsmiling, he looked almost joyful as the druid gave a long, deliberate nod.

Arthur squared his shoulders. He seemed to age several years just in the time it took him to draw breath.

All around the ring of stones the rooks grew quiet. Merlin watched a last cloud, no more than a wisp, disappear from the face of the sun. He glanced at Arthur's truncated shadow on the grass. The sun was at zenith—

The hour was a fitting one. He felt a great burden lifted. His labors were nearly done—

"In the name of the Savior get on with it!" King Lot shouted.

Arthur ignored Lot; the younger man's face was almost beatific in its calm.

Slowly, gracefully Arthur lifted his strong right hand, then moved it forward. He turned his hand over so that thumb and index finger were downward nearest the altar—

He grasped Excalibur's hilt.

For a moment there was total silence. All the petty kings and barons and even Lancelot stood riveted by the sight of the tall young man holding Excalibur's hilt. The ruby dragon in the pommel stone glowed a moment, then suddenly dulled. Merlin glanced up.

As on that other night clouds were sweeping from the north. Heavy, ebony clouds, bringing wind of incredible force—

Arthur stood motionless as the raging wind began to whip the grass outside the standing stones. The pavilions cracked and snapped. One toppled. Horses fretted and neighed, pulling on their tethers as thunder rumbled in the depths of the clouds.

Several of the barons drew their cloaks around them and hunched their shoulders. White lightning leaped between the clouds—

The next thunderclap shook the earth.

The wind grew stronger, flapping Merlin's wool gown around his spindly legs. He braced against the wind's push, a holy joy filling him at the sight of the young man facing the coming storm with his head tilted back and his eyes defying the flashing, rumbling sky—

One of the tethered horses snapped its line and went thunder-galloping away across the plain. Arthur's long hair blew around his head. His cloak stood out from his shoulders, snapping—

Limned in the lightning's glow, he held Excalibur firmly in his right hand. The ring of standing stones had grown black as midnight. Yet Arthur's figure was clearly visible, a focal point of light in a pit of darkness.

Suddenly a bolt cracked down from overhead. A squire screamed and fell to his knees, clutching his lord's legs. Even Merlin had to fight to keep from turning away as that monumental glare leaped down from heaven to touch the pommel stone—

The whitish radiance seemed to bathe Arthur's clenched hand and forearm, then flow like liquid flame across the backs of his fingers to the hilt—

To the blade, where the inscription caught fire and glowed—

Men turned away, hiding their eyes. But Merlin saw the whiteness streak all the way down the blade and strike the altar stone—

The thunderburst knocked him from his feet, drove

the wind out of his lungs, and almost deafened him. Above the reverberations, he heard a hideous squawking. All around the standing stones, the rooks were leaping skyward, wings flapping—

Merlin heard Lancelot's awestruck voice:

"*The stone is broken*—"

A few men uncovered their eyes. Merlin tottered to his feet. Even he almost gasped in wonderment. It was true. The firebolt had cleaved the altar into two great sections, uprooting both from their buried foundation. The halves lay to the right and left of Arthur, who had lifted Excalibur from its prison and now held the great blade aloft so that it shimmered and shone like a mirror of the lightning—

As rapidly as they had gathered the clouds dissipated. *It was as if the earth could no longer bear darkness*, Merlin thought. Gradually Arthur's shadow began to emerge on the ground. The wind gentled to no more than a breeze—

And the plain was suddenly suffused with brilliant noon sunlight that lit both the upraised sword and Arthur. Majestically, small bird-shapes wheeled and soared high against the sun's blazing disc.

Arthur seemed transfixed, gazing at the upheld blade. In the silence Merlin spoke in a ringing voice:

"My lords—heaven has shown you he who is rightwise king."

More men uncovered their faces, awestruck and afraid to speak. Arthur's trancelike state seemed to fade. His face took on color. He lowered the great sword to his side, but at an angle so that its point did not touch the earth.

It was Lot of Orkney and Lothian who spoke for the opposition:

"The stone was weakened somehow! More of your damned trickery, druid—"

Merlin shook his head. "A divine sign."

"No adulterer's whelp will have my allegiance—!"

"Then go from this place!" Merlin shouted. "And all

the rest of you who will not give Uther's son your loyalty!" His voice grew louder: "The sword in the stone has found its rightful owner—" He dropped to his knees in the grass. "*Hail to the high king, Arthur Pendragon!*"

Another moment of stunned silence. Then Hector and Kay knelt and all their men-at-arms.

Lancelot of Gaul followed, his handsome warrior's face a study in puzzlement and awe.

All around the ring of standing stones, barons and kings and captains stood forth one by one—and knelt. Perhaps two-thirds of all those assembled.

But Lot would not kneel, nor would some dozen of the other petty lords who sided with him. He watched the spectacle a moment longer, then whirled his cloak across his shoulder and shoved his two stout sons to get them going. One, Gareth, whirled as if to protest. But his brother whispered something to compel unhappy obedience.

Lot's hatred will be a danger to us, Merlin thought. The realization marred the perfection of the moment—as did the departure of the remaining lords who refused to kneel. Merlin heard them grumbling outside the standing stones, grumbling and cursing and ordering their servants to strike their pavilions, bring their horses—

The druid had hoped for more than this. He had hoped for total acceptance. The dark union at Tintagel would never be forgotten, he feared—

Quietly Arthur spoke to those who had remained:

"I would ask you to rise. Only one can claim the high throne. But we are all equal in our hope of holding back the Saxon darkness. We are all equal in our dedication to that cause."

Merlin clambered up, marveling. Was it a trick of hearing? Or was Arthur's voice actually deeper, somehow?

Arthur pivoted slowly, surveying each face with candor and cordiality. The kings and barons gazed at him with a mingling of dread and worship, but they saw nothing threatening in the calm, steady eyes.

"Let this day be remembered," Arthur said. "Let this ring of Britons be remembered."

Swinging Excalibur at his side, he walked around the shattered halves of the altar, stepped across some of the rubble left by its cleaving, and took a place between Hector and Kay. Only Merlin remained in the center of the ring.

"Let this circle of loyal men symbolize a new unity of purpose—to drive out the Saxon invader and to begin a new time of justice in which the smallest and the greatest shall be no different before the law."

He glanced at Merlin. The druid almost wept. Those eyes no longer belonged to a boy he knew, but a man he had never seen before, except in dreams, a man of magnificence and quiet courage, who spoke his purpose in measured syllables:

"So that this day and its meaning will remain fixed in our minds—and will come to be remembered, and spoken of, throughout all the island kingdom—the high king will no longer sit on Pendragon's throne, but at a table made in the design of a circle, which Merlin shall build. At that table every captain and every baron and every king may come and sit with equal honor and equal rank."

They cheered him then. Cheered him as no king had been cheered in Merlin's memory. The standing stones resounded with lusty shouts that drowned out the ominous drum of the dissident nobles galloping away across the plain.

CHAPTER 7

Excalibur

Arthur could not sleep.

The wind flapping the tent cloth did not bother him. Nor did the night sounds of the warrior standing sentry. Nor the nickering complaints of horses. He could not fall asleep because of the burden on his writhing mind.

He tensed, shuffling off his fur covering. He tried to force pleasant, lulling thoughts through his mind, but they turned upon him, transforming into gnawing beasts of doubt, whimpering dogs of worry.

The excitement of the evening had long since passed, leaving but one question:

Was he capable of bearing such an awesome duty?

With a sigh of resignation, he forsook his attempt to drowse, stood from his cot, and donned his clothes and cloak. Murmuring a word of explanation to the guard, he stalked into the night.

He walked a time.

He paced through high grasses and snarled woods, his boots swishing through the foliage. Finally he found a hillock overlooking the British encampment. Overlooking the standing stones and the lightning-smashed altar that had held Excalibur.

Excalibur.

He unsheathed the mighty sword. Its glossy metal

shone in the starlight. Hard, well-tempered metal it was, Merlin had said. Forged from ore taken out of a fallen star, or so Merlin claimed. It was hard and it was sharp. Sharper than any spatha or other blade that Arthur had ever seen.

A memory quivered in Arthur.

Amlodd's voice drifted back into his mind's ear:

"Oh, I'm not faulting your technique or potential power. You will grow. You will learn. But there's more *there. I can sense it . . . you lack something very important."*

"But what Amlodd. What?"

"Jove knows. Maybe the right sword."

How had the big Celt *known*?

Well, now he had the right sword. If there was one positive thing that he felt, sitting there on the bank, the breeze swirling through his hair, the night smells strong, it was the *power* that coursed through him, wielding his strange sword.

As though the sword had a life of its own.

Yes, that was it. Some men used swords as symbols. They held them as though proclaiming their manhood, chopping into battle. Some strapped them to wood and tilled the soil, seeding fertility.

Somehow, Excalibur was capable of bringing both life and death. Feeling its cold balanced solidity in his hands, Arthur knew that this was not merely an instrument of death. It was like a surgeon's tool, to amputate ruined arms or excise foul growths. It was like an ever-rigid phallus to seed life—good and just life—into this blessed soil.

It should be wielded with the greatest gravity. The mightiest wisdom. The sternest steadfastness.

Had he these qualifications, or had there been a dread mistake? If he failed, the responsibility would rest squarely on *his* shoulders.

None other.

He looked up at the sky. Which powers, what forces pervaded behind the facade of the stars? Clouds floated eerily past the milky orb of a half moon, past the blind, sheening cold, cold eyes that were the stars. He was familiar with the gods of many religions. The beliefs of his ancestors in their green glades, worshipping nature; beliefs of the Romans, with their many gods. And then the new god their number had brought to these shores, the religion of a single deity.

He was not sure of any of them, although he had believed in bits and pieces of each.

Did a diety author his purpose here, in this land he loved so? And if so, then what deity?

And *why*?

"Why *me*?" he whispered to the night wind.

Arthur sighed. The sound seemed the echo of the swirling wind.

"My lord?"

He jumped at the sound. Twirled. Excalibur was held at the ready.

In the gully formed of the waving hills, just below him, stood two figures.

Their capes twirled between the fingers of the wind. They held no weapons.

"Yes?" Arthur responded, not able to restrain a slight quaver in his voice.

"We have come to seek audience with you," answered one man.

"Who are you?" Arthur demanded.

"If you please, King, we arc the sons of Lot," answered the other in a throaty baritone. "I am Gawain. My brother is named Gareth."

"I have heard of you," said Arthur, lowering Excalibur to the frosted blades of grass. "You are praised for valor and bravery in your deeds and in your fighting. But what have the sons of Lot to say to me, their father's bane? And you address me as king. Do you acknowledge me as such."

A single word, spoken twice: "Yes."

Arthur raised his eyebrows. "Well. Then come up here with me. We must talk."

Together, they mounted the hill.

"I am sorry I can offer you no chairs," said Arthur, humor enriching his voice.

"My lord," said the one who called himself Gareth. "This land is your chair, your seat. It behooves us to sit upon it as well, beside you."

Any glimmer of distrust Arthur felt departed at the man's obvious sincerity. "Then sit we shall." He sat.

The brothers joined him. They formed a ring. Arthur asked, "Why have you come to me?"

"We have questions, and we have doubts," responded Gareth. "The display this evening was astounding. I have never seen the like."

"Nor I," Gawain concurred. "I admit I had a try at that sword, when backs were turned. It was like a piece of that rock. There can be no doubt that you are the proper successor to Uther Pendragon."

"Thank you for your confidence," said Arthur.

"As to the doubts," continued Gareth, "we merely wonder if you are worth following."

Arthur held his head back and laughed. "What? Do you think you can find that out simply by asking me questions?"

"What other way is there?" said Gareth.

"I am not so full of myself to think myself perfect," explained Arthur. "But when you consider the alternatives to joining in with me, I think that my way is the best choice."

Gawain said, "That is what I think. We are not happy with our father's attitude. We are most upset with the squabbling of the nobles, the small kings, while great danger surrounds us. The Saxons must be dealt with, and our only hope lies in combining our forces and cooperating."

"But are *you* the one who should lead us?" said Gareth.

"Why do you doubt so much, Gareth?"

"When a man's father shows such terrible characteristics, one's tendency is to doubt his issue."

"Ah." Arthur's tone filled with understanding. "I see. Well. I suppose I could spend all evening explaining myself. Telling you of Merlin and of my teachings. The things that I have learned. My dreams."

"Not all night. We haven't that much time," said Gawain. "Our father has his camp several miles away. If we are not there by sunup, he will suspect something amiss."

"No," said Arthur. "I would not keep you that long. Both of you. Touch the blade of my sword. Careful, though, it's very sharp."

The two put their palms upon the metal. Arthur could feel that they felt an inkling of what he felt in the weapon. "Now. I shall say but this." He took a deep breath, his thoughts coming rapidly. "Just as this sword, no matter what its qualities, can only be used if it is picked up, wielded, so too a man's life. You may let it lay or let others pick it up and use it for their designs. Or you may take it and decide its best use in light of your own convictions.

"Just as this sword is my weapon, the vessel that holds the means of my defense and offense, so am I a weapon of our people, a vessel of our spirit. Our people—not the Celts alone, nor the Romans alone—but their combined bloods, mingled visions that hold together more than the sum of their parts—they are my master. I shall have their dreams to lead me, to pick me up.

"I cannot persuade you to join with me, Gawain and Gareth," concluded Arthur. "That is a decision that only you can make. You must look to your own souls for the answer."

They took their hands from the blade. In unison they rose. Star and moon light showed thoughtful expressions. "Thank you, King Arthur." Gareth bowed slightly. He and Gawain paced back into the night.

Arthur took up Excalibur, feeling the true weight of importance in its heft. . . .

He held it up to the stars, to whomever lay beyond them.

"I have drawn my weapon from *its* sheath," he whispered, reverently. "May I be drawn from yours."

ii

King Lot of Orkney helped his bride from her horse.

Morgause's tresses draped over his face, filling him with her fresh Cornwall perfume of seascapes and chalk. She thanked him courteously, small, oval face composed and reserved, then followed the servants to the rooms designated as hers, to rest after the end of her long, tiring journey north. Lot watched her swaying tunic, feeling the stirrings of lust and anticipation.

Not only was the alliance with Cornwall firm now, but he had a new playmate for his bed. Perhaps he might even birth a new bunch of sons to replace the less satisfactory brace that Gareth and Gawain had become. How they had balked at the notion of merely invading the neighboring territory to consolidate their position in this land. After all, he told them, it was King Cei who had sent that band of cutthroats to snatch away his life. Retribution was necessary.

Of course, he had contrived the evidence that Cei was indeed the culprit; the notion served his designs.

His journey to Cornwall for the meeting with its rulers and the final agreement of a bond of marriage only whetted his appetite for the power and land he desired. Such a beautiful country, the South. He looked forward to moving his seat of government to a milder clime. As much as he loved the wildness, the austerity of his own land, he decided that his health could use long stays in the South.

He handed the reins of his steed to the stable boy, then paced heartily to the house, hungry for food and home.

Stomping through the door with his muddy boots, he bawled for attention. An obedient servant scurried in, took his order for some cold fowl and cheese and a large jug of his best Mediterranean wine. The tousle-haired servant turned to depart. Lot grabbed a handful of his tunic's cloth.

"And see that my new wife is well satisfied in her repast this evening," he growled menacingly. "She is woefully thin, and we needs must plump her up. The best of the larder, do you hear?"

Wide-eyed, the servant nodded and fled.

Lot grunted. Good enough. Tomorrow would be the celebration feast. Today would be reserved for rest and recuperation.

He tromped for his haven, his favorite room of the large Roman villa—its solar. Sunny and warm, it gave him great comfort. The Romans certainly knew what they were about when they constructed houses. Except for the fact that they would control Britain themselves if they were still here, Lot rather wished they had not departed. But then, when your capital is besieged and plundered by the Goths, it was logical that you call all your legions back to deal with the trouble at home.

Lot collapsed in a well-cushioned chair beside a louvred window. He yanked his boots off. The mud flaked off in great clumps, dirtying the animal-skin rugs. No matter. That was what servants were for. Speaking of which, where *was* his wine, which he'd ordered brought to him immediately.

The servant, too young and clumsy by half for Lot's taste, stumbled in, bearing the uncorked jug and huge pewter cup.

"There!" Lot barked, indicating the oak table beside him. "And pour me a draft. I'm parched!"

Obediently the doughy-faced boy poured an ample portion of the scarlet liquor into the well-crafted cup, etched with runes.

Lot snatched it up and drained half of the sweet, tart stuff in a noisy gulp. Taking the rim from his lips, the tang of the wine lingered on his palate. Delicious.

Lot waved the servant away, folding his hands

around the cool metal. He propped his lanky legs upon the sill of the window, sipped his wine, and considered.

All in all he felt quite well.

The sun slanted in, bathing the large room in swathes of muted light. Illuminating Lot's collection of art.

Lot fancied himself a cultured man. So he cluttered his rooms with all manner of curios, Roman, Romano-Briton, and Celt. They decked the tables and floors and walls like the grave of an Anglo-Saxon chieftain. No order or sense of space had been used in placing them. They were simply placed at random, and there they stayed.

Pots. Pitchers. Statuettes. Busts. Tapestries. Candlesticks and items of metalwork. The contrast in their workmanship was striking.

That tapestry for example. Although showing signs of age, its colors were still bright. It depicted a young woman pouring wine into the cup of a lounging nobleman. Birds winged in the forested distance. All in proper perspective, all with much detail, right down to the veins in the man's extended hands.

The Romans were practical people, and in this Lot identified with them.

But the early Celt items . . . they were entirely different. They stood for something just a little beyond the grasp of Lot's limited intellect.

They were in no way lifelike. Rather, they seemed the work of an artist immersed in the blurry world of dreams.

That mask there hanging on the wall, with its slitted eyes and long prominent nose. A good example. And the strange carvings, the weird human faces, the haunted birds, strange and alien . . . and the many-spiraled, crescent-shaped shields. *Poltao* they were called.

They revealed the odd, dreaming spirit of the Celts, who were led by weird priests, such as that bizarre Merlin.

Lot had no liking for that man at all. Mummery—all hoax and tricks.

No, thought Lot, finishing his cup of wine, feeling a rosy glow begin within. He had more affinity with the works of the Romans. And with the clumsy combinations that the Roman influence had brought to bear upon British artwork.

Lot refilled his pewter cup. The practicality of the Romans and the dreaming, visionary qualities of the Celts. It made for interesting possibilities of a truly great kingdom.

A kingdom Lot meant to own, just as he owned these objects of art.

The sound of footsteps interrupted his contemplations.

Gareth entered the solar, wearing soft clothes and a hard face.

With a perplexed, almost bemused expression, Gawain followed him in.

Lot stood.

"Sons! I have returned! Have some wine to celebrate." He grabbed a pair of ceramic cups from beside the ashy hearth and made to pour.

"We have not come to drink with you, Father," declared Gareth, waving away the offer sternly. "We have thought much while you have been away. Considered, Father."

Gareth looked to Gawain for support.

Gawain muttered, "Yes."

"Considered?" said Lot, perplexed. "What is there to consider? The power to own this land is within our grasp." Hand wobbling a bit from the drink, he raised a fist. "And I shall pass Britain to you both. What greater gift can a father bestow upon his sons?"

Gawain looked him squarely in the eye. "He can make himself a father to be proud of."

Gareth added, "A father without the taint of greed in everything he does."

"Greed?" Lot frowned, swinging his gaze sternly

back and forth between the two. "You would speak such slander about your own father? What kind of treachery is this?"

"We hear from the servants that you have brought a bride home." Gareth's fingers drummed the top of a chair. "Morgause of Cornwall."

Lot raised well-trimmed black eyebrows. "Ah ha! So that is it." His voice warmed a bit. "You're thinking that someone is taking your dear dead mother's place, and so you are upset."

Gawain slammed a fist into a palm, shaking his head fiercely. "No! That is not it at all, Father! We do not care for your underhanded machinations. You are working against the hope of Britain. You have made yourself a villain of British history, and we must stand up to you. For your sake. For *our* sake."

"Hope of Britain?" Lot sank back into his chair, as though hurt. "I suppose you mean that bastard of Uther Pendragon's, Merlin's puppet, Arthur."

"Yes, that is exactly who we mean." Gawain drew erect, standing his ground. "If there is any man under whom Britain can unite against the invaders, it is he."

"Just because of a few magician tricks you are impressed, eh?" Lot picked up his cup, stared into it, but did not drink. "I am surprised at you both. I thought I had trained you to be skeptical of such things instead of gullible."

"He proves to be beyond our skepticism," stated Gareth frankly. "It is you and your plans that we grow skeptical of, Father!"

Lot fingered his cup a moment. Then abruptly flung it down upon the floor. Wine sprayed, slapping crimson across the floor. "I will not be contradicted in my own home!" he yelled, purpling. "You will apologize and assume your proper position! I *am* your father!"

"Yes, and we will never raise our arms against you," said Gawain, obviously straining the words out through a deeply felt pain. "But until you see the error of your ways, neither can we support you."

Flinging his gaze angrily upon Gareth: "And what say you, Son. Does that 'we' include you as well?"

Choking on the word, Gareth said, "Yes."

Erupting in a contortion of fury, Lot sprang from his chair, eyes bugged. "No! I raised you to be *my* heirs! You will not go against my word! You cannot! You will obey my wishes. It is your duty, by God!"

With a curt shake of the head, Gawain said, "No, Father. It is our duty to follow our sense of what is right. We cannot tolerate what you are doing, and therefore, we must leave. We shall always love and honor you. That is our duty and our desire. But we do not have to agree with the manner in which you are trying to tear this country apart for your own gain."

Gareth swallowed back emotion. "We know the full extent of your dealings with the Saxons. You are betraying us all, Lot, in your crazy lust for the highest throne."

Lot stepped forward and slapped him. Hard. Blood leaked from Gareth's nose. But he did not raise a hand to protect himself.

Spinning about, Gawain said, "We must go, Gareth. There is no arguing with him."

With sad eyes, Gareth turned to follow his brother.

Stunned, Lot watched, unable to act.

At the door Gareth turned, wiping the blood from his lip and chin. "Father, we just pray to God that you see the error of your ways before the sword of King Arthur shows it to you."

With a muffled cry of outrage, Lot hoisted a Romano-Briton sculpture from a table and flung it after them.

It smashed to shards and dust against the wall.

iii

Lying in the thick grass at the brow of a low hill overlooking a narrow valley, two figures watched the roistering around the fires in the siege camp below.

Now and again the watchers caught sight of barbaric arm rings or brandished axes or plaited hair.

The Saxons were encamped beside a purling stream that wound its way up the valley. Farther on, where the stream widened into a large pond, other lights—torches—showed beyond the log-and-earth wall of a hill fort that stood on an eminence at the western side of the pond.

Few signs of activity could be detected within the besieged fort. The gates were closed against the invaders, who were singing and drinking themselves insensible.

"How many do you count?" Arthur asked.

"A hundred and twenty at most." Stretched out in the fragrant grass beside the king, Lancelot grinned. "Hardly enough to give us a good squabble, majesty."

"Have you spied Argist yet?" Arthur referred to the feared and ferocious leader of the invading band. "A fat man, they say. Heavily scarred. He wears a foeman's skull on a thong at his belt."

"I saw someone like that a moment ago. Yonder, past the farthest fire. He was sotted, I think. He fell down."

"He'll sleep it off by first light." It was the closest Arthur could come to reproving Lancelot for overconfidence. The hotheaded young Gaul always minimized the enemy's strength; worked himself into a state of laughing excitement before a battle was joined. Arthur permitted his captain this small failing because, in actual combat, Lancelot fought as fiercely and skillfully as a dozen ordinary men. Now Arthur said:

"There's nothing more to be gained from watching. I'll post a lookout, and we'll ride an hour before dawn."

"Twenty-five against a hundred and twenty isn't really a contest." Lancelot laughed as they began crawling away from the hilltop. "Especially since we have the horses."

"We only stood against seventy at the Thames," Arthur reminded him.

"Turned them back too. Without a loss. They never got within a spear-cast of Londinium."

"Yes, but then we had surprise on our side. None of the Saxons had seen a horse troop before. Since then we've been afield six months. I'm sure we won't startle Argist quite so completely."

Arthur's words tempered Lancelot's enthusiasm:

"How many can we count on from inside the fort?"

"Fifty to seventy, I imagine. But all on foot. King Leodegrance will lead them in person, once he sees help's come to raise the siege of his fort. He's elderly, but a stiff fighter—"

"And this is one of the most important outposts in the North, you said."

Arthur's brown hair blew in the night wind as he and the Gaul approached a campsite in a gully on the side of the hill away from the noisy Saxons. Shadowy figures all but hid the one fire Arthur had allowed for cooking. The summer air was alive with the stench of horse droppings. There were muffled sounds from the restless, picketed heavy horses.

"Leodegrance's fort is the only one in the North that is not engaged in outright negotiation with the invaders," Arthur said to the Gaul. "King Lot bargains with the enemy for a truce with one hand while he tickles his new southern bride with the other."

"What's the wench's name?"

"Morgause of Cornwall. A mere child compared to Lot. His other wife, the mother of Gawain and Gareth, died years ago. He wed again to solidify opposition to me in the South as well as the North—"

The two young men approached the fire. Arthur debated about whether to tell Lancelot about his blood ties with Lot's new queen. He saw no purpose in it.

The horse captains heard them coming, rose, and hailed the high king softly. Arthur quieted them, dispatched the lookout to the hilltop, then squatted at the small fire, gnawing on a beef joint. The meat had a faintly rancid taste, but he ate it because his belly was empty, and riders living off the land couldn't be particular. Sheathed Excalibur lay across his leather-clad thigh.

He gave the others the assessment that he and Lancelot had made of the enemy's strength. His men listened attentively.

"Remember our purpose when we go forth," Arthur counseled his men softly. "We must defeat Argist and relieve King Leodegrance. But, as always, we have a greater purpose than the winning of one battle." Almost unconsciously his hand closed around the hilt of his sword. "We must show this kingdom what it has seldom seen—that warriors can be compassionate when the enemy is beaten. I would rather convert a hundred Saxons to our ways and see them married and settled than slay them."

Lancelot glowered at that but said nothing.

"We must fight bravely but fairly if we mean to bring about the ascension of mercy and justice under the law," Arthur went on. "We must show by example that we mean to establish a new order of things. Otherwise, the people will never accept what we believe. Gawain, speak. What troubles you?"

A nervous smile flitted over Gawain's face. "Nothing, majesty—except that I've never had a little sermon on the eve of battle before."

Unblinking, Arthur looked at him, but it was Gawain's brother, Gareth, who answered:

"The realm never had a king like this before."

Arthur stood abruptly. "Rest if you can. Think about what I told you—" He saw a familiar figure watching from the perimeter of the light: Merlin. "I am going to take counsel with my good teacher for a little. I'll wake you when it's time. Someone put out that fire."

iv

Under the autumn stars the gully darkened as if no one were there at all.

Arthur led the procession of horsemen to the brow of the hill.

Leather creaked. Trappings jingled. Excalibur flashed starlight.

Arthur's sword hand was sweating. The Saxons were fierce warriors, and his horsemen were badly outnumbered. Yet there was a core of confidence within him, and from it he drew strength. Their cause was right. That helped outweigh the Saxons' numerical advantage—

Still, he was always conscious of the possibility of death.

He struggled to keep his face expressionless as his horse reached the crest of the hill. Below, starlight picked out the course of the stream where it meandered to the pond. Arthur noted the darkness of King Leodegrance's fort. He felt there were sentries on the tower, but none was visible.

Directly below, the Saxon fires had dimmed to embers. *How soft the autumn morning smelled*, he thought. They would be whiffing much stronger fragrances before long—

He tugged his iron cap low over his forehead, then adjusted the riveted leather flaps that protected the sides and back of his neck. Lancelot rode on Arthur's right, the great silver rowels of his spurs tinkling occasionally as he drummed his war-axe against his left boot. Lancelot hummed in anticipation.

"Who carries the dragon flag this morning?" Arthur asked.

From behind, Gareth answered, "I, your majesty."

"Then come up here beside me."

Horses moved out of the way. Lot's son took his place alongside the king. Arthur's lips hardened as his right hand rose. "Hold it high so they see it."

Excalibur flashed as he swept it down to signal the charge.

The strong war stallions from Gaul, sure-footed and heavily covered with plates of leather, carried Arthur and his captains rapidly down the hillside. They had gone about halfway when someone in the Saxon camp yelled. A silhouette scampered past one of the dying fires. In moments other voices blended with the first.

The wind swept against Arthur's face as he reached the relatively flat ground at the foot of the hill and kneed his horse to speed. Before half a dozen Saxons had rolled from their blankets Arthur was into the enemy camp.

A stout Saxon blundered into Arthur's path. Arthur rode him down, letting the slashing hoofs of his charger put the man out of action. He had other concerns: a trio of diamond-headed spears jabbing at him from the right—

Hand clenched on Excalibur's hilt, he chopped downward. The stroke cut two of the spears in half. Lancelot came galloping up and leaned sidewise from his saddle, his great axe scything back and forth. A Saxon dropped, decapitated. Another shrieked as Lancelot lopped off his extended forearm. A hand, still clutching the butt of a severed spear, went flying. The wrist fanned blood over Lancelot's thigh. Under the morning stars the Gaul's triumphant laughter rang.

The third spearman came on. Arthur's second cut missed the diamond-shaped head by a fraction. Wildly he tugged his rein to divert his horse to the left. The spear raked the right side of the horse's neck. The animal screamed and reared. Arthur tried to keep his seat but could not—

By now the camp beside the stream was alive with running men. Arthur's mounted captains were decimating the enemy, at the same time shouting to alert Leodegrance's fort that an attack was under way—

All these details blurred as Arthur was hurled backward from the saddle. Falling, he glimpsed Gareth battling on the far side of the camp, the dragon-flag staff in his left hand, a red spatha hacking and cutting in his right—

Arthur crashed into the remains of one of the fires.

He felt the sear of the coals, smelled the stench of burned leather. He rolled frantically and took a brutal kick from a Saxon boot that materialized out of the turmoil.

The boot caught the underside of Arthur's jaw, snapped his head back. His cap rolled off. Dazed, Arthur saw a hulking barbarian grinning down at him—a man with a pitted face. A skull with a thong through the right eyesocket bobbed at the man's thigh—

Argist the Saxon grunted his pleasure when he recognized Arthur's sword. In the past months the legend of Excalibur had swept the island, and there was hardly a man on either side who didn't know of the great blade. Argist closed both hands on the shaft of his battle-axe, hoisting it over his head to strike—

Arthur scrambled to one side, gained his feet. Too late, Argist tried to stop his stroke. Excalibur rang and sparked as it struck the axe-head in midair. Although he was rocked backward, Argist somehow held onto the axe. His gap-toothed smile vanished as Arthur's sword leaped out.

Argist darted backward. The lunge was short. Argist leaped sideways, turned, started the axe down again to chop Arthur's outstretched hand.

Arthur jerked Excalibur back. The blade absorbed Argist's blow, shivering and clanging and jolting Arthur's right arm with pain. He staggered, off balance, while the blade hummed in his hand. A lesser weapon would have shattered—

Maddened, Argist rushed three steps to his right, kicked the embers of another fire. Coals stung Arthur's face, forcing him to close his eyes. Argist hurled himself forward, his great poxed face looming larger and larger. The war-axe rose again, held in both hands, ready to cleave Arthur's exposed skull—

As Argist brought his axe over and down Arthur shot his right hand forward from his left shoulder. He felt the murderous impact as Excalibur cleaved the stout shaft of the descending axe.

The axe-head spun toward Arthur's feet. He jumped aside as Argist screamed in rage.

Arthur darted forward again, this time swinging Excalibur toward the Saxon's temple. Argist's eyes opened wide. Wailing his death-chant.

But Arthur struck only to stun. The flat of the sword felled Argist with one smacking blow.

Panting, Arthur leaned on the pommel. His mounted men were scattering the enemy like leaves in a wind—

Someone ran up with a raised sword. Arthur lunged, bowling the man over before he could gut the fallen Saxon leader.

"Let me kill him, majesty!" screamed the enraged Gawain.

"No! Lash his hands behind him with your belt, and let him be seen. Once a foe's fallen, savagery serves no purpose except to promote more savagery—"

Gawain scowled.

"Gawain, obey me!"

Grumbling, Gawain did. Soon he was ahorse again, the Saxon leader lying belly down across his legs. Arthur regained his own mount. Above the clatter of weapons and the cries of the wounded and dying, he heard another sound: a massed roar of voices from up the stream.

A Saxon spearman jabbed at him from the left. Arthur chopped the head from the spear. The Saxon spied Argist on Gawain's horse, flung the spear aside, and fled in terror.

The massed voices grew thunderous: King Leodegrance's foot soldiers come to join the battle.

With his free hand Arthur stroked his mount's neck. Surprise and the immense advantage of height that a mounted man possessed had proved a successful combination once again. Small numbers had prevailed against greater ones.

He rode among the litter of bodies and saw none of his own number fallen. To each captain he called an order that prevented the murder of already-defeated foemen. Only Lancelot, a scarlet-daubed figure in the rosy light just breaking, refused to listen to Arthur's commands. He gutted two wounded Saxons and chopped the hands off a third, an immense smile on his gory face.

With a sad look in his eyes Arthur let the Gaul finish his brutal work. He sheathed Excalibur and trotted through the corpse-field to meet the astonished King Leodegrance. The king was an elderly man. In full battle array he stood by the reddened stream, his expression perplexed. He had reached the site of the battle, but there was no enemy to fight.

V

His face flushed with happiness, Leodegrance tippled more mead, then continued his crowing:

"Thirty dead! Twice that many captured—including that villain Argist! The rest run off—" The elderly king wiped his glistening lips and leaned close to his guest. "Ah, majesty, it was a noble morning! Noble!"

The smoky long house rang with the merriment of the victory banquet. Arthur was letting his captains enjoy themselves. They took full advantage, pinching round feminine rumps, vying for the honor of consuming the most meat and drink, and generally creating a fearsome din that was compounded by the loud lute and the shrill singing of Leodegrance's gnomish minstrel, who had composed a lay in Arthur's honor.

In his cups Leodegrance nudged the high king—smirking at the lead entertainment. A moment later, horrified, he realized his error:

"Forgive me, majesty! I quite lost my head—"

Arthur smiled and touched the old man's withered hand where it lay on the greasy trestle:

"Yesterday's ways are changing—all of them. I am a man like you—no more, no less."

"I—I thank your majesty. I was only about to remark that everything I had heard about you was correct. That you are merciful and honorable. That your captains are incredibly fleet and deadly because they fight from horseback—some who saw you draw the sword blade from the stone scoffed at what you promised. Now we can scoff at them!"

"You weren't present at the standing stones—" Arthur began.

"No, majesty. Illness prevented it. Would God that I had been!"

"I imagine one of the scoffers you refer to is your good neighbor, King Lot."

Leodegrance fairly spluttered in fury:

"No good neighbor of mine! A traitor! My spies tell of secret visitors at his fort practically every day!"

Arthur nodded wearily. "I know he's trying to unite the North and South against me. He'll be dealt with in due course. Meantime, this is an evening for joy—"

Arthur lifted his mead cup, but only sipped. He wanted to keep his wits. He felt pressed by the realization that much remained to be done.

But Leodegrance had spread a great feast. He couldn't decline the old king's hospitality. And today's triumph *was* significant. When word that the siege had been lifted spread through the North, King Lot might have fewer visitors. The defeat of the notorious Argist might sway some of the barons and petty kings who hadn't quite decided where to align themselves—

Arthur hid a yawn behind his hand. His eyes smarted in the thick smoke that puffed from the hearth, where yet another boar turned on the spit. All at once Arthur blinked.

Leodegrance had nodded off. His head lolled against the carved back of his chair—affording Arthur his first unobstructed look at the young woman who was seated beyond Lancelot, who was on the king's right.

The handsome young Gaul was boisterously using his sheath knife to mark the surface of the table. Arthur followed the patterns of the knife, realized Lancelot was sketching the morning's battle—

For the benefit of the young woman to whom Arthur had paid only passing attention earlier—

Now, however, the girl's face was turned in the high king's direction, and Lancelot was bent forward over his crude map. Arthur was struck by the girl's great beauty.

Fair skin contrasted with rich, dark brown hair over which she wore a circlet of gold, the traditional adornment of a noblewoman. Her gown was deep yellow, the cloth dyed with saffron flowers to achieve the desired shade. The gown flattered her ample, almost lush figure.

The girl had a wide mouth and pleasing, alert eyes. Having imbibed a bit of mead, Arthur was much taken with the warm, vibrant earth colors of her skin and costume. She seemed to pulse with passionate life. But that energy was focused on Lancelot—loud, laughing recital of the victory—

Across the Gaul's stout shoulders the girl's and Arthur's eyes met for a moment. She lowered her lashes politely, although she didn't seem overawed. He saluted her with his mead cup. She smiled and returned her attention to Lancelot's description of the battle. Leodegrance, quite drunk, snored loudly.

Soon Arthur felt the table too confining. He rose, stepped behind his chair—and exclaimed softly as Merlin glided from a shadowed alcove.

"I thought you had decided to skip the celebration," Arthur said. "Aren't you setting off to see about conditions in the South, as we agreed?"

"They're readying the infernal horse right now," Merlin grumbled. "Meantime, I helped myself to a bit of food."

The flecked eyes showed amusement.

"I noticed an interesting exchange a few moments ago. I couldn't see your face. But Lady Guinevere's is not so high."

"Leodegrance's daughter is a beautiful woman. In the press of introductions earlier I failed to notice."

"Perhaps you will take more notice. Particularly if I put a purpose to it."

"What do you mean?"

"I know many things demand your attention. So I have hesitated to speak of another that I feel is important. I mean the necessity for marriage. For an heir—"

"God save us." Arthur laughed. "Don't I have enough to do, with the Saxons on one hand and Lot and his rebellious ilk on the other?"

Merlin shrugged so casually that Arthur knew his old teacher was dissembling.

"Of course. However, I do suggest that if you fancied the Lady Guinevere marital alliance with Leodegrance's house would greatly strengthen your position in this part of the kingdom."

Arthur felt almost light-headed. The mead, he supposed. "The idea is not displeasing—"

He glanced at the dark-haired girl laughing delightedly over some remark of Lancelot's. The realities of the situation weren't lost on Arthur.

"But I'm afraid mine was the only glance of interest. She's quite taken with the dashing captain from Benwick. Foreigners always hold a mysterious appeal for women, it seems—"

Merlin didn't respond to the mild joke designed to take the edge off Arthur's abrupt and rather painful realization. The druid, in fact, looked angry:

"You forget, your majesty—you are the master. He is the servant."

"And you forget he's my equal at the round table at Cam."

"I realize. However, at certain times, by the very nature of his role, the high king must be a man apart. Should you choose Guinevere that would take precedence over any other man's—"

"I wouldn't make such a request of her."

"Even if it would solidify the ties between North and South?"

"Not even then," Arthur said, hoping his face didn't show how deeply he'd been stirred by the girl's beauty.

Merlin shrugged again: "Very well. But bear this in mind. No king with whom you're allied would refuse you his daughter."

A servant appeared. Merlin bade Arthur a cross good-bye and slipped out of sight, bound south on a despised horse—

Guinevere's laughter rang bright as Lancelot leaned close to her. He touched her hand briefly, whispering something. Arthur turned away, more than a little embarrassed at the deep feelings the girl had stirred within him.

CHAPTER 8

Arthur, Guinevere, and Lancelot

"Would you keep *still*, girl!" scolded Mara. "You fidget as though insects inhabit your clothes."

Guinevere barely noticed the comfortable, familiar tugs on her scalp as her prating servant pulled the white bone comb through her luxuriant hair. She stared at herself in the looking glass atop her toilet table, astonished that such an ugly girl should attract the attention of such a man as Lancelot of Benwick. She leaned closer, hoping that she might catch a glimmer of beauty in her face or eyes that might merit his further interest. But all she saw were the too large eyes and lips she felt too wide to be beautiful. She wanted to smash the mirror in rage.

Mara slapped the comb down upon the oak table in exasperation. "Comb your own hair then. And maybe you can comb some of those thoughts of that arrogant Gaul from your head as well." She turned to attend to the turning down of her mistress's bed.

Guinevere made a silly face at herself, then mussed her hair in frustration.

She spun 'round to her servant. "Mara, do you think I'm pretty?"

"Yes, my lady," replied Mara dutifully and yet far too noncommittally for Guinevere's taste. Her words flowed with the same primness that she used to pull off those stitched-together fox furs. But on the other hand, Guinevere had heard it on good authority that Mara had been quite a comely maid, with a saucy way with the lads in her day. She needed all the advice she could get.

"How can I make myself more beautiful, Mara?"

The servant stopped her task, turned a thoughtful gaze upon her mistress. Her firm mouth seemed to soften a bit. Wrinkles smoothed, as though a reflection of the memory of a less harsh time. "The question, Guinevere, is not how to make yourself more beautiful. The crack of dawn is the most beautiful of sights in men's eyes, and yet they do not try to couple with it."

Guinevere stamped her bare foot on the wooden floor. "You know what I mean!" She leaped up and began to pace, arms folded under her bosom. Her long, free yellow tunic swished along the wood. "How do women catch and keep men's hearts?"

With spare, practiced movements Mara returned to her task. "Aren't you becoming a little designing, my Guinevere? This is hardly the place of a woman, to pursue a man. That is their province." But the tone of her voice was sarcastic, with a touch of remembered hurt.

"Didn't you *see* him, Mara?" cried Guinevere, clapping her hands together and placing them to her lips. "Didn't you see Lancelot? His bold manner, his manly pronouncements, his proud swagger?"

"His handsome face, his young, muscular body, his fiery blue eyes," continued Mara. "Yes. I saw your Lancelot. I do believe that most women at the celebration tonight took note of his presence."

A warm feeling suffused Guinevere. "Isn't he wonderful? So fascinating to talk with as well. Not like the boring old men around here and the empty-headed youths." She licked her lips, tasting the mead with fond recollection of the drink and of Lancelot. She even fancied that the smell of him—strong, musky—lingered in her nostrils. "He's *different*. He does not hide that he is above all a man. And yet, yet there is something in him. A deep-seated forlornness on his soul that makes me want to take him in my arms and hold him till all the pain goes away."

"All true perhaps, Guin," responded Mara, finished with her task. "But did you not notice the presence of another great man at the table?"

"Who? Arthur?" Guinevere shrugged. "I have broken bread with kings before. He seems nice enough, I suppose."

With the wisdom of age and experience, Mara said, "Of the two he may not be the more exciting. But I think he is the better catch."

Guinevere's eyes flashed angrily. "How can you say that? You haven't even talked to Lancelot."

Mara knew when Guin had her mind made up how difficult she could be. "Come. It is very late. It is time for bed." She shuffled over to the closet to pick out a nightgown.

With a heartfelt sigh, Guinevere said, "Yes. I suppose you're right. I do confess, I am so tired I am already dreaming."

Mara selected a beautifully embroidered blue silk gown and drew it off its peg. "There is nothing wrong with dreaming about such things, Guin. I confess in my youth dreams filled my head as much as anything."

Guinevere brightened. "Did any come true, Mara?"

"I found a husband. I serve the daughter of a good king. My stomach is full every day. My bones are not cold."

"But your dreams, Mara," breathed Guinevere. "Your dreams!" She sat on the edge of the bed, leaning forward intently.

Mara clutched softly at the silk. Her eyes grew distant. She raised an aging hand to her face, as though to brush away a tear. But no tears shone in her eyes. "Dreams, Guinevere? Perhaps they guide us to paradise. Or to perdition. But they disappear with youth, and if you are lucky, they leave you with peace and acceptance."

Guinevere clucked her tongue as she rose to shed her evening dress. "You try to sour me."

"I would not do that for the world, Guin. I am most afraid for your happiness. Fate plays cruel tricks on those it seems most to favor at first."

Guin slipped her yellow tunic off, then did likewise with her undergarment. She reached out for her night garment, and in doing so happened to gaze down at her bare body. The slight chill had raised goose bumps on the smooth white skin. "My bosoms are too big, Mara," she said with disgust. "My hips too wide." Quickly she accepted the nightgown over her head, half to warm herself, half to hide her body in which she found such dissatisfaction.

Mara chuckled softly. "Guin, you have a beautiful body. I would that I owned such large bosoms in my youth, such full-bloomed hips. They fill the hearts of men with raging desire."

Scurrying under the covers, Guinevere turned eager eyes upon her servant. "Really, Mara. Do they?"

"Yes, yes, they do, and you are a beautiful child."

"Oh, *am* I?" Hope filled her voice.

"Do you think that such a man as Lancelot would pay attention to you if you were not?"

"Oh, Mara," said Guinevere, scrunching under her warming covers. "He was but being polite. Perhaps it is just the custom of his country."

"Men are men in any country."

Guinevere sighed deeply. "No doubt I shall never see him again. He shall ride out of my life on the morrow, and I shall be miserable all the rest of my days."

Mara shook her head, care shining in her eyes. "Although you are almost a woman, sometimes you are such a child. Rest, my love. Let tomorrow take care of itself."

Guinevere accepted her fond kiss upon the forehead and watched her douse the flickering candles.

When the door snicked shut behind Mara, Guinevere promptly rose to a sitting position and brooded to the music of the wind rattling the roof and leaking through the cracks in the shutters.

She could not erase Lancelot's image from her mind.

It clung there, bright and intrusive, a memory more alive than her latest sigh.

What unfairness! How could a single man affect her so? And in such a short span of time?

She could control her emotions. Lancelot, after all, was only a man. One of those strange, rude creatures who slopped around with the beasts, shot beautiful deer, then stormed off to war to kill one another. She had promised herself many times before that never, ever could she be impressed by such as a *man*.

But then, how could she explain these feelings that moved within her? These soul-flickerings, these warm, demanding coursings within her breast and her loins. She trembled like a leaf at the mere thought of this man, this Lancelot.

A foolishness, certainly. And yet it was a foolishness that filled her with meaning. Meaning that she'd felt intimations of before, meaning that now crested toward the promise of completion.

The shadows that swathed the room seemed a congealing of mystery. Life was like the night, wasn't it, she mused as she tried to peer past the darkness. You have to *feel* your way through it rather than see it. If that was indeed the case, then the way she had responded to Lancelot must mean *something*.

She hugged herself with a kind of contained glee, the roundness and warmth of her body reassuring her. All of her life she had constantly asserted her independence—and now she longed to cast if off, to share herself. Surely this was a gift that Lancelot would not scoff at. Even if his attentions had merely been play, perhaps she still had the opportunity to convert them to more serious purpose.

Unable to sleep she lay there listening to the hush of

the wind scuttling through the elms outside, rippling off dying leaves. She listened to her heart, still excited, pounding within her breast. She listened to the crunching. . . .

Crunching? she thought, raising up to a sitting position again.

Yes. Crunching. The crunching and shushing of someone walking through dead leaves, outside. But who—?

A rapping commenced at her window shutter.

Fear seized her, stiffened her with a kind of paralysis.

A muted whisper: "Guinevere?"

She blinked. Was that the voice that had been echoing through her mind since dinner?

Again: "Guinevere."

The accent was unmistakable.

Lancelot!

She had to refrain from leaping from bed and from ripping the window open.

Containing her impulse, she instead slipped from bed and whispered back, in mock meekness: "Who—who is it? Keep your place, or I'll have my father's men at you!"

"No! Don't do that," whispered the voice. "It's just me. Lancelot. I had to talk to you again."

Guinevere smiled as she heard the slurred voice once more. Lancelot was a little worse for the mead. So much the better. Men tended to tell more of the truth in their cups, the elusive rogues. She tiptoed to the shutters but did not open them. The floor was cold against her feet. The air was full of the bittersweet smell of burned candles.

"How can I be sure?" she asked. "These lands are no longer safe."

"Believe me," said the voice again. "It is I who talked to you this evening. Have you forgotten me already?"

She smiled at that. Despite the chill bite of the night that invaded her nightgown, she felt a rush of warmth.

"Prove yourself. What words did you whisper in my ear?"

There was a moment of silence. "I—I do not remember, exactly. I was in the flush of drink and victory."

"Do such words flow to all women at such times, sir?" said Guinevere, a little piqued.

"No!" replied the man indignantly and most sincerely. "Truly! You must believe me, Guinevere. I spoke from my heart. As I recall I said that you were the most beautiful woman in Britain and that I would never be satisfied again in Gaul, knowing that such beauty existed across the channel."

Sweeping back her hair with satisfaction, Guinevere bit her lip softly with a thrill of happiness. That was much better than what he had actually said.

"Please," he begged. "Open the window. I could not sleep. I must see you again."

"Very well," she replied coyly. "But only for a moment."

Lifting the bolt, she drew the windows slowly open. Despite her caution they squeaked slightly.

Outside, a gibbous moon ruled the sky. No clouds marred its brightness. Stars shone in courtly attendance to the queen of the heavens. Lancelot's features were smoothly etched in shadow. He leaned in, laying his chin on his arms he had propped on the sill. "You look beautiful in the starlight!" he said.

"Why? Because you can barely see me?"

Lancelot seemed a little taken aback. "You do not take praise well, do you?"

"Why must men come girded in flattery when they visit women?" she spoke forthrightly. "I wish you simply wore no armor at all."

"You prefer your men unclothed, then?" asked Lancelot, the joke obvious in his tone.

She laughed softly. "That depends upon the man. Now tell me, soldier. What brings you to my window at this late hour? I hardly know you."

"That is why I've come. I wish that you did know me

better, for there is so little time. I leave tomorrow, as I mentioned."

"Why do you bother with me? The king would present you with your pick of this kingdom's women, and I'm sure the women would gladly acquiesce to the prospect."

"You wield flattery well yourself, Guinevere." His face was stern in the moonlight. Sharp, deep angles. Guinevere felt a delicious fear form in her. "But Arthur would never make a woman marry me. That is not his way."

"You have much respect for the high king, don't you?"

"I worship the ideals he embodies. He saved my life. And above all he is a good man. He is my friend, whom I would not betray though my soul were in peril."

"He does seem a goodly king."

"I fear I monopolized you at dinner. I wish you knew him better. You would see the meaning of my words. . . ." Suddenly he reached in and touched her cheek. His hand was not cold at all. Starlight shone in his eye, reflected off a wetness. "Ah, woman. Your beauty makes me weep. I cannot hold that back. On the battlefield I am often but a sword's swipe away from death. I know how fragile and short life is, and when I feel something I cannot hold back from professing it."

Guinevere raised her hand to touch his. She pressed it firmer against her cheek. "Feelings that arise over one dinner and many glasses of mead are often short lived, Lancelot."

He shook his head slowly. "The drink cannot dim or heighten that which I feel for you. How can I say it? My tools are my sword and shield, not words."

"Perhaps you should compose them at a later time."

"I thought I saw those feelings reflected in you, Guinevere. That is all I have come to find out. Can these feelings be returned, or shall I staunch them?"

In the distance an owl flapped. Leaves nodded with

the breeze. Some flew off branches, danced to their graves on the ground. The smell of the breeze was woodsy. The tang of death was on the air, and the taste of life. . . .

She turned her head, kissed Lancelot's wrist almost reverently. Despite the darkness she could *feel* his smile.

"I shall tell you no lies, Guinevere. I have known many women in my search."

"Search?"

"For one my head and heart tells me is you."

"That sounds quite romantic and quite unlikely."

A kind of threatening hurt sounded in Lancelot's voice. "Do not mock me, Guinevere. . . . If I could control it, I would. I wish I could not love. I wish that I were as my sword. Cold and steel and good in battle for the right cause."

"I would not hurt you for the world, Lancelot. I speak from practicality. You men may weave all the dreams you like with songs and poems and not change the truth one jot."

Lancelot's voice grew wistful. "All this I searched for . . . a body full anchored to the earth, beautiful as this island. And yet a soul that soars. I see in you, Guinevere, much that I have found in Britain. I must know your feelings about me."

Her heart melted with the yearning sincerity of his statement. "I cannot believe it," she answered finally, shaking her head. "I hardly know you, but you move me. As for my deepest feelings, words fail." She leaned into the night and kissed him softly upon the lips. The warm moistness coursed excitement through her. She made to back away, but his hand pulled her down again, and he kissed her again, long and hungrily. She grew dizzy with the headlong meeting of passion and passion.

He smoothed a hand down her side, tracing her voluptuous fullness, wrist brushing her breast slightly. Tingles shot through her. She answered with a sigh.

He took the exhalation as an invitation. With a leap, he scrambled halfway over the window's lip. But she halted his entrance with strong hands.

"No, Lancelot."

Astonished eyes rose to hers. "But why? I love you more than life itself."

"And I feel for you, Lancelot. But this could be but a vapor of the night. It is so beautiful I would not have it mock me on the morrow with a foolish indiscretion."

He let himself slide back to the ground beneath the window. "You are a remarkable woman indeed. . . . Yes. Yes, perhaps you are right. But this will not pass! I swear to God, by all that is holy it shall not, for my life will surely dissipate with it."

"We shall see each other tomorrow and see what feelings that meeting brings."

"Yes, yes. Clever girl." He leaned against the sill. "But at least a kiss before I go. One kiss from you is worth a dozen hay rolls with other women."

She laughed softly and kissed him long and hard.

With no further words he pressed her hand firmly in farewell and sped off.

Quickly he was swallowed by the night.

Guinevere had to pinch herself to assure herself that he had not been a dream.

Shivering, but not cold, she paced back to her bed after reshuttering the window. She immediately fell into a deep sleep, dreaming no dreams.

As though they were without purpose—now that her life had Lancelot.

ii

Late in the night, restless in the room King Leodegrance's steward had provided for him, Arthur raised up on his elbows, scowling. He couldn't rid his mind of the girl's face, the sheen of her hair, the color of her eyes—

Or the way she gazed so admiringly at Lancelot the Gaul.

The day's triumph had been blunted, somehow.

He tried to rid his thoughts of her. Stupid, foolish man, he told himself. You are a king, not a gaping simpleton. Women are mysteries no longer. They are people, your subjects as much as men. One should not impress you more than another.

Nonetheless incidents of the evening replayed in Arthur's mind as he lay squirming upon the bed.

He heard again the melody of her voice rising above the din of the feast. He had hoped to drain the tension of the battle into that celebration, yet found himself more unsettled than ever by the presence of Guinevere. A beauty to be worshipped and cherished rather than held. Every moment was elegant and expressive. Her laughter still seemed to sound in Arthur's ear, tinklings of bells.

Yet in the glimmer of her eye, the shapeliness of her figure, she had an earthy self-awareness. In this Arthur was reminded of Guenhumara, and his heart ached at the memory.

Thinking of her, Arthur lay tossing until the cocks crowed.

iii

Not long after the sun dawned clear and bright over the land, a hearty breakfast was served in the great hall of King Leodegrance.

Waking just a little before the sun, Guinevere found herself ravenously hungry. Her father had announced the usual early breakfast. Perhaps Lancelot would be there.

The thought made her giddy.

Not bothering to summon Mara for help, she donned a pale red tunic, accompanied by oddments of jewelry. Glass beads, porcelain medallions. She combed her own hair, then washed her face in the basin of cold water on the toilet table. The splash of chill wetness brought out the color in her cheeks.

Quickly she donned her beaded leather shoes and raced down for breakfast.

Lancelot was not there.

The only occupant of the long table was King Arthur.

Before him sat a trencher of cold mutton, pears, and apples. Untouched. Not seeing her, he fingered a brimmed wood tankard of fresh cider as though in contemplation. If she had not known his fearsome and just record these past years as high king, she might have thought him merely a beaten soldier, bitter with his wounds.

She paused a moment. Then remembered that as a duty to her father, King Leodegrance, she owed at least politeness and hospitality to this odd man who had fought so valiantly yesterday.

With a flurry of her tunic, she stepped full into the room and daintily settled opposite the king. She smiled good morning, then cast her eyes down to the table's contents. Besides the strips of mutton, there were chunks of last night's roast boar, wild scallions, fruit, rough loaves of delicious-smelling bread fresh from the fire. Pitchers of cool water and cider lined the table's center like alert sentries. There were even a few small kegs of ale for the more hearty.

As she selected a few slices of mutton and pondered if she should request cooked eggs from the attendant servant, she noticed that King Arthur had brightened considerably.

Yes. Now he looked more like a king. Not many years older than herself, he sat alert, eyes trained upon her every move. A handsome fellow, really, if you looked past the premature age in his eyes.

Guinevere smiled inwardly at his attention as she picked a bright, ripe red apple from its tray.

"The cider is very refreshing too," commented Arthur, tapping the side of a pitcher near him. "May I pour you some?"

"Thank you."

Arthur obliged, careful not to spill any.

Guinevere picked up her cup. Sipped. Cool, sweet, and tart. "You are right, my lord."

"You are Guinevere, the daughter of our host, Leodegrance," Arthur said, a trace of hesitation in his voice. *Surely not shyness*, Guinevere thought.

A king, shy?

"Are you not?" continued Arthur, punctuating his sentence with a flicker of a smile.

"That's right. And you are Arthur Pendragon. I saw you last night at the celebration. The feast would not have been possible without your help. Thank you. You are a fine leader." She toyed with her meat.

The man colored a bit at the compliment. He did have an expressive face—and yet it betrayed a certain unsureness. There was power there, no question about that. But beyond that power there was an essential questioning. Guinevere was intrigued. Truly Lancelot's king was a wonderful man.

"I would that I could win such victories daily. Protecting houses that shelter such as you is a pleasure rather than a duty." He stared at her a moment, then seemed to recover his sense of the moment. "Oh. Excuse me. You are no doubt hungry. Do not let our conversation keep you from your breakfast."

She nodded graciously and commenced her eating. She decided against asking for eggs. Her hunger somehow did not seem so important anymore. Here before her was the man who Lancelot loved dearly. His bosom friend. His leader and his king. Who would know more of Lancelot than King Arthur himself?

"I was most intrigued by your tactics of battle," she commented casually a few moments after washing down some bread and butter with a swallow of cider. "Your captain Lancelot praised them to the skies. His tales have the stuff of legend to them, King Arthur."

"Just Arthur, please." He barked a sardonic laugh, wiping a bit of fruit from his mouth with the back of his hand self-consciously. "It is Lancelot's bravado—and his high-flown language—that form legends. I simply work hard and speak seldom."

"He is a braggard, then, this Lancelot of Gaul?"

"Lancelot? I think there's a bit of bluster in him, yes. But he always stands on firm ground. Seeing him fight, knowing him as a friend, benefiting from his extreme loyalty, I sometimes wonder, though, if his speeches are not understatement to the truth."

"Which is?"

"He is my finest captain," stated Arthur, finally attending to the mutton before him. "I would sooner lose my sword Excalibur than Lancelot."

A few more guests had begun to shuffle in to seat themselves at the table, patting back yawns. But Guinevere barely noticed them. She had all her attention focused upon Arthur and his talk of Lancelot.

"And yet," she pressed, realizing that perhaps she was being impolite, "for such a great man as Lancelot to swear loyalty to another—why, the other must be an even greater man."

Arthur smiled broadly at that. He scooted his chair back with a scraping sound, put his hands to his belly, and laughed uproariously.

Guinevere blinked. Cocked her head inquisitively. Her unbound dark hair draped in swirls over her shoulder. "I am sorry. Does my boldness offend you, your highness?"

"No." Arthur stretched a hand out, waving away any import of her statement. "It is just so silly. I do not think of either of us as being 'great' men, Guinevere. We do what we *must* do. What is our duty, for our people, and our country, and our cause. We aspire only to what we *should* be. Excuse my laughter, but I do not take praise seriously."

Noting that he seemed more relaxed now, Guinevere felt more comfortable as well. More at ease with this complex and admirable man. Perhaps talk of Lancelot could wait. How often was it that she had breakfast conversation with the Pendragon himself?

Absently she fingered the ornate embroidery above her bodice. Running deer, in gold and crimson thread. She had worked on it long and hard. The bronze pin above it, though, was a gift from her father. It was a very old pin that had to be cleaned regularly to prevent tarnishing. Depicting the head of some dead and forgotten tribal leader, the pin was claimed by Leodegrance to be full of luck. It would lead her, he said, to marriage with a great man amongst their people.

She had hardly been aware that she had slipped it on in her rush at daybreak. Its hardness was a comfort under her fingers. The metalcraft was crude, but powerful. The head had an expression that was half smile and half scowl. She had always favored it because it reminded her of her father. Now it reminded her of another.

"Very well, then. I shall keep my praise humorous," she pronounced with mock airs of nobility.

Laughter rumbled in the hall. Heads turned.

Lancelot stood at the doorway, resplendent in clean clothes. From shined tall leather boots, up his straight and tight-fitting cloth breeches, his berry red tunic and dashing leather vest, he was the virile image of man. But his animate face, his twinkling eyes showed so much more to Guinevere. He was even more handsome in the light of day. The torch flame and the moonlight had not done him justice. Her heart lurched, as though to wrench away from her and join his.

Stalking forward, Lancelot grabbed a chunk of meat from the table and wolfed it down heartily, directing his attention to Arthur, not even glancing at Guinevere. He directed a long finger in a westerly direction. "I've heard it told that there's good hunting yonder. I've employed a few village lads to help me carry back the deer. I could use a hearty venison steak for midday meal today, before we take leave of this beautiful country. Would you care to join me, Arthur?"

A deep hurt speared through Guinevere. But she was careful to keep it from her expression. He hadn't looked in her direction. Lancelot had so little time here, and he chose to spend it slaying innocent deer? Had all his hot words of last night been for naught, after all? She looked down and addressed herself to the last of her breakfast, despite her sudden lack of appetite.

"I think not, Lancelot," responded Arthur. "I do not find hunting restful as you do. I think that after my meeting with King Leodegrance I will take my horse for a ride among these lovely hills. Good for the soul, I think. Fresh air, without the smell of blood."

Lancelot shrugged eloquently. "Each man to his own sport." He grabbed a loaf of bread. "Well, I must be off." He granted Guinevere a clipped bow. "My lady. I hope I shall have the pleasure of a good-bye before we leave this afternoon."

Anger filled Guinevere. The rogue!

She leaned toward Arthur. "I know the hills well, my lord. May I have the honor of guiding you about them?" She directed an abrupt and fiery look at Lancelot, who accepted it with a grin.

Arthur seemed surprised. "Why . . . if your father thinks it appropriate. I would not go against his wishes."

"My father generally wishes what I wish," she returned. "Excellent. Settled then. Lancelot shall spear animals. We shall ride horses and *enjoy* the countryside, not mar it."

Lancelot's grin turned a trifle lopsided at the barb. He saluted Arthur with the bread loaf, briskly turned about, and trotted off. His cape waved behind him.

Excusing herself, Guinevere went to encourage her father to get out of bed and take breakfast.

"He sleeps much too late for his own good after such celebrations as last night's," she explained.

"He drinks too much for his own good, as well, I fear," grumbled one of the nobles tableside.

"The two, I fear," commented Arthur, "go hand in

hand." He nodded at Guinevere. "My men will prepare horses for our ride. I will see that you are not kept waiting."

"That is very nice of you," said Guinevere. She felt a trifle guilty, using this good man so. But then, she'd done it on spurious impulse. To not go through with it would be dreadful.

Besides, already her heart had begun to ache at Lancelot's inattention. Was last night a dream, after all? Or had he just been very drunk and fed on her dreams like some bird of prey?

She desperately wanted to think that was so, but deep within she knew that the man was just not that way.

Her feelings seldom lied to her.

"I look forward to the ride, King Arthur," she said with her sweetest obliging smile. "I only hope that I am a suitable guide."

"And for my part," murmured Arthur, barely audible as he reached for the tankard of cider, "I hope I can keep my eyes on the scenery."

iv

The sunrise was a ruddy, bloody gash on the North Sea's horizon. The wind whipped the water into white-capped waves, which slapped against the longboat's sides monotonously. Spray lapped over the pontoons, splashing the rowers of Saxony on their way to the British shore.

Cynric of the Rhine Valley gripped the handle of the rudder in both powerful hands. The brine of the sea was heavy on his tongue. The reckless smell of the sea washed over him with the morning breeze. Cynric watched his private army dip their oars as one into the rolling surface, pull as one against the tide, lift again for another strong attack. As one.

He felt strong. He felt the gods were gracing him this time. With this *comitatus* under his command, he felt capable of any of the tasks ascribed to the Anglic hero

Beowulf. Tackle a monster or its mother? Why not? It would be child's play compared to battling this new British king and his captains, if his father, Cerdic, already in Britain, was right.

Fifty men he had with him for his first venture to Britain. Not ordinary warriors, these. Oh, no. As soon as his father had told him of the spoils and glory to be won on this distant island, he had begun planning to take them properly. His experience among the lands of the Angles and the Jutes had been wide. He personally preferred their fighting talents.

They had a hardness, a dourness achieved no doubt by the cold bleakness of the land. They fought with skill, power, and solemnity. They fit his needs like a fine-cured leather gauntlet about his hand.

He grimaced as a wave broke over the side, flinging the sting of cold water. Readjusting the angle of the rudder, he smiled grimly to himself.

Although it had taken some time to pick the very best from the various tribes, it had been time well spent.

For Cynric sought a prize higher than either glory or spoils.

He stretched like a healthy animal. Scratched at his wiry, uncombed beard. He was twenty-one with this year. The well-earned armband about his thick left biceps was comfortably tight. An emblem of his prowess. He had won it from a Frisian warrior after a drunken argument over the favors of a buxom woman. How gloriously his blade had shone in the torchlight as it streaked down, metallic lightning. To cleave the life from the old fool. Cynric admired the working of the metal, hammered to represent the image of Woden, his god . . . god of warriors. Cynric knew that Woden favored this journey. The Britons, their Roman protectors long gone, were ripe for gradual conquering.

His hungry wolf eyes roamed among the rowers, satisfied.

They halted on a young, burly man. Durnor, by name, as he recalled. The man was not rowing.

"Ho, lad! Durnor!" he bawled above the slapping of the other oars and the sea-sounds. "Let's have at it, fellow. We need your strength."

"I am ill and I am tired. I will have some rest!" groaned Durnor back. Limp brown hair hung in greasy locks down his temples. His face was pale with seasickness. The bilge-sopped oak planks that composed the boat creaked and sighed as though in sympathy. The shriek of a gull ripped the silence as the bird wheeled over the boat.

Cynric stabbed a finger in the air. "Land is near, man! Row, I say." He'd half suspected that Durnor might be a troublemaker. Strong, but too lazy by half.

Sullenly the Jute hunkered down, ignoring Cynric's command.

So. A questioning of his power already, even before their feet were firm upon British soil.

Cynric, disturbed by the swing of heads, the assaying glances from the other men, prodded the nearest oarman in the shin. He gestured to the rudder. The man nodded and took his place.

Conflict.

Confrontation.

Halting beside Durnor's bench, Cynric kicked its support violently. Durnow tottered but managed to cling to his purchase. "I do not tolerate stubbornness in this *comitatus*," pronounced Cynric. "Puke over the side if you like, but get back to work."

The slithering ring of metal against metal sounded. A blade shone in the sun, held up—half threat, half protection. "You are no hero, Cynric. You are a user. I heard you gasp your ambitions to that woman you had in your hut in Jutland. A whole land, you would own. You and you alone—"

Cynric sneered to hide his shock. His response was immediate. His fist slammed into the man's face. Nose cartilege crunched. With a grunt of pain Durnor lashed with his knife.

A jump took Cynric clear of the blow. The sharp point thunked into wood.

With skilled ease Cynric's sword erupted from its scabbard. Durnor sprang back, but too late.

The swing of the long blade caught him hard on the chest, biting deep. Blood squirted down the leather cuirass. Blue eyes began to film. Teeth chattered a death rattle.

Surging forward, Cynric plucked the big man forcefully from his stance, heaving him over the side.

Water splashed. A scream of horror wailed, then stilled. The thrashing man bobbled for a moment in a froth of blood, then sank beneath the waves as though tugged by something dark.

The oars stilled.

Eyes filled with respect.

Cynric sucked in a salty breath. "Entertainment is over!" he growled. "You can rest when we beach!"

He swaggered back to his post, victory filling his sinews with force and strength as it always did.

Grabbing hold of the rudder once more, he looked to the horizon as paddles once more chopped at the swell.

He searched hungrily for the first sight of the land that would be his.

V

Guinevere admired the way Arthur rode his big black roan horse. Poised and alert in the saddle, Arthur seemed to control the beast's movements as easily as he controlled his own.

She had a way with horses as well, but it was more a natural affinity than a skill. Firmly and comfortably planted on her young stallion, Asnar, she matched Arthur's speed stride by stride as they cantered across a field that lay in a dip of the hillocks. At the verge of a large copse of trees, foamed with green, choked with brambles, Arthur reined in.

Guinevere followed suit. Asnar's rapid compliance was rewarded with an affectionate stroking of his well-combed black mane. She was covered in familiar horse smell. It made her feel warm and composed.

"You ride well," complimented Arthur, smiling at her. "It is a shame more women do not learn to ride. They often have an equine grace that complements that of their horse."

"My father taught me," said Guinevere, answering with a smile of her own. "Riding gives me a sense of control. Power, if you will. Does riding this land of ours lend such a feeling?"

"At times." Arthur sighed, staring off into the trees. A woodpecker labored on the bark of a larch, dull red among the turning leaves. Yellows, vermilions, and oranges invaded the wealth of green as gray invades an aging man's hair. The smells of autumn wreathed the air in subtle and earthy scents. The rich sourness of decay wrapped up the world with sweetness and muskiness. Dying pink primroses clustered below holly. A blueberry bush, its fruits plucked nearly clean by birds, huddled amongst perfumy loosetrifes and pimpernels.

Guinevere had loved the flowers of spring and summer for as long as she could remember. The water lilies of lazy ponds. The bluebells wrapped in long bending grasses in nature's feckless arrangements. The oxslip and cowslip to pick and adorn your hair, fancying yourself some forest nymph, dancing recklessly and with the abandon of wild ivy through the forest. The windblown narcissus. And yes, the yellow poppies, sweet smelling as honeysuckle.

"But I would rather not talk so much of my duty," continued Arthur.

"What would you talk of then, Arthur?" Guinevere asked, adjusting the collar of her cape to cover her neck against the faint chill in the air.

"We live in a beautiful land, do we not?" asked Arthur. "I only need to travel to its wild midst to feel a sense of its destiny. But warriors grow weary even of what they fight for, Guinevere. I am but twenty-one, and already responsibility has weighed me down." Smiling with wry humor, he faced her directly. "Tell me. What is it like to live your life with little care? Exist in the way you choose, free to dabble in leisure so much. I envy you much in this."

"Your highness," she began in shock at his complaints.

"If you please, my lady, call me Arthur."

"Well Arthur, then, my lord. Every woman and man is driven by forces over which they have no control. The ways that we live are presented to us. We cannot even choose what body we are placed in. Indeed, if we could, then I would choose yours. For then I would be king and you can be sure I would not envy a life of leisure."

"That is what Merlin says." Arthur dismounted suddenly and tethered his horse to a low-hanging branch. Fingering an acorn, he continued contemplatively: "I am truly honored to be high king. I feel that the cause I strive for is *right*." He plucked the acorn. Tossed it at a clump of moss. Then gazed back at Guinevere almost pleadingly. "Why, then, does it all seem so wearying at times, so futile." He waved his hands with an air of frustration. "I wish I could live merely a peaceful life in this land. Enjoy a family. Yet it seems I must buy peace for myself and this land with war. A paradox, is it not?"

She looked down into his deep brown eyes, which met her gaze simply and straightforwardly. This man was painfully honest. Refreshingly so. He was a good man. Guinevere realized then just how much she liked him, how much she respected him. Instinctively she knew that she could trust him with her innermost secrets. A confidant and a king. Good company too it seemed. "You brood too much, Arthur." She watched a squirrel scurry raucously through the brush. "Worry, I have found, solves nothing. Thinking perhaps finds solutions. But thinking, if it is done properly, requires very little time or anxiety."

"You seem a wise and caring person, Guinevere."

"I fear my character lacks depth, actually." Such things she was saying to this man she had only just met. Not even Mara was privileged to hear such. But how good it felt to let it gush out. "I wish I were more mature and not so involved with such ephemeral concerns as flit through a young girl's head naturally."

"And what might those be? I confess, I have never been a young girl." Arthur showed fine, even teeth in a broad smile. Guinevere was touched by his warmth.

"Oh, silly things. How should I wear my hair today. I had better not eat so much; I am too fat. Oh, look at that kitten there, isn't he cute. Or such a handsome lad. I wonder if he notices me." She swept her hands out expansively. "The ocean, sky, and clouds like puffy woolen ships, the gentle slopes of hills, and the animals that roam in the dales; weighed against these majestic things, my thoughts seem silly."

A moment of pregnant silence came between them. Arthur bit his lip softly, then looked up and blinked.

"Dear me, I *am* sorry. You're up there and I'm down here. Would you care to join me."

She smiled brightly. "Why certainly, Arthur. My sore-rubbed rear would welcome the rest."

He hopped over immediately. Grabbed her by the waist. She could feel his iron strength as he supported her in her dismounting. And too his gentleness and slight awe of her. She placed her arms about his neck. Softly, with infinite care, he settled her down to the ground. Their arms lingered a moment. She met his wondering gaze directly, and a shiver raced through her. He turned away, swallowing. Released his careful touch. Walked to a tree and leaned against its crumbling bark, staring off to a heather-lined hill.

His foot scuffled at a pile of peat, as though he was in deep contemplation.

She stepped up beside him. "That bank yonder." She pointed. "There lies a large stand of rocks, smaller than

Stonehenge, perhaps older. Can you see?" The breeze flapped at her tunic.

He followed her pointing. "Ah. Yes. Those stones . . . I wonder what they mean. Why they were placed here."

"They will be here long after we're gone and forgotten," commented Guinevere wistfully. "Or I will be forgotten anyway. You, Arthur, have the promise of a great reign. Perhaps you will live on in the fireside tales of our people." She signed. "I, however . . . I am for the earth and the wind. I just pray that my ashes nurture this sweet, sweet land."

"No," said Arthur, gripping her arm vehemently. "We are more than that . . . *you* are more than that. You must be, can't you see." He shook his long hair. "We strive and yearn, and it must be for something, even though we cannot touch it, see it." He gazed on her in a manner that made her feel as though his eyes probed her very soul. "In you I see a representation of all that has moved me in this island, this Britain. The skys are in your eyes, misty and mysterious. The climate in your warmth. The gentle curves of the land in your body. The soul of our people and our homeland in you. You personify this all for me, Guinevere."

"You flatter me, Arthur," said Guinevere, disturbed, yet not quite understanding why. "You speak very well. But I am just a woman. No more and, thank God, no less."

"Yes. This is just an island. But our caring for it makes it something more."

"Caring. Yes. You are a caring person, Arthur." She strolled away in no particular direction. The high grass brushed at her breeches. "You are a good king. I am honored to know you."

Silence again.

She could sense that he followed her, hanging back a ways.

They traipsed through dead leaves, crunching.

She thought of Lancelot and the crackle of leaves outside her window.

Finally he said, haltingly, "I know of someone who cares very much for you."

She turned around, raising her eyebrows. "Oh, do you?"

Arthur nodded. "Yes. People call him a great man, and yet he is just a man."

That echoed what Lancelot had said last night. A suspicion grew in Guinevere. And a wild surge of hope. Was all this a plan forged by Lancelot? An odd way of wooing her, true. But on what better recommendation than King Arthur's could he express his worth to her. Who knew him better than his best friend? And she could be more likely to believe the good things from Arthur's mouth than from Lancelot's. How very clever of him! She liked Arthur all the more for collaborating on this amusing and worthwhile plot.

"This great man," she said, calculatingly, eyes averted, watching a gray kestrel wing overhead. "What are his feelings? I have learned that the truth in man is ill-served by words."

Arthur seemed to be choosing his phrases very carefully. "He is a man who distrusts words as well and prefers action. His feelings are genuine and deep. They are of love, Guinevere."

She turned on him, flashing her eyes in amused accusation. "And this man who loves. No doubt he has loved many women before."

"Not as he loves now, I think," answered Arthur, seemingly a bit taken aback. "I can vouch for his sincerity. I swear by my sword."

Arthur took a pace forward, touched her arm gently. "Guinevere . . ." he began.

His sentence was cut off by the clopping of hoofs on the ground. In a whirl of riffling cape and fluttering light hair, Lancelot pounded up the slope toward them. He smiled broadly as he neared them. "Greetings on this fair day. I trust I find you both well and amused."

Arthur looked a bit dour, but Guinevere thought nothing of it, wrapped in glad emotion at Lancelot's arrival.

"Lancelot!" she hailed. "We thought you were hunting."

The dashing captain halted his horse. "I decided against it." He directed his gaze to Arthur. "There is something that needs your immediate attention, my friend. A jeweled necklace taken from the dead body of one of the Saxons of yesterday's battle. Two men squabble over it. They will fight to the death over it, lest you intervene. They have agreed to abide by your decision on that matter. And only your decision."

Arthur shook his head, exasperation plain. "Greed. It is a human curse. A disease of Saxons and Britons alike."

He turned to Guinevere. "Dear lady, our talk has left me hungry for more. I feel our—friendship is something very special. We must leave your father's land soon. . . . But may I call upon you again to continue our discussion?"

"Why of course, Arthur," said Guinevere. "I anticipate that with much pleasure. Well, I guess we had better remount and head back—"

"And waste this beautiful morning?" Lancelot chimed in. "It is a matter that needs only the high king's attention. I shall take his place on the tour."

Guinevere looked at Arthur, who nodded. "Lancelot is right of course. You two enjoy yourselves. Duty calls." His voice seemed full of resignation. He strode to his horse, pulled himself up, and with a farewell wave started away, headed toward the house of Leodegrance.

At the bottom of the hillock he stopped, looked back for a long moment. Then kicked the flanks of his horse and sped away.

vi

The brook burbled happily, echoing Guinevere's feelings as she gazed into Lancelot's eyes. The water churned over smooth rocks, lapping hushingly at the fronds leaning over the verdant edges.

Time seemed to have stopped for Guinevere.

Her life seemed set into perspective, after this time with these two men. She felt on the verge of a fulfillment she had never thought possible.

Her head lay in Lancelot's lap. He stroked her long hair with measured care. They spoke from time to time, there on that soft bed of grass by the brookside elm. But the silences carried as much meaning.

Guinevere's mind ranged back over what she could recall of her sixteen years. All in all not an unpleasant life. A privileged existence, actually, with pampering from servants, a fond father who spoiled her, no great amount of work to accomplish save her own avocations, weaving, and jewelry-making. Filled with the delights only a nobleman's daughter could know. Fine linens and objects of art from the Mediterranean. Horses to train. Airy rooms, sunlight, a beautiful countryside that seemed hers alone. The songs of the curlew in the bush. . . .

In contrast with this time with Lancelot, her past seemed colorless. A desert, leached of meaning.

The day was an idyllic dream.

Morning had stretched into afternoon. The sun was clothed in shreds of clouds. Streams of light through breaks in the clouds played slowly over the particolored landscape. Ducks squabbled in the slow-moving stream. The breeze raked leaves into spurts of whirlpools, flinging the smell of autumn subtly about them in their resting place.

After a long, thoughtful silence Lancelot said, "I have never felt such peace." A breathy reverence filled his voice.

"Lancelot," she whispered. "I am so glad you decided not to hunt."

He tousled her hair playfully. "I never intended to. I wanted to be out here with you."

She sat up abruptly. "What? Then why—"

Lancelot put his fingers to his lips. "Your father plots."

"What is that supposed to mean?" she demanded, vexed.

"I believe he would like to have his daughter the wife of the high king. A good political move, that would be."

"Ha!" she said. "My father would never—"

"You have only known your father as parent to a cute cuddly child. You mature, Guinevere."

"Nevertheless, what does that have to do with the way you acted this morning?"

"If your father knew our feelings for each other, he would instantly forbid our meeting. If I had asked you riding with me, he would have suspected. He seemed most pleased that you were out with Arthur."

"And what will he say when he sees that Arthur is back and I am not?"

Lancelot shrugged. "*If* he does, then he will naturally inquire of Arthur. Arthur will tell him that I have been placed in charge of your countryside ramblings. So much more seemly than if we'd galloped off together." His eyes twinkled mischievously as he stared down at her. "Besides, who better than my best friend to speak for my qualities."

"Rogue! I thought as much!" She punched him playfully. "He did very well. I like him very much, Lancelot. And he speaks of me in very good terms. I believe we are very good friends now."

"And what did he say of me?"

"Only good things. And I even think he knows of how we have begun to feel for one another!"

"Really? I suppose he saw that at the celebration last night. He has seen me with many women—"

Guinevere raised her eyebrows.

Holding up his hands in mock defense, Lancelot grinned broadly. "I will speak only truth to you, Guin. Let me finish. Never, I'm sure, has he seen me so taken with a woman. No man knows as well as he how much I long for a great love." He held her close, smoothing his cheek against hers. "The love I have found in you."

"Yes, he spoke of you in that way just before you barged in. He thinks the world of you."

"And I of him. He is my king. His wish is my rule. Disobedience to Arthur would be like betraying myself." He kissed her softly. "But enough of Arthur. We have very little time together before I must leave."

A small pang grew in her. She blinked back unwelcomed tears. "Must you go? We have had only such a short time together."

"I fear so. There are urgent matters to take care of in Cam. Our following grows. We must organize it properly. The Saxons do not allow us time for love."

"Then you can find no time for me?"

"My life is yours now. But I could not love you if I did not serve the ideals of Arthur to my best ability."

"Yes," she murmured, a sadness beyond all measure in her heart. She grasped his hands tightly, urgently staring into his eyes. "Then if you've so little time here with me, you must avail yourself of my love, in manly ways. Now."

Lancelot blinked. Stiffened with perplexity. "What *are* you talking about, Guinevere?"

Kneeling near him, Guinevere placed his palms on her breasts. "I am not unaware of men's desires toward women. I would not have you forget me, Lancelot."

Strong emotion crossed the handsomely angled face. Lancelot craned forward, bestowing each of her eyelids with a gossamer-soft kiss. "Our love does not need such a start to survive," he said quietly. "Although it is a pure and treasured gift you offer."

"You do not think me chaste?" said Guinevere, feeling slightly relieved.

"Truly, it does not matter a jot to me," proclaimed

Lancelot. "Virgin or not, you are Guinevere. And our love is all that matters. We shall take that part of it when it comes, slowly and softly. Savoring it, one of the other."

He folded her up safely and warmly in his caress.

Nearby linnets chirped. A blackbird fluttered in the branches above. But all Guinevere heard were the breaths of Lancelot. And his strong heartbeat.

The song of his life lulled her into an ecstatic repose.

"It is time, my love," he said finally. "I must join Arthur's company."

"You will tell him of our love?"

"I will tell the world."

She beamed happily. Stretched. "When shall I see you again, Lancelot?"

"I have been thinking on that. We must wait to see how the land lies . . . excuse me. A warrior term. I will send you a messenger as to the exact time. As for the place, why not here?"

"It grows cold."

"We shall warm it with our love. And when winter whitens the world, we shall find some hayloft. The land will be ours, Guin. I have much to tell you. So very much!"

She touched his lips with a slim finger. "And I, you, Lancelot. Each day will be a year to me, before I see you again." She nuzzled close.

"I will take a kiss before we ride back, Guinevere."

"Gladly," she said. "And I shall take many from you."

Their lips met, and to her the world dissolved into inconsequence.

vii

The hairy hand slapped the scuffed felt pouch upon the feasting table. Dishes rattled. A gilded glass of ale tottered, then crashed onto the hard, bare ground.

Silence as thick as the British night above descended

upon the Saxon gathering. All eyes turned to the scowling man, standing above his plate of half-raw wild boar and smashed mussels. Cooking fires flickered upon sharp-etched features.

"Here is your damned *wergild*," growled Cynric. Contempt flared in his eyes at the thickset man before him. "Take it and begone."

The middle-aged man on Cynric's left spat a piece of fowl bone into the dirt. Took a draft of ale, gazing blankly at the table heaped with a partly devoured roast boar, shellfish, and huge pitchers of strong drink. "You should learn to control your temper, my son," Cerdic said tonelessly. "A foolish action may next time cost you more than gold."

The hulking Jute dragged the pouch off the table and tinkled the coins into his palm. His thick lips breathed a murmur as he counted, a facial tic contorting his rough features.

Suddenly he locked eyes with Cynric the Saxon. "One hundred shillings! My brother Durnor was not a *coerl*! You heap insult upon your pile of crimes, pig son." Hrothgar the Jute waved a fist under the Saxon captain's nose. "My family cannot accept this!" Outrage bulged the veins on his forehead.

Cynric half drew his bone-handled *gladius*. A quick motion of his father's hand halted him.

Cerdic looked up at Hrothgar placidly. "You will take what my son offers, Hrothgar. Be glad that you get anything at all. Your brother was a traitor." He glanced meaningfully at the score of warriors seated around the table. Nodded. Swords flashed. Axes raised. The warriors glowered with the humor power brings. "Yes, Hrothgar. Take the man-money my son owes you and take your life back to the cold land that spawned it. We want none of your rebellious ilk among our number."

"My brother was no peasant!" cried Hrothgar, indignant. "He was a proud and brave warrior! I will not take this!"

An iron-headed spear prodded his midriff.

Cynric paced to the Jute. "You are lucky I give you anything! I do have my honor!"

Contemptuously Hrothgar flung the pouch to Cynric's feet. "Your honor is a cheap thing, then. I'll not have its foul coins!"

The burly Jute brusquely pushed away the spear and pounded away into the darkness beyond the firelight.

Eyes wide with fury, Cynric unsheathed his Roman short sword and began to follow.

A sharp bark from his father halted him. "No! Leave him be. There are other Jutes among our number. Warriors we value," Cerdic said, stern emotion creeping into his voice. "Brave, courageous men." He smiled and laughed as he gazed upon the surrounding group. "Dissension is hardly reason to pursue Hrothgar, my son. In killing him you may well kill our friendship with these other good Jutes. No. Take the money back. Distribute what foolish Hrothgar will not have among his able brethren." He cocked a furry-browed eye at his audience. "Am I wrong?"

Laughter and cheers swelled. The atmosphere of tension that had cloaked the welcoming feast dissipated immediately, as Cerdic's servant took the purse and began to distribute the coins to the Jutes in the crowd.

"And as for our Anglish friends and our Saxon fellows let it be known that they shall have an equal portion's worth of money on the morrow. There is plenty for all!"

More hurrahs thundered.

Dissatisfied, Cynric slunk back to the table.

Cerdic patted his back. "There, there, my blood. Cool yourself in some drink. All is well now. You have done well. You've brought forty-nine of the best warriors I have seen. With my strong and able men and those we recruit from the countryside settlers we will form a force that will smash the Latinized swine into their British soil!"

The graying, muscular middle-aged chieftain erupted to his feet, hoisting his horn-cup high. "Let us drink with renewed joy at the coming of Cynric, my son, who will lead our ranks to riches and glory."

Cups and glasses clanked together with a boisterous ring. Even the serving women smiled as they poured more ale for the men. Their bright-jeweled brooches glinted in the firelight.

Grumbling, Cynric drank his yeasty ale and found that the bitter, warming stuff did indeed douse some of the fire that poured through his veins. He chomped down a few fresh oysters and slaked his thirst three cups further, listening to the renewed heroic songs and tales the drunken tribesmen were wont to tell. The dinner scents, the odor of the unwashed bodies, lulled him into a comfortable drowse. Perhaps his father was right. Anger of the moment seldom contributed to long-range ambition. Let that fury smolder and use its power for fighting that contributed to his goal.

His father was a wise man, when he forgot about his lechery.

Cynric noted with good humor his father's antics with the plump-breasted maiden he'd sat in his ample lap on a pretext of adorning the dark-haired beauty with rough, barbaric necklaces—linked lumps of amber and crystal, colored glass beads and amethyst—his wrinkled hands found plenty of opportunity to fondle her softer parts, resulting in girlish giggles. She had the blunted features of a maid of this region—part British, part Saxon.

Cynric shook his head good-naturedly as he drank yet again, spilling almost as much as he swallowed. Father would be plowing these British fields tonight.

The Saxon chieftain diverted his attention from his jolly sport. The din was unbelievable. Drunken songs assailed the air. Men wobbled before the fire in imitation of dance. Burps and farts resounded amongst lip-smackings and gurglings. They were beyond all hearing now. Cerdic no doubt concluded that he could speak to his son with no concern of understanding ears overhearing.

"We must begin rallying our armies immediately," he said, a seriousness cutting through the glazing that drink had brought to his eyes. "A curious occurrence has made it necessary to make our attacks less casual and random. We now must have solid leadership for a drive into more British land."

"I thought it was ripe for plunder."

"And so it is, my son." Not gently Cerdic hefted the girl off him, whispered something in her ear, then slapped her rear playfully. He turned his full attention to Cynric. "We have pretty much ravaged the riches of these areas of this island we now own. Our people settle. Our families grow. Sons are born, lusty lads who will praise Woden with their swords soon. But beyond the plunder to be had deeper in the land, beyond the Roman towns that yet stand, there is the threat that the small kingships that now squabble amongst themselves are being united by a higher king. If this king rallies his people too well, there is the threat that we may be driven into the sea, forced back to our homeland."

Gazing off into the familiar dark past the campfires, Cynric said, "Who is this high king you speak of who is so effectively uniting his factioned people?"

"Captured Britons call him Arthur. His seat is at Cam, and they say that a magic man named Merlin is his consul. All this brews fear in the hearts of our men, Cynric. We must make gains into the land, or our lads will lose heart."

"How do you propose this be accomplished?" asked Cynric, turning his gaze back to his father.

The yellow and red of the dying fires reflected an intensity and glee in the Saxon's eyes that made even Cynric quail deep within.

"I have thought long and hard on this, my son," responded Cynric. He adjusted the length of his cape with his arm. By a trick of the light it appeared that he was huddling the night closer into his body. "I have a plan. And the heart of it is that we must strike soon. Strike hard." His eyes gleamed. "And strike deep."

viii

Arthur walked with Merlin among the Roman ruins.

Thickets and ivy already covered the remains of the roads and villas. Blackened shafts of wood attested to the way in which the town had met its end. A rabbit hopped timidly to the cover of a dilapidated stone wall.

Arthur felt a sadness and wonder at this sight.

Catching sight of something interesting, Merlin hobbled forward. With the end of his staff he scraped at the pile of rubble, unearthing a round thing that glimmered dully in the bright daylight. Leaning over, he scooped it up, brushing off the dirt.

He handed it to Arthur. "A Roman coin. The face stamped upon it is that of Agricola, onetime general of Roman forces in Britain. A shame we don't have his troops and weapons now. From the records I have their catapults were quite effective and their warriors well trained."

"I am tired of war already, Merlin," said Arthur. "I could use weapons to storm a heart."

"Still thinking of Guinevere, Arthur?" The druid placed a fond arm on Arthur's shoulder.

"Yes. All the time. Are you pleased?"

"I am indeed. The bond that marriage would produce will help strengthen our fighting forces," stated Merlin, stroking his straggly beard. He waggled a finger at Arthur. "But you must not shilly-shally about it, Arthur. Ask for her hand immediately."

Arthur turned away. He leaned against a crumbling wall of mortar shale. "How can I? I barely know her. I spoke with her only a few minutes."

"She liked you, though, did she not?" Merlin's tone was encouraging, insistent.

Arthur pawed at the air in a helpless gesture. "She said that she thought of me as a good friend. I tried to tell her my feelings for her, but Lancelot interrupted us." He turned mournfully to face Merlin. "Can't you see? I can't *make* her love me. And that is the only way our marriage would have any meaning."

"Meaning?" Merlin waved his hands, portraying his frustration at such piddling matters as love. "You speak of meaning when such a bond would assure so many troops under your command—as well as the strong possibility of the aid of Leodegrance's many allies of the North." He shook his hairy head. "Is this the Arthur I have known so long, the Arthur who loves his land and his people more than anything else?"

Arthur was silent. He barely noticed the sweet scent of the hawthorn, the honeysuckle vine winding, riotous with color, about the wall by him. He kicked a rock with his boot.

"Look, my boy," continued Merlin. "Look around you, please. I show this to you for a reason. This was part of our heritage, this city of Avium. And look at the result of the Saxon's savagery. Ruin. Destruction. This is the work of barbarity, Arthur. It will eat us up as sure as age has gobbled up the glory of what Rome achieved in league with our peoples. And you would betray our goal just because you are not sure of the emotions of a fickle woman. No . . . *girl*!"

Arthur wheeled upon the druid, angry. "Have you no feelings, Merlin?"

Merlin threw his arms up in exasperation. "Oh, I wish that I could divine the ways of women! The commonest have more sorcery than I! They twist men's souls about their fingers just to see the funny shapes they create!" He sat down hard upon a rock, covered his face with his hands. "You know, Arthur, my detractors claim that I was sired by an imp upon a demon. It is not far wrong. I never knew my father . . . killed by Saxons for dabbling in the so-called elemental forces. And my mother was such a shrew! The Saxons did me much harm in sparing her!"

A feeling of concerned warmth grew in Arthur. "What became of her?"

Merlin peeked through his fingers. "She died while I was yet a youth, screaming for aid from the powers I was learning, powers she had once abhorred, then wailing to the Christian God and drooling upon a cross. In her last moments she grasped my neck as though to drag me with her for company. My interest in Christianity dimmed with that exhibition." Merlin's odd-flecked eyes, deep set and old in his finely boned skull, gazed up at Arthur. "That is why they have so much power, my boy. They naturally possess the power to steal men's souls."

"You malign them, my friend," said Arthur. "Their healing powers would bind this world together if they were given a chance." He looked out upon the autumnal land and drew his cloak closer as much for its touch as its shields from the brisk breeze that stirred the multicolored leaves. "I think they unearth a nobility and kindness in men that normally would be foreign to male natures. It is men who war, and women who suffer for it."

"Aye, aye," muttered Merlin, holding up an arm for help in getting up. "I must admit, I have a weak spot for them myself. The student instructs the teacher."

Arthur gladly pulled Merlin up. "You need not feel left out in not being able to divine them. I know of few men who can. And those that seem to are as mysterious to me as women. They think with their feelings and follow no straightforward path in life."

"Like our Lancelot, Arthur?"

"Lancelot, I think, is torn between the two." Arthur snapped a twig from a low-hanging branch. "It is his weakness and it is his strength. He breathes love as fierce as he wields a sword."

The two walked on awhile in silence, Merlin limping pronouncedly.

As the sun dipped toward evening, lengthening the shadows, touching the somberness of autumn with the cold dread of a long winter, they set out for the warm fires of home.

Partway there they were met by a galloping rider whose mantle and clothes fluttered about him.

The rider reined in. His horse's breath plumed mist.

It was Bedivere.

"Arthur," he said, breath quickening. "I am glad I found you."

"We were just on the way back to Cam," said Arthur. "Is there something wrong."

"Something important," said Bedivere, drawing his ruddy face near. "I wasn't sure you were returning today. I had to find you."

"What's the problem?" Merlin's face showed concern as he jockeyed his horse close to catch the conversation.

"Late this morning a visitor arrived at the fort gates," said Bedivere. "A Jute."

"Indeed," said Arthur. "What do you think, Merlin? A spy?"

"Let's hear him out."

"His name is Hrothgar, and while we certainly do not trust him beyond the lengths of our swords, he does seem sincere. He wishes to give us information that we might use against the invading Saxons."

Arthur's eyes widened. "Say on."

"He claims to have been wronged by a Saxon leader and wishes to be avenged."

"In matters of vegeance the barbarians are most sincere," commented Merlin.

"Aye," concurred Bedivere. "He brings much in the way of revelation about Saxon position and plans."

"Plans?" said Arthur, dread moving in his breast. "Plans for what?"

"The Saxon Cynric and his father, Cerdic, are gathering a great force to drive into our lands, it seems."

"No!" Merlin's word was exhaled in a breath of disbelief.

"Yes, very soon," Bedivere said, face a grim study. "This Hrothgar talks of many powerful men in one army. This drive would not be for random plunder and

destruction. It would be for more land for the Saxons."
"Of everything," said Arthur, feeling an emptiness deep within him. "This is what I have feared most."
A wind as cold as ice blew over his face.

CHAPTER 9

Merlin's Vision

His message grasped excitedly in her hand, Guinevere hurried from her rooms to meet her Lancelot.

Her feet trod over the Roman-type mosaic in the solar, long her favorite piece of artwork in her father's house. Often, in her journeys through this room, she would stop and gaze for many minutes at this large picture in the floor. It portrayed Daphne, followed by Apollo, and it reminded her of all the grand tales of Roman and Greek mythology she had learned. With all the delicate detail and shade Guinevere would often gaze at the design for hours, finding new meaning in the labyrinth of display. But today she simply gave it a passing glance as the hem of her tunic dragged over its surface.

Today she would be with Lancelot.

The message had come mid-morning. Fortunately her father was out seeing about the storage of certain newly harvested grain, and she, stationed near the front entrance in hopes of just such a message, intercepted the weary Celt lad who had ridden all night to deliver it. It said:

Guinevere:

My time is short. I write with fondness, remembering our friendship and thinking of our day together. Would that we could spend another . . . this very afternoon. But I must leave now, hoping you and your great father are well.

L.

The message was in tersely scripted Latin.

How clever Lancelot was. Even if Father had opened the folded paper he would not have understood the real meaning of the thing between her and her captain.

Simply it said that she should meet him at the same place as their last meeting . . . this very day!

Eagerness lit her expressive eyes as she slipped out the back entrance, heading for the stables.

Only five days had passed since that golden afternoon, and already Lancelot was coming back. Obviously he could not stand life without her . . . not seeing her, touching her . . . being with her in mind *and* body. At his first opportunity he was flying back to her arms!

The outside breeze caught and belled her ermine-fringed brown cape. Below this, she wore two tunics, girdled at the waist. The inner was a lustrous white, with long rippled sleeves. The outer was dyed a strong red with scallop juice; an elaborate embroidery of flowers intertwined with ivy had been sewn by herself around its edge. She wore her hair long and free. It waved, as though with the inner joy she herself felt.

She had washed her face a dozen times, and it felt new and clean in the brisk outside air.

She entered the stables, a blast of horse smell meeting her.

Good. No one here.

Quickly she untethered a horse, mounted it, and was off through the fields and forest, toward the glen by the brook where she and Lancelot had spent that glorious afternoon.

Today, their love would bloom further.

Of that she was sure.

She waited.

The wind picked leaves from the elm nearby. They floated down to the stream's surface like dry tears and were swept away in the swirling waters.

She tossed pebbles into the stream, and she brooded.

These dour thoughts were merely an extension of her previous misgivings.

She had been brought up, nominally, as a Christian, and her training had not been ignored. Christian doctrine stated that man and woman should not fornicate. The word was ugly and in no way resembled the glorious feeling she had for Lancelot—the desire she had for him. Nevertheless she could not shrug off trepidation concerning what surely awaited her. What she longed for.

What she had promised Lancelot, would have given him last week at his merest suggestion. A mere symbol of the giving of her soul, after all. A fleshy symbol.

Marriage was impossible now. But it would come soon, she knew. Such a love she had for him, and he seemed to own for her, did not go frustrated. Soon they would be together forever. They would have time . . . just as each had the other.

It seemed almost destined, preordained. Lancelot was to her soul as water was to thirst, food to hunger.

Nevertheless a lifetime of candlelit crosses, chaliced wine at the altar, droning Latin, bent knees, and bowed head could not be shed so easily as clothing. Doubts and questions persisted, like whining, demanding children.

She leaned against the rough, mossy bark of the elm, staring across the countryside. Even now for the most part it was green. The land clung to the color stubbornly, even when winter threatened. In nearby valleys and fens Guinevere could see pockets of mist roiling languidly. Out on the heath were bogs and crags . . .

to the north. They reminded her of death and of death's mystery, which was a part of this land.

She had heard of lands sunny all year 'round. Of bright days, clean rains, sparkling winters, moon and starlit nights. In these lands, it was said, life was all about, like a wash of sunlight over flowers.

But in Britain there was the taste of both. Beauty beyond bearing, sadness that struck chords of despair. A land of light and shadows, golden sun and damp drizzle, one's heart fluctuated wildly through the gamut of emotions. Somehow, looking out upon the mist in the hills, thinking of dreary days and the harsh northlands, Guinevere knew that her feelings were deepened in knowing both extremes.

In Lancelot's embrace was the hint of death, just as there was the throb of life. His kiss would bring the mist into her life, just as it brought the sun.

In his arms would be the pain of death as well as the joy of life. She knew this almost instinctively. But she did not shrink from the thought. Her life had not been so sheltered that she did not know the stink of death. She knew that life was just a slide from the womb to the grave, but she had long since accepted it with her mind.

In giving herself to Lancelot she would be accepting it with her heart.

These glum thoughts filled her head as she waited by the purling, gurgling stream.

She had waited for over an hour, certain that some terrible thing had happened to Lancelot on his journey to her, when he finally arrived.

Even though she had been constantly searching the horizon for him the sight of him surprised her. He emerged from a copse of beech to the south, his horse's hoofs kicking up sprays of dead leaves. His cape flew flaglike in the wind of his haste. Even at this distance she could hear a jingle—his leather cuirass, chain-mail sewn upon it. *Why did he wear battle apparel?* she thought, running to meet him, breathlessly.

Through waving reeds she ran, through tall grass that

whipped, stinging, at her legs. She barely noticed the pain, nor the smell of the hill's heather. Nor did she notice her tunic becoming sodden from the wet leaves she brushed.

All she saw was Lancelot.

He dismounted some yards from her, a smile underlining a burning gaze.

Guinevere slowed to a halt. Her breaths were hard. They turned to vapor and misted away like ghosts of thoughts. She stepped toward him hesitantly, arms held out partly in welcome, partly imploring. "Lancelot?"

His sheathed sword swung as he paced to meet her.

She felt buoyed by excitement, her heart fluttering like a small girl's at the sight of father holding a present.

They met with a lunge.

Lancelot gathered her up in his strong hard arms. He pressed her close to the chilled metal of his mail. His gauntlets were rough on her back, but she did not notice any discomfort.

His nose burrowed deep into her hair, as though to suck the scent of her in a single inhalation. His breaths were warm upon her neck. Clasping hard about his neck, she raised her head, eyes closed with pleasure from the sensation.

Every muscle seemed to relax as she sank into his embrace.

He brushed his lips against her cheek in a way that made her sob. "Lancelot!"

"Ssshh," he whispered. "This is no time for words."

She opened her mouth to ask why and found it covered with Lancelot's mouth. His kiss was dizzying—it was so long. He moved his head away a moment, and she was astonished by the passion he seemed to radiate.

Abruptly she felt herself lifted. Her eyes fluttered open, and she found herself staring into the blue of Lancelot's. He was carrying her across the field.

Arms wrapped snugly around his strong neck, she felt as though she floated. A pervading sense of safety and security infused her being. She studied his honest open face, darkened only by those eternally haunted fires in his eyes, and knew the full force of trust.

Relaxing, she knew only happiness as she rested her face against his shoulder. She hummed an air her nurse had taught her as a child. It had always seemed to her a sad, aching kind of tune. One that bespoke a nameless yearning. But now it felt as gay as she.

Lancelot stopped.

Guinevere gazed up. The muted sun beamed through the bent bows of an elm. Their elm, arched and gnarled, yet timelessly elegant.

Gently he set her down on the ground.

He took her hand in his and looked deep into her eyes.

"Lancelot, I—"

He placed his finger to his lips. "Answer me only this. Are you ready?"

The words were soft and caring. She knew that if she said no it would not change the way he felt.

A dozen reasons to defer arose in her mind, undergirded by a basic fear she could not dismiss. But more than any logical argument she could bring to bear against them, the trust she had felt in his arms told her to be guided by her heart, not by her reason.

"Yes," she said. "If *you* are."

He laughed his delightful laugh and cupped her face in his hands lovingly. "I would that we had a roof over our heads, a bed, and a fire in the hearth."

She stroked his battle-worn hands. "The sky has always been my roof. This land has been my bed." She flung back her hair. It floated back dreamily. "As for the fire, my heart will be our hearth."

"And mine," breathed Lancelot.

He flung off his cape, laid it on the moss and grass. She rolled onto it, smiling warmly.

They held each other long and hard.

When passion and desire demanded release, Lancelot began exploring her with a gentle hand, showing her the treasures of feeling he could unlock within her body. His fingers traced the outline of her back beneath her linen undergarments, tickling, stroking, caressing. His mouth found her bared breast as a baby finds its mother's. His sucking gave them both sustenance.

She returned his embraces, exploring his body. The cold of his mail was soon gone, the warmth of his broad, hairy chest bared.

When passion rose beyond bearing, she surrendered to him fully. When he entered her she knew pain, exquisite pain, a javelin of agony. An odd, clear thought arose in her mind. She wondered if this island were alive, as she was, and if it felt this pain each time an invader landed upon her shores. A welcome pain, to be endured for the pleasure that would come next.

She opened her eyes into Lancelot's, a Gaul's eyes, and she saw concern and love, and the pain suddenly dissolved into a building pleasure.

Under Lancelot's expert guidance, she was shown through trembling worlds of ecstasy.

When they were both finally spent and lay together, the earthy smells of the loam and their love mingling with the cooling of their skin, she said, "You have done this before."

"I told you. I have had other loves, but incomplete," he murmured, clutching the cape tight about her to shut out the slight chill of the air. "But now I know what love is for."

The thought of his departure rang a sudden hollowness through her. She flung herself at him, holding him tightly. "I wish you were as other men, content in one place."

Lancelot said, "Yes, but if I were as other men, you would not love me."

"That is not true. I would love you were you the lowliest peasant or the loftiest king. It is *you* I love, Lancelot, not your trappings of position or importance."

"Yes, yes, my dearest." He kissed her lightly on the forehead. "I understand because I feel the same. I will promise, though, to keep myself safe. Not for myself, but for you. I cannot stand the thought of you grieving for me."

"How could I grieve," said Guinevere. "In your death I would die as well."

They held each other long and lovingly, until the last possible moment, full of the awe that such a love could exist.

When Guinevere watched Lancelot disappear into the woods with the setting sun it was as though she watched the departure of her soul.

ii

Cynric struck.

His sword gored through the stomach of the Celtic peasant. The man screamed, writhed, and died. His blood pooled on the dirt.

"You see how easy it is to kill a Celt." Cynric laughed, jerking his blade away. He gazed at the bodies lying hither and yon amongst the mud-thatched huts. Somewhere a baby wailed bitterly.

The cry ceased suddenly.

Cynric looked upon the recently harvested fields, the pens of fowl, horses, pigs, and cows. "Find the granary!" he bawled hoarsely above the havoc. "Slaughter the livestock. We will feast for many days after this victory of our strength and glory!"

He waded through the scene of smoky death as his men put the Celtic huts to the torch, to supervise the hauling of the ample plunder.

In his path was a body.

A woman.

No, it was a girl, not quite a woman. Her clothing had been ripped to rags where it had not been stripped. Her face was blue with bruises. His men had had their fun.

He leaned over her, touched her swollen cheek. Something like regret moved in him, canceling out some of the pride he felt in this, a victory that could well feed his army for a moon.

How beautiful her hair was. Even now it shone in the light of the fires building in the huts.

She groaned.

Cynric snatched his hand away as though from a burning coal.

He raised his sword to finish the job.

Then lowered it. No. This would not do. If this was going to be his land, then he must not treat it so harshly.

Who knew what fine Saxon lads this girl could bear.

With awkward gentleness he picked her up into his arms. Her eyes opened wide with fear at his touch, then lulled back into rest when she saw no harm was imminent.

She was so small, thought Cynric. So helpless.

He carried the limp girl back to his horse, wondering why he was doing this.

iii

Merlin stared at the scrap of pink root on the work-table of his cave. Rubbed his dirty hands on his robe. He licked his cracked lips, contemplating.

Was it worth the risk?

Of late, the dream stuff had begun to cause bad reactions. Headaches. Nausea. An increased stiffness of the limbs, along with a difficulty of drawing in breaths.

The druid had the feeling that if he abused his drug too much he would be irreparably poisoned.

Despite his fear he'd dug a fresh bit of it from Hollow Hills soil. Newly taken from the ground, the root was most powerful.

Was it worth the risk?

Hobbling over to the corner, he grabbed a half-empty jug of mead. By rule he did not drink much in the way of ale or wine. He preferred the water of the multitude of fresh streams from the heart of this island. He felt as though he were nourished by the land itself, with the sparkling, clean drink.

But of late he had taken comfort in the bottle. Intellectually that disturbed him greatly. Physically it gave him ease and rest. That was, if he did not overindulge.

He poured. This jug was old and potent.

He tasted. Gulped. Fire seemed to spread through his aging sinews as he sat down before his pile of Latin scrolls.

Yes. Now he felt better. Much better.

Ah, he thought. For the strength of youth once more! For the power of determination and decision! This was a time of great crisis. Arthur needed all his support.

He closed his eyes and heaved a sigh. The memory of the audience with Hrothgar burned like a Saxon war-torch.

Raunchy stench.

That was her first impression of the tall, brutish Jute hunkered in the guest chair, slurping down good wine almost insatiably. Foul smell, then those coal black eyes, sparked with the hint of a flame that could consume them at anytime. Robed in poorly cured furs, he looked more a beast than a man.

A barbarian.

And what *of* these barbarians. Who *were* they? Always before Merlin had merely thought of them as embodying the powers of darkness that threatened the light of Britain. And yet direct and unhostile confrontation with one brought forth odd feelings.

Certainly here was savagery. But Hrothgar seemed to wear his savagery as he wore his stench and his stained clothing. He *knew* no better. This was the way he was . . . just as the Celts of the distant past knew nothing but the ways of their tribes.

Here was a man, Merlin felt, who could be washed, taught, and possibly *changed*, to a certain degree. At heart he was no worse than that scoundrel Lot. And Lot was a Celt. Reasonably civilized at that.

After the encounter curiosity drove him back to his cave in these hills to consult his texts.

As the barbarians themselves kept no records it was left to the Romans to interpret these peoples. They were Roman enemies, mostly, for barbarians had little understanding of anything between victory and subjugation. Only by conquering them could the Romans change them. And so the Celts were conquered.

But the tide had turned. The barbarians were overrunning the world. Indeed, Britain was a microcosm of the entirety of the European continent.

If they overran all of Europe, then total darkness and ignorance would sweep over humanity for who knew how long. But if the flame of civilization was kept alight for long enough to prove as an example, perhaps they could be changed so that mankind could progress unimpeded through its grand destiny.

Coming to these conclusions, Merlin realized that this had always been his essential goal.

It was a goal worthy of sacrificing his life for, if necessary.

He rose and ground the root in a mortar. Added a large quantity of mead.

Quaffed it quickly.

He retreated to sit beside his ball of crystal.

The warmth of the mead shut out the chill of the cave.

He waited.

The root's magic roared upon him like a consuming, fiery wind:

But it was not a vision of the future. . . .

His father, standing before him, eyes wild and wide, warning.

Clustered about the elder druid's heels were a group of the small Hill People, eyes shadowy, haunted.

"Merlin, my son," said his father, looking just as he had the day he died. "You have done well. There is now hope. But be forewarned. In your failures there will be victories. And in your victories will be failures

that will seed a victory beyond your comprehension."

Suddenly with an explosion of heat and light, a great cup appeared before his vision. "After your time," said his father, "there will be peace. But it will only be the eye of a storm. The keepers of the light must be reminded of your great vision."

As the light ebbed, Merlin saw that it was a golden chalice.

A grail.

iv

Winter had closed an early fist around the north country. Even now Arthur felt its chill in his extremities. As the servant ushered him before King Leodegrance he stamped his feet and blew on his reddened hands.

Leodegrance sat in his solar in a creaking Roman wickerwork chair. Flanking him was a brazier glowing with lighted coals. The homey scent of controlled burning eased Arthur's tension.

"Wine?" asked Leodegrance.

Arthur handed his cloak to the servant. "Thank you. I could use something to unclog the ice in my veins."

Leodegrance poured. Arthur drank, then sat in a sturdy oak chair well-stocked with embroidered cushions.

"I'll not mince words with you, my friend," said Arthur. "I'm going to need your help immediately." He detailed the situation with Cynric, already encroaching upon their territory. "He's heading toward Cam," Arthur concluded.

"Serious," said Leodegrance. "Most serious." He folded his hands upon his broad chest, contemplating.

Taking the opportunity of the pause in conversation, Arthur leaned back in his chair, letting his muscles unknot.

Warmed, he felt better.

Marvelous, these Roman-style villas, he mused, looking about him. After the spartan youth of Hector's fort, these comforts were an always welcome surprise.

Beneath these fine houses were hypocausts—short pillars of stone or brick propped up the floors. Through these was circulated hot air from a nearby furnace. Vents and box-flues allowed the heat to seep directly into the room as well. Obviously the Romans, used to the hotter climes of the south, did not care much for the chillier falls and winters of Britain.

"Yes," said Leodegrance. "I will send half my forces at my disposal. I am now aware of the importance of your maintaining power."

"That is most generous."

Leodegrance fingered the tassle of a cushion. "I grow old. And yet I can yet wield a sword." He stared straight at Arthur. "May I accompany you in this campaign?"

Arthur was taken aback. "Well of course! You would be much welcomed! You may lead your own men."

Leodegrance nodded sagely. "I ask but one consideration."

"Anything within my means, Leodegrance."

The older man's grayish eyes twinkled. "You remember we spoke before of Guinevere. You had, I think, a chance to speak with her. What were your impressions?"

Averting his head, Arthur murmured, "Your daughter's beauty extends well through her spirit. I was much taken with her."

"Excellent. And she has spoken well of you. Guinevere is of marriageable age. I have been noting you, Arthur. Watching your actions, sizing your character. I have heard reports from others concerning you. I am much impressed. I would have you as a son. In return for my aid—which I will benefit from as well, I know—I merely ask that you *strongly* consider the possibility of an alliance through blood. It would strengthen both our houses—"

"You want me to marry Guinevere?" Arthur was astonished.

"That would make an aging man quite happy," replied Leodegrance.

"But what does Guinevere say to this?"

"She is a willful girl. But in this she will obey her father."

"I don't wish to marry her if it is against her will."

"There are certain *harsh* necessities that arise from political life, Arthur," said Leodegrance. "You might well consider this a pleasant necessity." He finished his wine. "But there is no hurry. You have other matters to dwell upon for now. Give me your answer within a year." He placed his cup back on the table. "Now, I must tell Guin that you are here. She has been looking forward to seeing you again."

With a good-humored flourish of his brightly dyed evening dress Leodegrance nimbly walked from the room, leaving Arthur to his thought.

He felt stunned. Marry Guinevere?

The thought, of course, had entered his mind before, but only as a wistful wish, a delicious fantasy. To have that wish clothed in reality was surprising.

In essence Leodegrance was *offering* his daughter to him on a silver platter. Like a piece of property. . . .

The comparison appalled him.

And yet to have her as a wife . . . to have her near, always.

This life, so devoid of pleasure, full of care and responsibility, would become lively and joyful once more. The burden would seem to be less with Guinevere about.

And the possibility of a constant alliance with the land and people of Leodegrance. Merlin would be overjoyed at the notion, as well he might.

It could well be the salvation of Britain.

With Leodegrance's aid he might even be able to handle that scoundrel Lot.

Forgetting the mead in his cup, he stared down at the floor, and he thought deeply.

V

"Arthur? Here?" Guinevere looked up from the game of fidchell she played with Mara. "Now?"

"Yes," responded Leodegrance. "He would speak with you."

"Did you hear that, Mara?" said Guinevere gaily. "The high king to speak to *me*."

"I think this is merely the secondary purpose of his visit," said Mara soberly.

"Mara, of course!" chided Guinevere. "But let me have my moment of fantasy!"

Leodegrance chortled resonantly. "Do not discount your charms. He seemed most enthused at the notion of being permitted to see you."

"Really." A thrill of good feeling passed through Guinevere. Her good friend, Arthur . . . how good it would be to see him.

And to hear of Lancelot.

"You *will* be nice to him, won't you, Daughter?"

Guinevere blinked up at her father. When he spoke in that tone it meant he was to be obeyed. How Arthur was like her father . . . such exterior strength . . . and yet in their hearts was much warmth and humanity. She realized that the reason she understood Arthur was because she knew her father so well.

"That should be very easy to do, Father," she replied demurely.

"Oh. And Mara. See to it that things are kept in order here. I will be gone for a while."

"Gone, Father?" said Guinevere, eyes bright. "But where?"

"I will leave in a few days to join Arthur's campaign against invading Saxons."

Her father, gone. That would mean that Lancelot

could—but she couldn't think about that now. Now she must concentrate on Arthur.

vi

"Arthur?"

The voice was pleasant memory, given volume and timbre. He had heard it a thousand times in his dreams.

Swinging his head, he saw Guinevere enter the room with regal grace softened by the warmth of her smile.

"Guinevere." He stood nervously. "So good to see you again." He looked past her. "Where is your father?"

"He said he had something to take care of." She stepped up to him. Her tunic flowed along like music-made cloth. She took his hand in her warm, lithe fingers. "So good to see you again. How have you been?"

She sat him down on a couch and demanded all the news. "We are so out of the way here. I hear nothing until it is ancient history!"

"I am quite well, thank you. Better, now that I see you."

"Oh, nonsense."

"You look quite well," he insisted.

"The winter suits my complexion, I think. Inside, I am bored to tears. Ah, to be a man. To venture forth and *see* things."

Feeling more at ease, Arthur said, "We long to see things of beauty, Guinevere. Like yourself."

"Oh, Arthur, truly I think we are close enough by this time to dispense with the formal flattery."

Chided, Arthur felt embarrassed and stupid. Could he never say anything right?

"Now. I want to hear of your captains. And what is this I hear of invading Saxons?"

Somberly Arthur told her of the situation.

He explained about Hrothgar and how they had learned of Cynric's intentions. Now, already Cynric seemed to be in the process of systematically spreading terror. Conquering.

"My father tells me he is sending soldiers and himself to your aid. I am glad." She shook her head. "And yet cannot this be settled more peacefully?"

"How do you mean, Guinevere?"

"Is there no way that you could persuade this Cynric and his savages not to trouble us?"

The naiveté and innocence of the remark almost caused Arthur to laugh. But he staunched the reaction.

No. Perhaps she had something there.

"Just what do you mean, Guinevere?"

"I have heard it said that the Saxon villages are in themselves quite peaceful. The Saxons *are* capable, it seems, of a quiet life."

Arthur snorted. "They are bases of invasion. I would drive them into the ocean if I could."

"Ah, but that is the same attitude that they have about our people; could there not be some halfway point? People, after all, are people, Scot or Saxon, Roman or Celt."

"Yes, yes, I have thought on that. But they are our enemies."

"Why?"

Arthur shook his head, flustered. "Because they wish to kill us! Take our land away from us! Squash all that is good and right within us!"

"But, Arthur. You cannot see such things from only one side! What is the ultimate thing that life does to us . . . a thing that none of us can stop?"

Arthur answered bitterly, without the slightest hesitation. "It takes us to our graves."

"Yes, and it gives us pain and sorrow. And yet is life our enemy?"

Arthur thought awhile on that.

"We must do our best with it," Guinevere continued.

"You are very wise," said Arthur. "A man's mind would only think of matching death-dealer with death. I will give your words thought. Perhaps something might be arranged similar to what you suggest."

"Nevertheless," cautioned Guinevere, "I should be sure you are well prepared for such a meeting."

"In what way?"

"Perhaps an army to your rear would do well." She touched his hand gently, smiling. "I should hate to lose a good friend."

"I would that we were better friends, Guinevere." Arthur covered her hand with his own. "Sometimes, I hate being king. The responsibility. . . ."

"It must be very heavy."

"Yes." He rubbed her hand. It felt soft as silk but warm, yielding. "Sometimes I would trade places with a peasant."

"You know that is impossible, Arthur." Her face was solemn—yet it wore a luminous caring. Such sincerity moved him with a subtle support that Arthur did not know he needed. It gave him a feeling of fullness. Completion.

For just as a king needed to be a warrior and a leader—hard, decisive, and firm—so, a king needed a counterpart to encourage his softer, merciful side: a queen. Justice had to be laced with mercy, knowledge with emotion.

"Guinevere," he murmured. "I am awed by you."

"Me?" Her eyes widened. Mirth gleamed in them. "You are awed by a woman?"

"No. I don't know if I use the right term. . . ." He groped for the words. "I . . . I've not that much experience with women, Guinevere. I never knew my mother. Merlin has told me that somewhere I have sisters, but they are unknown to me as well. But I see something I would have in you . . . a kind of wisdom beyond the ken of man."

"Arthur, we each have qualities of our opposite sex. I see much in you that is said to be the province of women. Love. Emotion. Gentleness. To have these things does not in any wise make you less a man."

"No. You don't understand. You see these things in me because you bring them out." Arthur's words became impassioned. "I wish I could have you by my side, always."

A wave of controlled surprise passed over Guinevere's face. She took her hand away from his and sat down, as though digesting some new piece of news.

"Guinevere," he said, unable to bear the silence. "I—I have great feeling for you. I cannot interpret it—but I know that somehow I need your friendship by me constantly. I have spoken with your father. He urges me to take you as a wife."

She looked up, alarmed.

"But I would never do that without your consent, Guin. Never. Nor have I decided on it." He licked his dry lips. "Tell me this. If I accepted your father's offer . . . took you as wife . . . would it please you? Do you think you could live with me as my queen?"

She was silent a moment more. Then she spoke, her tones controlled and precise. "It would be a great honor to be queen. And I naturally would do as my father and my king wish."

Arthur shook his head. "But what would *you* wish, Guin? I care for you too much to take you against your will."

"You do care for me, Arthur?"

The king's voice choked. "Yes . . . yes, I do."

"And this marriage . . . this marriage would be political. It would be important in the scheme of things, a bond between North and South."

"You are very wise, Guinevere."

"Arthur, I must obey what you say. What my father says. That is my place."

"What are your feelings?"

"They are unimportant. But could you do one thing for me? Could you wait some months before deciding? That way you can think more on this."

"Of course." *She wishes to think on it as well,* Arthur thought. It is too soon for an immediate answer. He just prayed that events did not necessitate this union before she had a chance to decide.

She brightened. "Thank you. I admit you have surprised me. I have only thought of you before as a friend."

"As you are my friend, Guinevere. Is this not the proper way to begin? There are many marriages that begin with much less than friendship."

After Arthur had departed, declining the invitation to sleep in the villa, Leodegrance said, "Well, have you anything to say, Daughter?"

"He asked if I would like to be queen, Father."

"And would you?"

She stared straight into his eyes a moment, then averted her gaze. "That is really not within my realm of decision, is it?"

"Arthur believes it to be."

"He is the finest man I have met."

"He wishes you to love him, I think. Do you?"

"I do not know. May I go to bed? I am very tired."

"Of course." He took her hand. "Guinevere. Know that I would not let any man have you I thought was not worthy. And Arthur is more than worthy."

She nodded solemnly. "I know, Father. I know."

"You must take care of things around here. I have settled my plans. I leave in three days, once my forces are gathered."

"Yes, Father. I will miss you." She tiptoed up and kissed him on the cheek. "Good night."

She walked away toward her room.

A tear dripped down her cheek.

vii

A crusty layer of snow mantled the earth. The hoofs of Arthur's horse crunched through the snow. Torchlight threw back sparkly reflections.

The Saxon village lay dark in the distance, outlined in the flares of cooking fires.

Merlin said, "You are sure that you wish to do this, Arthur?"

Flinging back his cape, trying to ignore the cold, Arthur said, "Yes. The response to our message indicated Saxon willingness to a parley."

"Honor is nothing to them. They cherish only their tribes and their families." Merlin shuddered. His face was pale—as it had been since he had returned from visiting his cave a month back, Arthur noted. But the old druid would not speak of what he had done there.

"I would that Lancelot were here."

"As I would, Merlin." He glanced back at the twenty men he had picked to accompany him. "His presence would double our numbers. But he works well at recruiting forces . . . that is why I have sent him north. Should this meeting come to a bad end, we shall need all the forces we can muster."

"King Leodegrance has asked him to stop at his home, to check the welfare of his household, is this not true?"

"Yes. The old king worries. I would set his heart at rest . . . he has been a strong ally here."

"His men to the west of us will come in handy should trouble arise this night," concurred Merlin.

"That is why they are camped there."

"Arthur." The druid drew near, lowering his tone to a confidential whisper. "Are you sure it is wise?"

"What?"

"Allowing Lancelot to visit Guinevere."

Arthur's hand tightened on his reins. "I see no harm in it."

"But I have told you. It does not bode well."

Arthur relaxed and laughed. "Ha! You fear Lancelot's charm with women. But Merlin—don't you understand? Lancelot is that way with all beautiful women. His ardor is but on the surface. It is a *game* with him."

"And Guinevere? Is it a game with her?"

"She has the wisdom to know Lancelot's fundamental insincerity. Of that I am confident." He reached a hand out. "Do not worry, my old friend. They are both my best of friends. If they had feeling for each other, they would tell me."

"And what would you do then?"

Arthur shrugged. "I would respect that feeling. I love them both."

"But our bond with the North. . . ."

Arthur waved away Merlin's objection. "Do not worry me about such things now, Merlin. We have plenty to attend to at this very moment."

He motioned his men onward.

The group moved down to the field of the Saxon settlement. An uneasy stillness surrounded them as they moved, their horses' hoofbeats muffled by the snow.

A sentry stood just on the outskirts, jumping from foot to foot to keep himself warm.

The hefty man started at the sight of the Britons. He opened his mouth to wail a warning. Merlin held up a hand, speaking the harsh and gritty language of the Saxons. Used to the mellifluous tones of Celtic, Arthur found the alliterative language grating.

Merlin's explanation seemed to suit the man. He spat out a stream of words and motioned for them to follow. Merlin turned to Arthur. "He says we are expected. Their leader awaits in their main long house of this village. We are to follow."

"Where did you learn Saxon, Merlin?" asked Arthur. They had employed another interpreter for speaking with Hrothgar the Jute. Merlin was along to serve as translator for this parley.

"There are two dictums that are especially useful," Merlin answered, spurring his horse on through the crackling, glinting snow. "Know thyself. And know thy enemy."

"I should learn their language," mused Arthur as he kept pace with the druid. "And yet I quiver at the very sound of it."

"The Saxons hate ours as well, calling it all flimsy, weak sounds. Theirs is as hard as granite." Merlin looked thoughtful. "And yet one wonders. What things might occur if the best aspects of both were combined. Language is a living thing, Arthur, and that combination would express both the hard and the soft of life."

They wound through the collection of mud and thatch roundish hovels and larger long houses. Even with the cold the smell of Saxon life was strong—the stench of human excrement poorly disposed of, unwashed clothes, and tossed away, half-eaten animal carcasses.

They were led to a house of wood. Arthur noted that it was well built. The wooden frame was covered with overlapping planks and wattle hurdles covered with mud daub, colored grass green. The roof was quite odd; covered half with thatch, half with wooden shingles.

Standing by the door was a brace of warriors. They appeared to be quite drunk, for they weaved about as though buffcted by some phantom wind.

The sentry parted the warriors with a burst of guttural words.

He turned back and motioned the Britons to follow him in.

They entered.

Arthur immediately perceived an acrid smoke, the stench of animals. His eyes adjusting to the bleak dimness of the interior, he saw that the long house was in two parts. One side, partitioned off by a wattle screen, housed the domestic animals. Cows lowed. A sheep bleated. The thin wall did not keep out their smell.

A fire was in the center of the side for men. Above was the outline of a hole in the roof, covered over to keep out the cold. The chinks in the outer walls and the shingles were supposed to let the smoke through. Eyes watering in the haze, Arthur noted that they did a poor job of it. Even now the flames of a fire licked around a shank of mutton. Cowered figures huddled around it, seated upon long backless benches.

The sentry ushered in Merlin and Arthur. The others had to wait outside.

"I do not like this," whispered Merlin, nervous. "It was a condition of the meeting that we have our men by our side constantly."

Arthur patted Excalibur. "Don't worry. I've allowed for this. Besides, this will keep us alive long enough for a rescue should things go awry."

Heads turned as they entered through parted hides. Grease-smeared faces shone in the flickering firelight. The harsh roar of voices stilled to a mutter, quieted totally as a tall, bearded man broke from the group and stepped forward to welcome them.

"Greetings, Britons . . . you have arrived just in time to share our drinking," the man said in jerky Celtic. He grasped a long horn cup from another man. Its foaming contents slopped over onto his arm band and the sleeves of his faded yellow tunic. He did not seem to notice.

They were certainly a collection of savages; their half-drunk, sneering visages showed that. But there was a certain order to their chaotic barbarism that struck an ancestral chord in Arthur. This was a heroic society—a society built up around the individual. The strongest and bravest reaped the best in life. The weak were shunned and weeded out. Britons were not very far from this after all. . . .

Arthur shot Merlin a glance.

"I will taste it—to see," murmured Merlin, taking Arthur's meaning immediately.

He shuffled forward, trying to hide his limp, and took the horn.

Sipped.

He grimaced. Then swallowed.

Arthur's heart lurched. He feared for Merlin's health. What if the Saxons had poisoned the drink?

But Cynric grabbed the horn and lustily quaffed a healthy portion. White foam clung to his beard, splattered as he spoke. "You see! Not poison. Here! Drink!"

Arthur took the proffered horn. He slowly drew it to his lips, repulsed by the crust of questionable material about the rim. These folk certainly did not take much stock in cleansing their drinking cups. He drank. Almost choked. Strong and a touch rancid, but cool and warming.

He handed it back to Cynric. "I thank you."

"I shall give you your own cup!" Cynric cried enthusiastically. A wave brought forth a finely crafted piece of metalwork, crusted with rough jewels. Arthur recognized it as Celtic workmanship. A relic of plunder.

A woman quickly filled it with the brownish brew. Arthur accepted it with thanks and made a show of drinking some of it, not showing its immediate effects upon him.

Cynric seemed to take great interest in how he handled the drink. "Now," he said expansively. "You have come to convince us not to take your land from you, true?"

"You get right to the subject, don't you?" commented Arthur.

"I—how do you say it—I have few words to work with," said Cynric.

Arthur gestured to Merlin. "I have a friend here who knows your language very well."

"Who, him? He is a druid. I have heard of him. He will twist my words and yours. No. I have some knowledge of your language. I have dealt with Celts in the mainland before, and these months I have been here, it has been my enjoyment to take to bed one of your women. She has taught me much."

Arthur worked hard to control his temper. "Very well. I have come to speak with you. We are enemies."

"That we are."

"And yet I would that we were not. We do not ask your people to move from this land. We only ask that you stop your raiding. Your killing. Your plunder."

"You speak most forcefully," crowed Cynric. "Yet you speak with little knowledge. Do you think that your people are so innocent?"

"What are you speaking of?"

Cynric spoke a few words to his men. Laughter exploded.

"What's he saying?" asked Arthur.

Merlin's eyes bulged a bit. "I don't think a translation would be appropriate for a peaceful visit here."

Cynric turned back to face Arthur. "No. You perhaps do not realize that your people are guilty of raiding our settlements as well."

"I make no claim that we are without guilt," answered Arthur. "I have only just begun to exercise my leadership. I have heard of raiding parties of Celts and Britons, true. But don't you realize that this is in retaliation?"

"Small point," said Cynric. "We shall not haggle. Tell us. What do you offer in return for our cooperation?"

"Peace."

Cynric growled a laugh. Smirking, he looked down to the bench. There sat an older man. Yet a man every bit as muscular as Cynric. Gristled cords of well-exercised muscle wrapped around his body like protective armor. The older man showed rotting teeth in a grin and spoke to Cynric in their native tongue.

Nodding, Cynric turned his attention back to Arthur. "My father, Cerdic, suggests that the essence of the discussion be boiled down. Peace is something we do not care for and is certainly not sufficient reward. We are a strong people, and we crave land to build and grow. That land is within our grasp, with only your people between it and us. So we sharpen our teeth upon you. It is only the natural way of things."

"Then why did you agree to this parley?" A wave of anxiety filled Arthur. Had they indeed been led into a trap?

"There is one way in which this might be resolved," answered Cynric. "It simplifies things."

"And what is that?"

"I am well aware of what you have been doing amongst the tribes of your people, Arthur, King of the Britons. It is you who stands between me and what I want. You and you alone. Without you, what you have built up will split into warring factions again. Your part of Britain will be ripe for the plundering. The taking. Now, if I kill you, then the way will be open."

Arthur's hand sped to the pommel of Excalibur. "So, you intend to break your oath and attempt to kill me now. I warn you. I have taken precautions."

"But of course you have," said Cynric. "As have I. We are both not stupid, Arthur. No, no. You still have my oath upon my honor against treachery. What I suggest is really much more open than that." His eyes glinted with amiable self-confidence. "We shall fight, you and I. Now. Fight to the death. If you win, you will have my father's promise to draw back our forces for two years. That is the longest we can keep ourselves in check, and we cannot speak for other tribes of warriors. Besides, I will not be around to lead them."

"And if I lose?" said Arthur.

"Then you lose only your life. And Britain will be without a strong and worthy leader. Think, Arthur. You will no doubt save thousands of lives in this manner."

"Arthur," said Merlin. "You mustn't! This is not in the plan. If you are killed, *everything* falls apart!"

Arthur ignored his druid counselor. He shifted from foot to foot, firming his resolve. He stared at Cynric for a moment, measuring the man's prowess. The Saxon was bigger and broader than Arthur. In a match of brute strength to strength there was no doubt that the man would win.

But then, Cynric did not have a sword the like of Excalibur. Nor the resolve and dedication.

With smooth effort Arthur whipped out his king-blade. The firelight flashed upon its metal with a sheen of blinding brilliance.

"Very well, Cynric," spoke Arthur, voice deep and resounding. "To the death!"

viii

Lancelot was like a man possessed.

In Guinevere's chamber he made love to her with a violence that would have done him proud upon a battlefield. A wanton, unchecked wash of emotion raged from him like light and heat from the sun. Guinevere had meant to speak to him of important things, but the spark of his desire had ignited them both.

She was swept up into his passion like a leaf in a gale. Thoughts were washed away in the torrent of his kisses and touches, strokings and grasps. He led her upon a whirlwind journey of gasps and throbs, where feelings lived like people, each with its separate identity. In her own passion she learned the complexity of herself.

His manhood probed the depths of her body and being recklessly, relentlessly, and she knew ecstasy as she had never known it before. His desire seemed endless, and his hard body capable of expressing it.

When he had shuddered the last of it away into her, they held each other's warmth and cool sweat, their souls as naked to each other as their bodies.

"I should not be here," murmured Lancelot. "I should be with my king."

"He sent you here," she murmured gently, running her fingers through his hair.

"Yes, but not for this."

"This is fire and wood, Lancelot. We cannot blame ourselves," she whispered. "We cannot check it."

He had arrived in the early evening. The servants had provided him quarters in another wing of the villa. They had supped together sedately under the watchful eye of Mara. Then they had retired.

Lancelot had sneaked into her bedroom while the rest of the house was asleep. Their love had consumed hours upon hours. A hint of rosy dawn now fingered the cracks in the window shutters.

"No. I wonder what will become of us."

With a pang she remembered what she had to speak to him of. "Lancelot. Do you remember when we talked of my father's designs for me?"

"Yes. I dare say he would very much like you to marry Arthur. So?"

"Has Arthur spoken of me to you?"

"No. Why?" His voice seemed hesitant, troubled.

"He was here two weeks ago." She licked her lips, burrowed closer into Lancelot. "He loves me, Lancelot. He would have me as his wife."

Lancelot was still for a long time. She could not see his face. Their meager tallow candle had long since spent itself. Finally he said, "And how do you feel?"

"I love him as you love him, Lancelot. No more, no less."

"And you would marry him?" His voice was thick with emotion.

"I must obey my father and my king. But he is such a good man, Lancelot, that he says he will not ask for my hand unless I am willing as well. He has given me the winter to decide." The word gushed out with sobs. "Tell him about us, Lancelot! He would never take me as wife if he knew of the depth of our love! If you could but mention it to him. . . ."

"Yes. Yes, I must." Lancelot quivered vulnerably in her arms. "But it will be hard."

"I could never tell him. It *must* be you."

"And yet it will tear my soul! Right is on *his* side. His truth is what I serve, and his goal would be mightily buttressed by such a marriage."

"Lancelot, I cannot believe you are saying this," she said, a little angrily. And then she paused, thinking. "No. No, I see what you mean. Why should this cause suffering for us? But I can't connect the two, my love. All my world is you now. I care not about anything else, except my duty. I am torn."

"Yes. Duty. There's a word for you," murmured Lancelot. "And yet, my dearest, I do not think you know its true meaning."

"You will speak to Arthur then."

"Yes, when I return to Cam."

He heaved a sigh. "Now I must go."

She wrapped her arms tightly about him. "No. Love me once more."

Tenderly he took her again, and it was as though it were the first time—and the last time.

ix

The ring of torches blazed bright, held aloft by a circle of men, half Saxons, half Celts.

They surrounded armed figures facing each other.

Ankle deep in snow, Arthur crouched in battle-ready position. He held Excalibur in both hands like a broadsword. Despite the cold that swirled like a warning of death's chill he felt hot and damp beneath his battle-mail.

It was a perfect, beautiful winter's night. Solemn and still it held a full moon in the arched sky, with wool tearings of clouds ghosting through the star-speckled blue-black. The evergreens on the wood verge were crusted with icicles. A fire crackled and spat nearby.

"Are you ready, Arthur of Briton?" said Cynric the Saxon in a sarcastic tone, jerking from side to side in limbering exercise. His grease-smeared face was split in a huge grin.

In his ham-sized fists he held two weapons. A Roman-style long sword was gripped by his right hand. His left grasped a Saxon Scramas axe—a swordlike knife. He had donned his full battle armor—including a heavy coat of mail and a helmet formed of an iron frame, between which was a horn with a boar on the crest. He seemed relaxed and ready, as though ardently anticipating this bit of hack and slash. His eyes glowed a furious self-confidence that was echoed in his darting, ferret-like movements.

Arthur waved Excalibur up and down, renewing his feel for the fine balance of the blade.

"I am never ready to kill a man. But if this has to be, let it be now."

He took a step forward, careful of his footing in the snow.

Standing by one of their own warriors, Merlin held a torch, a fretful expression upon his face. Arthur had asked that he not use any of his tricks. The battle would be fought honestly and fairly, an example of the fair play he envisioned as the hallmark of his reign over Britain.

With a savage cry Cynric hurled himself toward Arthur, swinging his weapons wildly. Arthur could see no strategy in the blows—like a volley of scattered slices they were directed at nothing in particular. But if you stood in their path, you could not escape a goring.

Nimbly Arthur stepped aside, placing Excalibur lithely between one of the random blows and his body. Metal rang. Cynric's weapon slid down the edge of Arthur's blade and buried itself in the snow.

But with incredible speed the Saxon jabbed at Arthur's torso with the Scramas axe, wrenching himself away from his former lunge.

Arthur dodged.

His left foot slipped from under him, shot out, and kicked Cynric in the shin.

The Saxon howled with pain even as he brought his sword to bear and chopped down. But the blow was askew, biting into the earth. Snow spumed over Arthur's face as he rolled away, cloaking himself in the cold white stuff. Hopping to his feet, he brought Excalibur back to position.

The Saxon regained his stance and dived into tumultuous battle once more, heaving breaths like the roar of some monster.

Even as he lightly and quickly parried the berserk swipes and lunges, Arthur realized that what he was battling was not simply maniacal strength and years of sword-bearing experience, but raw selfhood.

The Saxon spiced his onslaught with harsh, single-syllabled cursing, his face frozen in a rictus of fury.

Blows rained upon blows. Clangs echoed bangs as they spent their strength upon each other.

Cynric backed away a second, breathing harshly, pausing to rest. "You are very good," he gasped raggedly. "And your sword is swift. I will claim it when you lie dead and bloody in the snow."

Arthur heaved a breath. Phlegm clotted his throat. He spat it out, making it a gesture of contempt. "That is what I think of your plan. Would you like to quit now and keep your life?" He thought to match bravado with bravado, will with will.

Cynric's eyes bulged with fury. Blue veins stood out on his temples and forehead. "I shall meet you in your hell first!" he screeched.

He charged Arthur, raging.

Arthur brought up Excalibur to fend off the blow, expecting the Saxon to halt to aim it. But Cynric forged on, banging into the blade full force, knocking it back. Eyes blazing, he slashed his Scramas axe about.

He twisted to avert it, but the tip found the soft underside of shoulder. Pain arrowed through him as the knife ripped over mail and ribs. Blood welled.

With a swiftness borne of desperation Arthur backed away. With an undercut Excalibur smote upward, slicing the knifelike weapon away from Cynric's grasp, two fingers along with it. Blood spurted, crimson and bright against the sparkly white of snow.

Cynric howled and retreated, staring disbelievingly at his ruined hand.

Arthur, biting back his own pain, said, "Will you call this off now?"

Cynric struggled to smile through a face full of agony. "It is but a scratch," he growled.

He plunged forward, renewing the fight.

Straining, each blow driving more pain into his shoulder, Arthur defended himself. For long moments Cynric threw blow after sword blow at him with unflagging vigor. He ignored the blood that smeared his clothing and the ground they had tramped to slush.

But if the Saxon's tactics of brute force were impressively difficult to fight off, so they were full of errors. It was just a matter of moments before the man left himself open.

Then Excalibur sang true.

Whipped down with its strong metal bite, it struck the hilt of the Saxon sword so hard that the blade was driven away from Cynric's grasp. It buried itself in the snow.

Releasing Excalibur with his left hand, Arthur struck the Saxon across the face with a fist. The blow was hard.

Cynric staggered back, dazed, then toppled into a mound of snow.

Pain driving mercy from him, Arthur raced to his enemy; Excalibur raised for the final blow.

Someone wailed.

A woman parted herself from the crowd of onlookers and threw herself upon the fallen Saxon.

"No!" she cried, tears smearing her pretty face. She held up a hand. Arthur checked his blow. "Don't kill him!" She spoke clear and lucid Celtic.

The sight of her swam before Arthur. This must be his Celtic woman. He lowered Excalibur. "Do you concede this fight, Cynric? Will you abide by the agreement of your defeat?"

Cynric's eyes twisted in hatred. "Never!" he began, but his voice was muffled immediately by the woman's hand over his mouth.

"Yes! Yes he will! Just, please, don't kill him! I am carrying his child!" she cried.

From the expression on the barbarian's face Arthur surmised that the news was fresh to him too.

"Yes," whimpered the woman. "I want him to know his father."

Hand staunching the blood that dribbled down his chest, Arthur said, "You are a brave and valiant fighter, Cynric." He turned and signaled his men to depart with him. Stalking away, he had a second thought and turned to face the Saxon again. Suddenly he felt a kinship with the man—deeper than words. "But you have not reckoned with the charms and power of British women." He gestured in the manner that Merlin had taught him meant extreme respect to Saxons. "And neither have I."

He left, the sound of Cynric's laughter rich in his ears.

x

"What is wrong?"

Lancelot dismounted his horse in great haste, seeing the alarmed expressions of the men about Cam, hearing the clamor.

He grabbed the nearest warrior.

"Didn't you hear me, man?" he demanded. "*What has happened?*"

Although the sun was bright, it warmed the day not at all, and Lancelot's words were framed by his misted breath.

The man stared wide-eyed at Lancelot a moment, face red with the chill. "Captain Lancelot!"

"Yes, yes, man. That's my name. Now tell me what's all the excitement about?"

"It's Arthur, sir. He's won a great personal victory. But he's wounded."

Lancelot relinquished his grasp upon the man's tunic. "Wounded! Where is he?"

The man pointed a dirty finger toward the interior of the fort. "Resting, sir. Merlin is tending to him. He just rode in at noon. On a stretcher. I—"

The man's words faded with distance as Lancelot

hastily strode across the courtyard to the nearest doorway. His thoughts and emotions buzzed insistently within him. Guilt hung heavy.

"If only I had been there!" he muttered between clenched teeth, hating himself. "God, if he dies—"

His heart hammered at the notion.

He banged through the door, pacing through chambers, dodging and thrusting through groups of alarmed people.

Bedivere was standing outside the king's chamber door, a grim expression upon his face. Lancelot made to forge through him, but the captain stopped him.

"I *must* see him!" cried Lancelot, half mad with fear and self-loathing. Wounded! While he lay in bed with Guinevere.

It was a warrior's nightmare of lost honor.

"Steady, steady, man!" Bedivere snarled. "What's got into you?"

"Arthur! I heard he was wounded."

"Yes. But it's nothing that can't be healed. Though he came awfully close to death the other night."

"What happened?" His voice choked with concern.

Bedivere told him of the duel.

"I should have been there! He'll never forgive me!"

"Nonsense! *I* was there, and I didn't lift a finger." He chuckled grimly. "No, there was nothing you could have done." He assayed Lancelot with a cool eye. "Yes, it was for the best that you weren't there, I think. You would have jumped in to help the king. I was pressed to stop myself from doing so."

"He is in there?"

"Yes, but Merlin has demanded peace and quiet from all. The king needs—"

"Lancelot!" cried a voice from within, muffled through the wood. "Is that Lancelot's voice I hear?" The tone was hearty, but quavering.

"Yes, my lord," answered Bedivere.

"Show him in. I want to see him."

Lancelot needed no more invitation. He brushed past Bedivere and through the door.

Inside, Arthur lay propped upon a bed. Merlin sat beside him, tending a large bandage upon his right shoulder. The druid gave him a cold stare, then returned to his work.

Arthur extended a hand. Lancelot stepped forward and grasped it firmly, meaningfully.

"How are you, my friend?" he asked, unable to keep a wetness from his eyes.

"Hurting. That Saxon gouged me good. What a fighter! I thought for a while there that I'd have a snowy grave. But a few of your sword tricks helped me."

"I wish I had been there to help you, Arthur." He waved his hands helplessly. "I feel I have failed you."

"What? That's absurd, man. There was—" Arthur's eyes bulged. He howled and gasped, staring down at some ointment that Merlin was pouring on top of the bandage. "Dragons and trolls, man. What do you think you are doing? That hurts worse than the Saxon's knife."

"Just a poultice, Arthur. It will help the wound to heal quicker," Merlin soothed in an authoritative voice.

"It feels like liquid fire," said Arthur. "Here, Lancelot. There's a jug of mead over there I sent for. Get some cups. Want some, Merlin?"

"I admit I could use a drop."

"Three cups, Lancelot." Arthur scrunched around to a more comfortable position. "And make them big ones."

Lancelot saw to the mead, pouring and handing the portions around. Arthur sipped long and noisily and said, when he was finished, "So then. What of your trip?"

"Arthur, it was nothing. I want to hear of your meeting with the Saxon."

"Every word the Jute spoke was true. If he chooses to stay, I think we should give him some land and welcome." Briefly Arthur related the confrontation. Lancelot time after time cringed inwardly.

"But we're rid of him and his men for two years."

Lancelot blinked. "You *trust* him?"

"He is a man of pride and honor. His own barbaric sort, true, but then our values are handed down from barbarism as well. Yes, I trust him. If he said he would leave us alone for all time, why, then I would not trust him."

"So we have a time in which to group ourselves. Arm."

"Yes. How did your recruiting fare?"

"Excellently. One hundred and twenty men have sworn allegiance, and they will join us in the spring."

"Wonderful. I was most impressed with Leodegrance's men. We shall need them." His voice softened. "Tell me, Lancelot. How is Leodegrance's daughter?"

Clearing his throat, Lancelot glanced away. *Now is the time, man! Now! Tell him. Tell him!*

But guilt held back his words.

No, he must wait. Wait until the king was back to full health. A little time would not hurt. . . .

"She is well, Arthur. She sends her greetings."

"I am glad you get on so well, you two," said Arthur. "It does my heart good."

Lancelot had to turn away to hide his expression. He wanted to blurt everything out then, beg his friend to understand that he and Guinevere loved one another . . . that it was she that he had dreamed of all these months, none other.

But it would have to wait. Later, when Arthur was alone, they could speak, man to man.

He turned back and smiled. "I drink to your health, Arthur. May you soon recover from this small indisposition that you may beat other Saxons into the snow."

"Aye," pronounced Arthur. They drank. "And soon. Just because we dealt with Cynric's bunch doesn't mean that we'll not have to worry about more of them. I have the feeling that this will be a busy winter for us all."

"Yes," said Lancelot. "I promise my sword will compensate for my brief absence from your side."

"There, that's the Lancelot I remember!" Arthur suddenly began to cough violently. Merlin tended to him, then turned to Lancelot. "Perhaps you had better go, Lancelot. The king needs his rest."

"Of course," said Lancelot. "We will talk later, Arthur."

He spun on a heel.

Perhaps it would not even be necessary to tell Arthur. Surely he perceived that there was something between the Gaul and Guinevere . . . surely he was not blind.

As for matters of state bearing on the subject that was silly. Arthur would never let that enter into his thinking. It was not at all like Arthur. He would see that Guinevere did not love him as a woman loves a man . . . there was really nothing to worry about at all. He would tell Guinevere that everything was all right.

"Oh," said Arthur. "Lancelot."

Lancelot turned around to answer. "Yes?"

"On your next mission north would you tell Guinevere to write to me. I am tired of the boring correspondence of men."

Lancelot managed a smile. "Yes, I'd be glad to, Arthur."

xi

"Where is the high king?" asked a messenger some weeks later.

Merlin stood in the doorway. "He is out on business," replied Merlin.

"I have a letter for him, from Guinevere, daughter to King Leodegrance."

Merlin's bushy eyebrows rose. "Do you? Well, I am the king's counselor. I can take and hold it for him."

"Very well," said the young man, handing the letter

to Merlin. "But I was supposed to deliver it personally to his majesty."

Merlin fumbled in his robes, pulled out a gold coin. "You *did* give it to King Arthur personally, didn't you?"

The young man palmed the coin. "I certainly did. Thank you." He was off.

Trailing his long robes over the wood-planked floor, Merlin sped for his private study. The correspondence could be of high importance. He should study it immediately. This situation was most delicate and called for some high level meddling on his part.

At his desk he unfolded the letter. The words were in nicely rendered Latin. Definitely a woman's hand. Guinevere's.

He read it. Twice.

Then he rubbed his eyes wearily and leaned into his hands.

No. No, this would not do at all. The note was much too cordial. In between the lines it was obvious that Guinevere would not care to become queen and would do so only if her father and Arthur thought it necessary.

It was obviously written to discourage Arthur's intentions.

Women, Merlin thought. *They make mincemeat of the best of plans. Didn't the creature realize the importance of a bond between North and South? If it did not come about, then Arthur would not be able to have the full power he needed to stem the Saxon tide.*

Merlin stared at the letter again. He had parchment like this. The hand would be easy to imitate . . . yes, it would be easy to rework this letter, add a word here, a phrase there to make it much warmer.

Events to the north were mounting to the point where Arthur would have to take advantage of Leodegrance's offer soon. A woman's feelings should in no way deter him.

Merlin found the right parchment, a quill pen, and ink and set to work scribbling.

xii

In the chaotic months that followed, Arthur saw Guinevere again and again, although always in imagination:

He saw her in the face of a baron's young wife, after his growing host of mounted soldiers swept all the way to the eastern coast to harry a band of Saxons into the sea and to administer a bloody defeat. On the troop's triumphant ride west following the victory, the roads were lined with common folk and even some nobles and their retinues. The baron's wife watched Arthur as he rode by at the head of the battle-weary company, Excalibur's hilt glittering like a cross of light in the sunshine. He saw only Guinevere.

He saw her in the face of the peasant girl whose father was a cottager near one of the Christian abbeys where Arthur stationed a few men to insure that the barbarian plunderers would not destroy the monastery's precious store of handwritten books or its priceless heritage of mercy and compassion.

He saw her in the face of a farmer's wife who came with her spouse to plead for a small parcel of land seized by a neighboring lord. Arthur decided in the farmer's favor. The crowd of plain people in the hall cried his name in praise. A month later, when Arthur returned to the same district to judge legal disputes again, the self-same lord who had been adjudged the guilty party before now found a matter of wholesale poaching to his benefit. The astonished lord knelt in genuine respect before the young man who dispensed justice with such evenhandedness—

It seemed to Arthur that he spent more time in the saddle than otherwise. But the fellowship of his round table was growing, and the Saxon line was slowly being pushed back toward the seacoast. Unexpectedly, in countless places, he saw not only the accomplishment of his plan but the eyes and mouth and hair of the daughter of Leodegrance.

xiii

Rain drenched and saddle weary, Lancelot flung off his muddy cloak as he entered the main hall at the fort by the river Cam. A white mastiff slumbered on the paving stones between the young Gaul and the great round table where the high king and his captains were poring over an immense parchment map.

The captains—Kay and Bedivere, Gawain and Gareth, and a dozen more—bawled greetings. Kay rose to pull back Lancelot's vacant chair with its high carved back.

The jovial welcome—and the smile on the high king's face—did nothing to improve Lancelot's seething frustration. He booted the mastiff out of the way. The dog whined and slunk off. As he slumped into his chair Lancelot noted an unhappy flicker in Arthur's eyes.

At each man's place around the table a red dragon had been painted on the thick oak planking. Otherwise the table was undecorated. It was heavily marked with the gouges of knives and the rings and grease splatters of innumerable meals.

Overhead, a crude cross-shaped fixture held stubby tallows whose flames flickered fitfully. Rain drummed on the thatching of the long house. The hall was silent, cordiality dampened by Lancelot's sour look.

He was ashamed of his treatment of the dog, but he couldn't reveal the real reason for it. His temples hurt from pondering the insoluble problem. Perhaps he had been a fool not to speak to Arthur—but the time seemed past, the moment he should have seized gone, and daily he knew his friend's love for the lady grew.

"You look like you've had a hard ride, brother," Bedivere rumbled from his place next to the one chair that was always empty. Merlin, in his mysterious pronouncements, insisted that the chair be reserved for someone special. The druid refused to name the person, however. The captains had christened the chair the Siege Perilous, making broad private jokes about the physical endowments of the captain who would be man enough to fill it.

"My men and I came straight through with only stops for food," the Gaul said to Bedivere.

Studying his newly arrived captain, Arthur frowned and asked:

"Does that signal a change in the state of affairs in the North?"

How quiet and determined his voice, Lancelot thought. How different from the light, carefree voice of the comrade he remembered from the days when Arthur first came to Benwick to purchase horses—

Lancelot stared at the high king, a heaviness weighing on his mind and his emotions. He yearned to go back to those first, joyous months of their friendship, when they laughed and drank and spoke their dreams aloud, as equals. Now that young Arthur was gone, vanished inside a man who physically resembled the companion Lancelot recalled, but only in a superficial way. Arthur had been high king a little more than three years. The responsibility had aged his face noticeably.

"Lancelot—?" Arthur prompted. Merlin, bent with age now, had slipped up behind him. The druid stood watching with those damned, unnerving eyes.

"We spied on Lot's fort as instructed," Lancelot said. "We saw the banners of four of the northern lords raised over the long house."

"Another parley, then?" Merlin asked. Gawain sat slouched down, one hand over the lower part of his face. The continuing resistance of his father was embarrassing to him and to his brother.

"Yes, but different than the ones before," Lancelot said. "This time, the kings came with more than small retinues." His somber eyes met Arthur's over the map of the island. "I counted close to a thousand men camped outside the walls. More were arriving every hour."

Arthur pondered that. "So your conclusion is—?"
"The obvious one. They have finally decided to move against you."
"I anticipated that," Merlin said to Arthur. "In the beginning I'm sure some doubted whether you could gain the loyalties of the common folk. Now all doubt has been removed. Unless you're cut down soon you will have too many supporters for Lot to risk open warfare."
Again Arthur thought, then sighed. "It grieves me not to have won the northern kings without a fight. I would have preferred for them to come to the dragon standard in peace."
Unhappily Gareth said, "I know my father too well. Even before his alliance with Cornwall's house, it would never have happened." Gareth sighed tiredly. "My father's gall is matched only by overblown pride."
"Compassion can generate false hope," Merlin said. "Now it seems the time for compassion is over."
"If they mean to march and corner us—" Arthur began.
"I have no doubt of it," Lancelot interrupted.
"Then we must move against them first."
The pronouncement stirred the captains out of their tense silence. There were smiles, glances exchanged. Clearly all the men at the table had looked forward to this moment. All, that is, save Lot's sons. Both continued to stare glumly at the table.
Arthur rose, moved to stand behind their chairs.
"We'll gather our men and ride as soon as possible. I exempt both of you from fighting against your father."
Gareth protested: "We wouldn't ask—"
Arthur interrupted:
"I know you wouldn't. That's why I spoke first."
Lancelot finally smiled. "Well, the breakneck ride was worth it, then. We've ignored Lot's treachery too long. The sooner we're in battle, the bet—"
He broke off. Arthur was shaking his head.

"I must ask you to do one more task for me. While we ride against Lot, I want you to return to King Leodegrance—"

Lancelot felt a chill stab of fear in his belly. Did Arthur suspect?

But Lancelot saw nothing to indicate that. Arthur mused aloud as he walked back to his great chair.

"If we engage Lot and his northern allies, it will inevitably bring new trouble. For a long time I've pondered ways we might offset some of that turmoil. The best way is through an alliance with the house of one of the most respected kings of the North."

He looked at Lancelot. "As soon as you've rested take your men and proceed north again. I'll give you a petition asking Leodegrance for his danghter's hand in marriage."

Everything blurred then. Lancelot felt as if he'd been dealt a mortal blow. He fought to keep his face expressionless.

For a moment he almost hated the king across the table. He pressed his clenched fist against his lips, bit his thumb as Merlin smiled and Kay exclaimed:

"Wise planning, majesty—"

Kay stopped. Arthur had raised a hand.

"Something disturbs you?" he asked Lancelot.

The young captain from Gaul rose abruptly. "Weariness. I beg permission to retire."

Arthur nodded. Lancelot spun and stalked from the hall.

Like a blind man he stumbled into the spring rain. He walked toward his quarters while the hurt and frustration rose within him like a raging wind.

Beside the fort's high wall of logs and earth, he failed to see a provision cart standing in the darkness. He collided with the cart's huge and solid wooden wheel.

Cursing, he struck his clenched hand against the wheel.

Again.

Again.

His head was bowed. His cheeks were wet with rain and something else.

xiv

The hillside breathed out the scent of spring flowers. Lancelot tethered his horse and shielded his eyes against the noon sun.

There she was, among shimmering trees at the summit of the hill. She was alone except for her palfrey.

Leodegrance had told Lancelot where to find her, thus complained about Guinevere's refusal to take an escort when she rode outside the fort. The king had instructed Arthur's emissary to bring Guinevere back without breaking the news—

She saw him coming. His heart broke as she began to move toward him down the windy hillside. He cursed the night he'd sat beside her at Leodegrance's feast and drowned in the depths of those dark and lovely eyes.

Now, climbing toward her and seeing her against a background of green trees and brilliant sky, he almost wished they had never shared those times together.

She called his name and a moment later flung herself into his arms. He smelled the sunny warmth of her hair as he held her. When the embrace ended her smile remained gay.

"Why are you looking so serious, my darling? I didn't expect you back so soon—and here you are!"

"Guinevere—" He wiped his mouth with the scarred back of one hand. "This is not another rendezvous of the kind we've had before."

"Then what is it?"

"A—matter of business with your father. I have just seen him. He told me to fetch you back and not reveal—" He halted, then burst out: "I've brought a petition from the high king. A petition for your hand."

Thunderstruck, Guinevere gazed at him to see if he could be teasing her. There was no mirth on his stark face.

Lancelot said, bitterness spilling out with every word, "A state marriage. To unite the North and the South. Women have no choice in such matters, you know. Besides—"

His smile grew cruel with self-mockery:

"You should feel fortunate. What can I offer besides the miserable life of a soldier's woman? Widowhood after a battle—?"

"You offer all I care about," she cried, throwing her arms around his neck. "The love we've shared in these fields and woods—"

"Secretly," he reminded her, seeing her tears. From the depths of his own pain he went on, "That's over. I made a vow to Arthur long ago. I vowed to follow and serve him faithfully. I—I love him for what he stands for, and I love you as a man loves a woman, but—I pledged to serve him before we ever met. I can't put myself in the way of a marriage that will benefit Arthur's cause."

Guinevere turned away, covering her face with her hands. She spoke in a choked voice. "Yes. Arthur's cause. We are trampled under the hoofs of Arthur's cause."

"What must be, must be," muttered Lancelot. "He is our king, the embodiment of this land's hope."

She took her hands away from her face. Nodded slowly. "For our country's life, we must die a little." To Lancelot, it appeared that she had aged years . . . no, not aged . . . matured. It made her all the more beautiful. "No. It is not too great a price to pay," she finished in a small voice.

"Come. We'll fetch your horse, and I'll take you back," said Lancelot. "We must tell your father. He will be pleased."

He started to move around her. She caught his arm, her lovely face tortured and pleading.

"Kiss me before we go."

A soldier's instincts made him glance around the horizon: the hills so redolent and fertile, their warmth heightening the warmth he drew from her hand. Southward he glimpsed men plowing, protected by some of Leodegrance's soldiers. He abandoned caution, seized her around the waist, and tasted the sweet burning of her mouth—

And her own tears, when he pressed his cheek close to hers one last time.

CHAPTER 10

Morgan Le Fay

The burning watchtower toppled, engulfing a hundred brawling men in fire. A moment later screams and groans rang from the spark-shot smoke where the tower had stood.

Sweaty and begrimed, his leather armor cut and his mail severed in a score of places, Arthur stormed on horseback among his milling men. He pointed forward with Excalibur. The blade shimmered in the light of the torched palisades:

"Through the gap past where the tower stood—*follow me*!"

A thrown spear slashed past his shoulder, frightening his horse. The animal almost stumbled over a mound of corpses. Arthur regained control, twisted in the saddle, saw Kay gory but grinning, close behind. More mounted men were forming up at Kay's rear. With a shrill yell and another whirl of the great blade over his head he led the charge toward the breach in the wall.

The closer his mount carried him to the simmering rubble of the tower, the more dangerous he knew this entry would be. His cheeks stung, then scorched in the heat. He slowed the animal's pace slightly, bending low over its neck as he guided it around burning timbers. If he and Kay's riders could only negotiate a path through that inferno of smoke and charred wood, Lot's fort would be penetrated—

With just seven hundred men, and only half of those mounted, Arthur had surprised the encamped thousand just at dusk. During the initial melee, he had watched whole companies on foot flee in despair because, as always, Arthur's audacious surprise tactics and the advantage of mounted men proved superior. The rebel king had retreated inside the fort at the end of the first hour's fighting.

But Arthur was tired now, tired and bleeding from a neck wound that soaked his linen shirt beneath his armor and mail. The horse stumbled, whinnied wildly, almost pitched him off into a pile of beams still red hot from the flames started by his fire-archers. Frantically Arthur roweled the horse. It raced ahead, sure-footed again.

Arthur saw a path he could take through the gap in the wall. There was only one sizable obstacle—a pile of burning rubble. With a sharp command to the horse he galloped toward it. Too late, he heard a vengeful yell high on his right—

The horse leaped, responding to the dig of Arthur's spurs. On a sagging watch platform overlooking the gap where the tower had stood, one spearman still lay, panting his last. All other defenders on the ramparts had retreated from the roaring blaze that was rapidly reducing the entire wall to ruin. But this one, ugly mole-cheeked thrall had life left in him. And he had his weapon—and a hatred of the conquerer just jumping his horse through the gap below—

The man on the platform flung his spear. It wobbled, not a good cast, but adequate. It caught Arthur in mid-air, piercing a rent in his link-mail. The iron point buried in Arthur's shoulder, then tore loose a moment later as the great warhorse completed its leap.

The spear tumbled away as Arthur's charger struck the ground inside the fort. The high king was pale, almost unconscious from the searing pain—

Wildly he veered the horse to the right so that Kay's stallion would have a clear jump over the burning barrier. Like a great black silhouette, captain and rider cleared the flames and landed hard. Kay cursed and wheeled aside.

One after another, a whole procession of mounted men leaped their horses into the besieged fort. Staying upright only by sheer will, Arthur saw the figures of a few remaining defenders blur and elongate as they fled shrieking before the awful specter of the horsemen jumping the last barrier and fanning out, swords swinging, axes flashing—

"Kay!" Arthur cried, pointing with Excalibur. The blade felt heavy as stone.

He waggled the sword at a man scurrying toward the stable. Kay finished an enemy soldier with a quick thrust through the ribs, turned his horse, and charged off to pursue King Lot, who had disappeared into the stable.

Kay didn't bother to dismount. He ducked his head and rode straight through the stable's open door. In a moment a bubbling wail told Arthur that Kay had found his quarry.

Arthur cantered ahead, saw with satisfaction that several of his own men had unbarred the rebel king's gate from within. The moment it was opened he heard cheering—the thunderous cheering of his own soldiers. His face convulsed in a weary smile.

He spied four stoutly armored men being driven into the fort on foot. That too gave him pleasure. The four were the petty kings who had conspired with Lot and who had been surprised before they could move their combined army against Arthur's.

Jogging across the fort yard, Arthur saw two of the kings watching him with outright dread. He heard their captors—his own men—boast of coming execution.

A disgusted Kay appeared in the stable door. The reason for his disgust was apparent a moment later.

Blood-soaked and gasping, King Lot came crawling out on hands and knees.

"It wasn't my stroke that got him," Kay called to Arthur. "The fool was in such haste to mount and escape he slipped and fell onto a hay fork."

Kay spat, indicating his opinion of that kind of finish for a traitor. Then he clambered down from the saddle, flexing the gloved fingers of his right hand. He transferred his sword from his left hand to his right.

"But I'll finish the work the tines started." The sword flashed up.

"Let him live!" Arthur shouted. The effort made him wince and sway in the saddle. "We've beaten them—"

He swung slowly toward the quartet of rebel kings and their guards. Bathed in icy sweat he called to his men:

"Spare them too—on one condition. I demand an oath—a sacred vow—that they'll never take up arms against the high king again."

One of the rebel leaders, a stocky, red-bearded man, ran forward before his guards could stop him:

"Gladly, your highness. Lot led us to expect butchery. No quarter—"

Arthur winced again. "I'm sure Lot said a great deal in order to commit your men to his cause, King Ulric." He glanced at the others through a blur of sweat and pain. The remaining three were suspicious and unconvinced. To them he said, "You need not love me, my lords. You only need to love this kingdom—and serve me if I call for your swords in its defense. Surely your consciences can accept—"

Unable to finish he slipped from the saddle and struck the ground, Excalibur pinned beneath him.

He felt a remote sense of elation that the northern resistance had been broken. But it was tempered by the immediacy of his pain. When Kay tried to help him up Arthur almost screamed aloud.

"A litter!" Kay bawled. "Poles and hides—*quickly*!"

Arthur fell back against Kay's forearm.

"I will live," he panted. "Never—doubt that. There's—still far too much to be done—"

His head lolled forward.

Terrified, Kay knelt and pressed his face near Arthur's mouth. He felt thin breathing. Bedivere, burly and blood-splattered, rode up.

"Find the household women!" Kay yelled to him. "Tell them the king must be tended. *Damn you. Don't stand there*—!"

Bedivere's huge hand pointed a stained war-axe at the unconscious Arthur.

"He's trying to speak to you."

Then Bedivere dismounted and lumbered toward the long house, knocking its door open with the axe. Inside, women screamed and wept while Bedivere bellowed.

Kay leaned close to the high king again. Arthur whispered:

"See to Lot's wounds also."

"What is he saying?"

Kay's head snapped up to see who had spoken. It was Ulric, the red-bearded rebel king who had pledged his loyalty.

"He's saying King Lot is to be tended."

"By Christ," Ulric said fervently. "He is all they say he is."

Kay nodded. "And more."

"I'll bear his litter myself," the defeated man vowed.

When it was rigged Kay lifted one end and Ulric the other. It was Kay, carrying the head end of the litter toward the long house, who stumbled against someone in a coarse, cowled robe.

"Watch out, woman!" Kay snarled. "The king needs no fortunes told. His future's very clear. He'll die unless his wound is shut with a hot iron—"

The two litter-bearers passed on. The fortune-teller melted back into a group of cowled servants. Reflecting the glow of the flames consuming the outer wall, lynx-like eyes shone within the fortune-teller's cowl.

ii

Morgan faced the small hearth in the queen's chamber. She preferred that her sister not see her expression.

She was a handsome, even beautiful woman, with reddish-gold hair. But her fine features were subtly marred by a too-severe mouth and lines around her large eyes. The household servants feared her. They called her le Fay because it was said she pursued arcane studies. The most superstitious claimed Morgan's wrinkles came from slitting her eyes when she communed with the Evil One, who sat in a cloud of billowing flame—

Across the room sat her sister, fairer and much more delicate looking. Morgause thrust a bone needle through the fabric on her embroidery frame, plucked it out again.

Morgan's eyes seemed to focus deep in the hearth. Then, her face smoothing, she turned and helped herself to wine from a ewer.

"What you've said makes me happy," she said at last. "I'm glad your husband will live."

Morgause's soft, almost sad eyes lifted from the needlework. "Thanks to God's mercy—and the high king's."

The last words produced an almost physical convulsion within Morgan, so consuming was her hatred of the man who had lain in Lot's house a full week, spared from death by quick attention to his battle wound. But Arthur was still delirious, the servants said.

She listened to the rain drenching the long house, the stillness. It was late at night. A sense of imminent opportunity made her catch her breath. She had a chance to work her scheme, if only she didn't let her hatred show.

"Will Lot resist Arthur any longer?" she asked.

"When I spoke with him earlier this evening he said no. He's tired of the struggle. So am I. Of course I know your feelings about Arthur—Heaven knows you spoke them often enough when we were children! But he *has* held the Saxons back—for years now. If we can't love him, we can at least make our lives easier by not fighting him."

The hatred filled Morgan like a poison. She feigned sighs of weariness:

"Perhaps you're right. Perhaps it *is* time we made amends."

"I never thought I'd hear you say such a thing."

"I don't do so by choice. It's a necessity. He has too many followers now."

She almost laughed at the way the lies came so easily. And yet Morgause, always open and trusting, acted as if she believed them. Choosing words with care, Morgan continued:

"It might also be well if you made some tangible sign of your new allegiance. The household women are tired of tending Arthur, I'm told. If you were to humble yourself and relieve them for a night, the king would surely hear of it when he finally awakens—"

Morgause pondered, then laid aside her handwork. "That's a sensible thought. I feel quite awake. Perhaps tonight—?"

Morgan's shrug was studied. "Only the deed matters, not the time."

But her heart was thudding with frantic expectancy. She ran her tongue over her teeth, pivoting away again in case she betrayed herself. *Yes, go to him,* she thought. *Go to him, your own half brother—and bring me back an heir who mingles the Pendragon blood into Cornwall's—another of this breed who can challenge Arthur's throne.*

Her breasts rose and fell quickly as she stared into the fire. Her tongue kept moving back and forth across her upper lip, the only visible sign of her excitement.

Morgause rose, rubbing her arms. "I think Elwina is

watching the king tonight. Old as she is, she'd probably be grateful for extra rest—"

The younger woman glided to the wall near the hearth. She studied herself in a scrap of polished metal that served as a mirror. She began combing her hair with quick strokes of a turtle-shell comb.

"You might want to warm yourself with a little more wine before you go," Morgan said to her sister's back. As she spoke she drew a bit of gnarled root from the charm bag at her waist. With deft movements she crushed the root into a powder that drifted down into a half-full cup. She lifted the cup, swirling it—then held it out toward Morgause:

"Here."

The young girl faced about, took the cup, drank, then sighed and murmured appreciation of the wine's warmth. She left the room.

Morgan could hardly contain her laughter as she flung the rest of the cup's contents into the fire. A quick puff of blue-green flame burst upward. A foul stench spread as the last drops of the potion evaporated.

"Yes," Morgan whispered. "Go to him and sin with him like a slut." *Then bring me the child who will bring him down.*"

iii

Bedivere roused on his stool outside the king's door. He pulled his dagger as rapid footsteps rustled the straw strewn along the corridor. A face appeared at the periphery of light cast by a cresset. Bedivere's greeting was mildly astonished:

"Good evening, my lady."

"Good evening."

"Is there some way I can help you?"

"Yes, sir captain, there is. When my husband woke tonight he bade me show proof of our submission to the high king." Morgause smiled in an ingenuous way; it quite disarmed Bedivere's natural suspicion. "I have come to sit with the king through the night." Morgause paused.

"So Elwina may sleep."

Bedivere gaped. "You're going to sit with him like one of the household women?"

"Aye. Do you object?"

Before he could answer she fanned back her cloak. "You may satisfy yourself that I've brought no hidden weapons. The offer is sincere."

Hesitantly Bedivere touched various folds of her garments. He found nothing to convince him that Lot's wife meant harm to Arthur. As she moved past him, he nodded in a pleased way:

"This is a good thing you do, madam. It's a sign that will be spoken of far and wide. It will help the king's cause."

"So I thought," Morgause replied, her speech oddly thickened. She opened the door and slipped inside.

Above Arthur's feverish moans and thrashing Bedivere heard Lot's wife murmuring with the crone Elwina. He recalled Morgause's face—

Had the light played a trick? Or had her cheeks glowed with a faint sheen of perspiration—? Yes, he was sure they had. On such a cold, rainy night, that was very odd.

Yawning and smiling at the thought of going to bed, old Elwina tottered out. The door closed again. Elwina disappeared and Bedivere sank down on his stool. He was soon snoring.

iv

The chamber where Arthur lay was windowless, stuffy. The high king wore only a woolen shirt, open at the throat to show the hard musculature of his chest. Morgause perched on the stool beside the bed, staring at the brown hair already streaked with white.

Arthur tossed back and forth, asleep but restless. Occasionally he clenched his hands in the coverlets and murmured someone's name. Whose, Morgause couldn't tell.

Very quickly, she didn't care. A strange warmth stole over her. Her body felt languorous.

Surely those few sips of wine couldn't have affected her this way—was she coming down with a fever like Arthur's?

She couldn't keep her eyes off the place where his shirt fell away. Deep in the recess of her mind a faint but shrill voice cried out against her shameful thoughts.

He is your half brother! You dare not!

Morgause threw her head back, her eyes glazing. She moaned softly. The warning voice died.

There was a dazed, slack-lipped look about her—a coarseness—as she rose slowly. Still moaning, she unfastened the brooch and let her cloak fall. With a shudder she clasped hands to her own breasts, squeezing them in a futile effort to contain the lust raging within her.

v

Dark hair billowing in the wind.

Dark eyes like great lakes in which he drowned—

Rousing a little, he wondered where he was. He felt he should know—

He realized he was in a bed. Dim lamps burned around the room. A pale figure hovered—

A woman. A lovely woman.

Because of the accursed fever, his eyes refused to focus properly. But he heard the woman breathing, a rough sound, full of passion.

His left hand lifted. He had to touch the vision. Define its reality—

Immense joy suffused him, soothing away his aches, as the imagined room disappeared. He saw *her*, limned against the medallion of the sun in a scented meadow bursting with summer color.

She bent toward him, whispering her desire. Somehow he found strength to grasp her. The sunlight was unbearably bright. The heat of her flesh seared him as he folded her nakedness into his arms and sought her mouth, mead-sweet and hungry—

Kissing her, he cried her name ecstatically:

"Guinevere—"

She held his head and kissed him fervently, never hearing.

vi

A few snowflakes drifted down. Mournful singing from the chapel sent Morgan hurrying by in the dark yard. She abominated holy places.

She slipped back into the long house. It was deserted. Almost all of the servants had gone to the chapel to say prayers for the soul of King Lot.

The king's wound had grown infected. Death had claimed him as the first winds of autumn tore the scarlet and yellow leaves from the trees.

Lot had lain ill all summer—long after the high king had recovered and gone south. He had never seen the swell of his queen's belly or the horror and agony in her eyes as, day by day, she was reminded of the terrible sin she had committed.

Earlier this same evening, Morgause had gone to her confinement filthy dirty. Her hair was dull, her eyes lackluster from the constant realization of what she had done. Morgan cared nothing about that—or about the foul talk in the household. All she cared about was—

Abruptly a figure emerged from the queen's chamber. Old Elwina, wiping hands on her apron.

"My sister—?" Morgan began.

The elderly woman gazed at her with dumb sorrow. "She's dead. I don't think she wanted to live past this hour."

Morgan's face showed no expression. "What of the child?"

Elwina shuddered. "A boy. Healthy, it would seem—"

For the first time, Morgan le Fay smiled.

vii

A hundred boys' voices pealed the wedding song in Latin. The soprano notes echoed and multiplied under the vast arches of the Londinium abbey.

Half the kingdom had come for the celebration, it seemed. It was springtime of the year following Arthur's defeat of King Lot and the rebels of the North. With Lot dead, most of those who had fought beside him had ridden to the old city to fill pledges of loyalty to Arthur.

Lords and ladies knelt as the high king entered from one side of the altar. He wore his robe of state and the dragon diadem.

A second door on the other side of the altar swung aside. With her hand resting atop her father's Guinevere moved slowly toward the man who would shortly be her husband.

Excalibur heavy at his hip, Arthur waited in a shaft of sunlight slanting down from one of the abbey's high slot windows. Guinevere's white linen gown showed her dark coloring to advantage and made him catch his breath. She was lovelier than any woman had a right to be. And the knowledge that she was his drove out the weariness that had given him an old man's eyes despite his youth.

If only old Baron Hector had lived long enough to see this, Arthur thought sadly. Kay's father had died just two weeks before, a half-full glass of his delicious mead in his hand.

Abruptly while the music soared he saw Guinevere's eyes move toward the benches where the captains knelt. It was no more than a glance, but Arthur recognized its object:

Lancelot.

Unlike the others the Gaul had not bowed his head.

For one terrible moment Arthur saw the unquenchable pain communicated between the man and the woman—

Old Leodegrance made a dry, rasping sound in his throat. Guinevere returned her attention to the high king waiting at the altar beside a richly clad bishop. Arthur's eyes sought Guinevere's and held them only a moment. She glanced away.

Not from modesty, he knew, sorrowing. From shame.

Time and again he had tried to forget what Leodegrance had revealed only last night, at the great feast preceding the wedding. Tippling too much, Leodegrance had spoken of his conversation with Guinevere when Lancelot brought Arthur's petition of marriage.

Even drunk, Leodegrance quickly realized his error. He tried to amend his words, but the damage was done. Arthur knew. But of course, he had known all along, although he had denied it to himself. Leodegrance's story only confirmed what he knew in his soul.

And where surpassing joy should have reigned, he felt only a dull ache.

The pealing choir and the holy sunlight of the abbey were mockeries. Like a wooden thing, he turned beside Guinevere as they faced the altar and knelt. Arthur was glad to bow his head as the prayer began. His bowed head hid his grief.

viii

A light supper of duckling and wine had been laid in the large chamber set aside for the bridal night. The room was unnaturally still.

Arthur, clad in a light blue tunic over clean leather breeches, fretted in a chair beside the small table. He roused only when Guinevere entered, her hair undone and her figure emphasized by the modest yet closely cut bed gown.

"My lord—" she began.

Almost angrily he shook his head. "Sit a moment. We must talk."

She tried to tease him:

"I didn't think new bridegrooms wanted conversation."

He took her hand gently, guided her to the chair. He saw how false and strained her smile was. As soon as she was seated, he said:

"You know the purpose of this marriage—"

Again she tried to smile. "Yes, my lord. I learned those facts from my late mother."

He gestured, almost angry: "I mean the state purpose. To unify the North and the South. I intend for the marriage to be confined to that purpose. I—I will not prevail on you in any other way."

Guinevere seemed stunned. *Or perhaps*, he thought, *miserably relieved*.

Her reply was appropriately dutiful, however:

"Why, my lord?"

"Guinevere, we are legally man and wife—so there must be no lies between us. I think I've loved you since the first time I saw you at your father's table. But I know you can't return that feeling. I—" Agony made his voice hoarse. "—I know who it is that you really love."

She whispered. "How did you learn—?"

"From your father. No, don't say anything—it's not something for which you should blame him. Anyway I think I've really known for a while what secret Lancelot carried in his heart. So although conditions in the kingdom made this marriage advisable, I want to spare you the pain of making it anything more than a marriage in name only."

A long silence. Tenderly Guinevere asked:

"And you want to spare your captain, too?"

Arthur nodded.

"Taking all the pain for yourself?"

His mouth twisted. "Oh, I think there will be pain enough for all of us."

He rose abruptly. "I will take the antechamber for the night."

"My lord, there is no need to relinquish your rights as—"

Arthur looked at her, heartbroken and overwhelmed with a love that could never be fulfilled:

"Yes there is. Good night."

Guinevere rushed after him: "Anything that might have existed between your captain and me is done!"

"Except in your hearts."

"My lord, I would *never* dishonor you."

He touched her face. "I know that, Guinevere. That alone makes you prized among women."

A moment later the door closed softly.

Guinevere sat again. Her hand lifted slowly to her eyes. The silence was broken by the sound of her weeping.

ix

In the cool cave Merlin moved with an animation and ebullience that he'd thought he would never experience again. "And here, Nimue—" His hands embraced the curvature of the crystal sphere. "—here is the seer's glass handed down to me by the last high druid."

Morgan le Fay emerged from the damp darkness into the flickering glow of the lamp on the worktable. She feigned awe at the sight of the crystal, touching it hesitantly. Merlin stared at her, an almost foolishly worshipful expression on his seamed face.

She had come to him a few months ago, at one of the forts he had been visiting with the high king. Since then his entire life had been transformed.

The girl called herself Nimue. According to her own statement she sprang from peasant stock. But she had an aptitude for learning—and a consuming interest in the lore Merlin had accumulated over the years.

The druid overheard many of the crude jokes about an elderly man falling in love with a younger woman and making a fool of himself. He paid no attention to them. This lovely child seemed genuinely fond of him, genuinely interested in all he could teach her—

Morgan bent to peer into the crystal, then clapped her hands in delight.

"Oh, this whole day has been a miracle. When I sought you out—begged you to teach me even a few of the principles of natural science—I never imagined I'd be privileged to see this place. Many people doubt it even exists, you know."

Merlin smiled. "That is a view I've fostered very carefully. In truth I had doubts about inviting you. No one has ever been here before."

"I'm touched, master. Eternally grateful—"

"No, I'm the one to feel gratitude, Nimue," he said quickly. "Perhaps I've worked too long in the high king's cause. Been preoccupied with attending to his needs—"

"He has a wife for that now," Morgan said.

"That's true. And as he grows in stature he needs me less and less and less."

Merlin sighed, gazing at the array of jars and pestles on the littered table.

"So perhaps it was time for my life to take a new turn. In any case—" His eyes were moist. He clasped her hands between his dry, veined ones. "You have made an old man's days bright again."

"Come!" Morgan laughed. "You're not so creaky as that! We've proved it more than one night, haven't we—?"

Merlin actually turned pink. "To my astonishment."

"Have you ever told the king about us, master?"

"Never. He would call me a senile idiot."

"Ah. But we know differently!" She touched his chin. "And you're wrong to minimize your importance to Arthur. Everyone knows the druid is the first one to whom he speaks about a new alliance or battle plan. But now he must share you—with me!"

She gave him an almost chaste kiss on the cheek.

Turning pinker still, Merlin made a delighted sound deep in his throat.

Morgan's eyes sparkled in the glow of the flame shimmering in the bowl of oil. "You promised to show me some of the secrets of medicine. The balm for deep wounds—"

Merlin began to rattle dishes and pull down sealed jars from a shelf. "Aye, and so I will. But I don't have all the ingredients. Some must be completely fresh. While I prepare the table—"

He turned her by the shoulders toward the dim spiderwebbing of sunlight and shadow at the end of the tunnel leading outside.

"—you climb the hill above the cave and bring me four of the scarlet flowers you'll find growing near the summit."

"Very well. I'll be back soon." She scurried out of sight. The spiderwebbing of shadow and light shivered as she pushed through the tangle of brush that hid the cave's entrance.

Humming, Merlin began to arrange the jars and utensils. He felt alert, alive as he hadn't since the high king's marriage—

All at once an odd rumbling reached his ears. The rock walls of the cave began to vibrate. The sound grew louder moment by moment. Alarmed, Merlin limped toward the mouth of the cave.

Seams opened in the rock overhead. Dust drifted down. Merlin's face went blank with astonishment, then turned fearful as he struggled to comprehend what his senses told him:

Somehow, a rockslide had started on the slope above the entrance—

Had the pupil who had become his lover dislodged some of the great stones by accident? Perhaps she was injured—

He dashed toward the entrance as fast as he could. The rumbling increased. Terrified, he cried her name:

"Nimue—?"

Above the roaring he heard cruel laughter outside: "I am not Nimue, druid."

"What? What are you saying?"

"I am *Morgan*!"

With a scream Merlin flung himself at the brush over the entrance—only to see it hurl inward under the enormous weight of great boulders tumbling down. They filled the tunnel, roaring, grinding, spilling inward—

"You deceived me!" he shrieked, out of his mind with anger as he flung himself at the rocks blocking the passage. He pulled away a few of the smallest. Most were too large to be dislodged—

The passage was completely sealed.

Only then did he understand.

In his eagerness, his misguided passion, he had allowed himself to be flattered, seduced—destroyed by an enemy he had long since forgotten.

A last, dull grinding on the hillside signaled the end of the massive slide. Merlin thought he heard the laughter again. Not warm as it had been while she teased and tricked him, but vicious, vengeful. Gradually the voice faded—

Panting, Merlin again attacked the rock barrier. Pulled and clawed and battered until his blue-veined hands were wet and red. On his knees, knowing he was sealed here forever, he scourged himself bitterly for his foolishness. He richly deserved the fate that had befallen him. Sorrow and fear mingled in his voice as he looked at the immovable wall of rock that would mark his grave.

"Arthur, your mercy on my folly," he whispered. "I never dreamed she still lived and plotted against you. Arthur, be wary. Be wary—!"

Frustration and fury overcame the druid then. With an anguished cry he slumped forward against the stones, beating on them with bloody hands.

X

Arthur was tired. He gazed down at Gawain and Gareth standing by the round table. The day had been insufferably long. Or perhaps it was only his spiritual weariness that made him feel that way—

From his high-backed judgment seat on the dais at one end of the main hall he spoke to the two captains who saw to the ushering of petitioners:

"Are we finished?"

Gawain said, "Yes, majesty. Except for one woman who refuses to name herself or her purpose in coming here."

"She's got an infant with her," Gareth smirked. "Probably some cottage wench who dropped a bastard and wants the king to order the father to wed her."

Arthur raked one hand through his white-streaked hair and straightened in his chair.

"Bring her in," he said.

The sons of Lot circled the table and left the hall.

Arthur pondered in silence, uneasy.

Much that was stable and familiar in his world had disappeared during the past year. Old Hector had gone to his grave. And now Merlin had vanished without a trace.

Arthur had heard stories that the druid had adopted a young girl as a pupil. It was said that Merlin was last seen in her company. But the reports were sketchy. Inconclusive.

The tension of living a marriage of pretense was taking its toll too. There were haggard shadows beneath Arthur's eyes and hurt in his heart because he constantly fought the impulse to become a husband in deed as well as in word. He always held back, remembering his vow to Guinevere on their wedding night.

He seldom saw Lancelot. The Gaul had taken to staying almost constantly in the field, campaigning against the Saxons. What few meetings they did have were strained and uncomfortable—

An infant's squall roused Arthur from his gloomy reverie. He glanced up to see an attractive woman crossing the hall. She carried a bundle in the crook of one arm.

She was well dressed, in ankle-length tunic with a knee-length gown over it. This was no farmer's child. The cut as well as the color of her clothing testified to that. Only the well born could afford the madder root that turned fabric crimson.

Around her brow the woman wore a gold circlet. There was some kind of device enameled in an oval at the center of her forehead.

Gawain and Gareth looked apprehensive. They fingered their sword hilts as Arthur said:

"You may approach."

Gracefully the woman moved to the foot of the dais and regarded him with startlingly large eyes. Arthur saw the enameled device clearly now.

It was the griffin of Cornwall.

The bundled infant wailed all the louder, forcing Gareth to shout:

"Kneel to the king, woman."

The woman continued to regard Arthur with faint arrogance. The lynxlike eyes alarmed him a little. The woman spoke to the brothers while gazing up at the dais:

"Is it required when I bring the king his own son?"

Dread froze Arthur then. He sat upright, his hand dropping unconsciously to the hilt of Excalibur lying across his knees. The hall, silent and filled with shadows at this twilight hour, seemed to give his voice a harsh echo:

"Who are you?"

"Morgan, daughter of the Duke of Cornwall."

Arthur sat back in his chair, astounded.

"I imagined you long dead."

"Of course, majesty," she murmured, still smiling that cruel, unnerving smile. "It would be impossible for the high king to be aware of all the humble persons of the realm."

The woman's hatred was no longer concealed. She lifted the bundle in both hands, just as Gareth said sharply:

"What's this babbling about a son? The king has no heirs—"

"But he does," Morgan replied. "Not conceived with the great morality he professes, but a son all the same."

She held the bundle high. Arthur pressed against the back of his chair, feeling unclean. Softly Morgan went on:

"Has his majesty forgotten a certain night when he lay feverish from his wound at Lot's fort? A woman came to watch over him—and he took her—"

Sickeningly Arthur did recall the vision of Guinevere. Real as it seemed afterward, he had assumed it was no more than a product of his sickness.

Morgan's moist mouth grew sinuous as she smiled. She bobbled the bundle back and forth:

"The child is christened Modred. The mother was my sister Morgause, who died bearing him. The father—"

"We heard nothing about a child when we learned of Queen Morgause's death!" Gareth thundered. His sword was half drawn now, and Arthur was dismayed by the cruelty he saw on the captain's face. He sensed dark, immutable forces gathering—

How could Lot's sons display such naked wrath? he thought sadly. The answer was simple: out of loyalty for him.

Yet their anger ran counter to all he had taught them, all that the dragon-painted table in the center of the hall represented—

"The child's birth was kept secret," Morgan said. "I did not wish my sister's shame to be widely known. The father, you see, is his majesty. My sister's half brother."

Gareth pulled his sword and ran forward:

"You foul-mouthed harlot—!"

Arthur raised a hand sharply. "*No.* Hear her out."

He dropped his hand to the carved arm of the chair, gripped it until his fingers turned white. Even as he spoke he knew he had little hope of disproving what she said:

"We have no evidence Queen Morgause actually birthed that child, woman."

"Ah, but there are scores who will testify to the size of her belly months after you left Lot's house. The king himself was too enfeebled by his wound to have—"

Morgan chose the next words carefully, seeming to take obscene pleasure in them:

"—fulfilled the husband's role."

"Then some other man got her with child!" Gareth cried. "Your identity makes it clear why you've come here with your filthy tale—"

"Be silent!" Arthur cried. Gareth took a step backward.

The high king rose unsteadily. The premonition of dark powers gathering grew sharper still as he descended to the paving stones.

At Morgan's side he lifted the coverlet away from the hideously red, howling babe whose skull was capped with brown fuzz. The child's miniature fists seemed to flail the air in defiance.

Arthur stared down at the infant with a strange mingling of wonder and foreboding. He pronounced the child's name:

"Modred—"

"Majesty, deny her charge!" Gawain cried from the gloom.

Arthur's face was bleak. "If it were possible, I would. In Lot's house, I—" The terrible admission wrenched forth. "—I did take a woman. I thought it was someone else. The child could be mine."

"He *is* yours," Morgan purred. "Your royal heir. There is an old midwife in the North who will testify that Morgause came to your bedchamber. And was in the presence of no other man during the time when the child was conceived."

Again Gareth protested:

"Even if his majesty knew the woman's identity, she was only a half sister—"

"A quibble, captain." Morgan smiled. "The sin remains the same."

Arthur was certain denial would be fruitless. Morgan exuded confidence. He knew the midwife must exist.

His sense of his own uncleanliness worsened. He jerked his hand from Excalibur's hilt, as though his very touch would soil it. Somehow, against his wishes, in defiance of his struggle and his dreams, a taint was coming to stain all that the sword and the round table stood for—

In an empty voice, he said to the woman, "What do you want of me?"

"I only want you to take your child and raise him in a way that befits his birth. I give you Modred as a gift—"

Arthur's eyes locked with hers. An almost supernatural clarity of mind warned him that if he dared accept the squalling bundle he would bring about his own—

He cut off the thought, speaking it aloud instead:

"A gift to destroy me?"

Morgan dropped her gaze. Her polite reply bore just a trace of mockery:

"Why, no, majesty. Who would wish to destroy Arthur of Britain?"

Gareth stormed.

"Majesty, forgive me, but you dare not acknowledge—"

"I believe I have no choice." Arthur turned away. "Give the babe into the keeping of my captains, woman. Then take yourself out of my sight."

Face averted, he listened to her small, pleased laugh. She murmured something he failed to hear. His head was throbbing all at once.

Gradually Morgan's footfalls died away. Gawain and Gareth had closed the hall's doors from outside. With a bitter curse Arthur walked slowly to his place at the round table. He sank down in his chair and stared at the painted red dragon—

The piercing scream hurled him from the chair and sent him running to the doors. He jerked them open—

"Christ save us!"

White, he saw Gareth stalking toward him. The sword in Gareth's right hand dripped a trail of red droplets on the straw.

The big man's other hand held something hidden by a winding of crimson cloth, cloth already dyed a deeper red—

Gareth shook the cloth loose. Dangling by the hair from his stained fingers—

Morgan's head.

Arthur would have struck his captain, but he was too weak with horror. He could only gape and cry out:

"In the name of God—*why*?"

Gareth looked shaken. "To prevent her from spreading her slanders, majesty. Even if her story is true—"

"Isn't one evil enough? Must a second one be added to it? You've done *murder*!"

Gareth swallowed. "In—in what I thought was good cause—"

"*In defiance of everything we have tried to establish in this kingdom*!"

"I beg his majesty's forgiveness. But—" Gareth spoke louder. "— it was necessary. The child should be destroyed too."

"*No*! I won't have him touched! Do you understand that?"

Gareth nodded, stunned to silence by Arthur's rage. The high king pointed with a trembling hand:

"Take that vile thing away. You have mocked and befouled the purpose to which we've dedicated our lives!"

Gareth retorted without thinking:

"I was not the first!"

Arthur struck him across the face.

Gareth reeled back, more hurt than angry. Arthur tried to offer an apology, rubbing his left hand against his leather-clad leg. At the moment of the blow something had struck him there.

Arthur's shoulders slumped. He walked back toward the round table. He heard Gareth's running step diminishing, then the sound of anxious voices through the long house. The servants had been roused by the dead woman's scream—

Arthur glanced down. Gareth had indeed been knocked off balance when he was struck. His sword had touched Arthur's leg—

Leaving blood.

In that glistening stain Arthur saw the irrevocable corruption of everything he had labored and fought so hard to create. At that moment there was a grief and a dread in him greater than any he had ever known.

xi

The soldiers sped their horses through the gloomy wood. It was an accursed place, long ago the haunt of druids and, in more recent times, thieves.

In the past year a new inhabitant had terrorized those who lived nearby. Freemen who tilled fields near the wood occasionally glimpsed a tall, powerful figure peering at them from the trees, a frightening figure in filthy clothes, with tangled hair and beard and wild, staring eyes—

The clopping of the horses muffled other sounds along the dim track under the arching trees—until a sudden, loud noise brought the half-dozen riders to a halt. They fingered their swords. Eyed one another—

Louder and louder, the wild laughter rang in the silence.

"It's the ghost of the wood. The one the farmers have seen!" one man whispered, drawing his dagger with one hand while making the cross-sign with the other.

The leader of the soldiers pondered. "We've heard

that tale almost a year now. I've always doubted there was such a creature—"

Booming, almost maniacal laughter rang out. Jays chattering in the treetops fell silent.

"Until now," the leader added.

Ignoring the pleas of his men that they ride on, he pulled out his spatha and turned his horse into the tangle of brush beside the track. "Those of you who wish to can stay here. The rest of us will split the bounty the king promised to any man who captured this phantom—"

Three followed him. Two remained behind.

Slowly the leader and his three cohorts negotiated their way through wild shrubs and tangled vines. The laughter pealed, now deep and bass, now high and cracking. The leader began to regret his decision.

But he pressed on, finally nosing his horse through a last screen of brush. Sword trembling in his hand, he beheld a tall, bearded man kneeling on the other side of a forest pool.

The fellow was riffling the water and peering into it, as if searching for images. He heard the horsemen, scrambled to his feet. Berries spilled from a torn pouch at his waist.

The leader stared in astonishment. The filthy hermit darted backward from the pool, his eyes huge with primitive terror—

The wood-ghost's worn boot tangled on a root. He tumbled, crying out. The soldiers dismounted and circled the pool, and the leader was sickened as he matched a memory with that bearded face.

The hermit tried to struggle to his feet. He couldn't. He fell back to the ground with an exhausted, despairing cry.

The leader led his frightened men to the fallen man. The man's eyes were closed. Cautiously the leader sheathed his sword, crouched, and touched the man's forehead.

"He's burning with fever! No wonder he stared at us as if he didn't see us."

The leader gestured. "Pick him up. We must take him to the king."

"Why don't we just leave him?" one of the others grumbled. "He's nothing but some crazed wanderer—"

"Aye, crazed." The leader nodded. "But I saw that face the night Arthur burned King Lot's fort and our lord swore loyalty." His voice a whisper, he continued, "I can't explain why he's taken to living in this wild place—but he was once one of the high king's greatest captains."

Staring at the slumbering figure, he shook his head. "His name is Lancelot of Benwick."

xii

Ulric, whose people called him the King of the Wall, stared down at the man lying unconscious at the foot of his judgment seat. Beside Ulric, a slim and lovely girl with wheat-colored hair also studied the fallen captain. Her eyes brimmed with a luminous pity and tenderness.

Ulric stroked his red beard shot with spikes of gray. At last he said, "I can't imagine what brought him here. But we must tend him."

The girl touched his arm. "I'll see to it, Father."

"Very well, Elain." Ulric shook his head. "It's puzzling that one who held such a high place should fall so low—"

The leader of the soldiers stepped forward. "Perhaps we should send a messenger to inform Arthur."

Frowning, Ulric replied, "Not just yet. We don't know what brought on Lancelot's madness. Nor whether he left Arthur's table of his own choice—"

The king's eyes brooded on the still figure. He added softly:

"—or was driven out."

xiii

The May wind warmed Lancelot's cheeks. Sunlight danced from the scythes of the farmers weeding in the fields of Ulric, King of the Wall.

The sight of the tiny figures among pleasantly green hills soothed the Gaul, who had lain in Ulric's long house all through the winter. The ministrations of the king's daughter had finally restored him to a semblance of health and sanity.

Clad in peasant's clothing, Lancelot sat on the edge of the old Roman wall, which stretched from horizon to horizon, crumbled in many places, but affording a splendid view of the district.

Although still long, Lancelot's beard was neatly trimmed now. But the deep-set eyes that roved over the sunny landscape still showed glints of pain and—at times—unreasoning fury.

A shadow fell across his knees. He glanced up, smiled in a cheerless way. The lovely wheat-haired girl had stolen up silently behind him. He almost couldn't bear to look in Elain's deep blue eyes. He was afraid of the emotion he saw there.

The girl gazed at Lancelot adoringly. She was slender, no more than eighteen or nineteen; yet her figure was full bloomed. With a deep sense of guilt Lancelot felt almost forgotten physical reactions stir as she came even closer.

Elain didn't speak. She seemed content to gaze in silence at the lovely scene south of the wall. Lancelot scrambled up, brushing the dust of crumbled mortar from his tunic.

"Perhaps we'd best start back."

He regretted his decision to go strolling with Ulric's daughter. They had never been alone before. Even when she sat by his pallet during the winter, feeding him broth and meat as he strengthened, one of the household women had always been nearby.

"Yes, I suppose so," the girl answered, looking at

him with such passion that he grew scarlet. "But first—"

She stopped, embarrassed.

"Go on," he said.

"I begged you to come walking out here so that I might ask a question."

In somber silence he stared at fleecy clouds moving slowly through the sky.

"The question is presumptuous, I know. But I can't help it. Please tell me. What brought you so far from the high king's table and—"

Again she stopped.

"And drove me to wander witless for months?" Lancelot's mouth twisted. "Why, child, the oldest complaint known to man. Love."

Elain's beautiful face showed her hurt. "A woman you couldn't have?"

Images of Guinevere stirred in Lancelot's mind. He saw her dining at Arthur's side, saw her among the arbors where she walked with her women, disconsolate, saw her when he encountered her once by chance in the long house and, almost against her own will, she touched him—

"Not quite," he said at last. "I could have taken her for the asking, I think. But I would not ask."

"Why?"

"Let's just say that to do so would have betrayed her, betrayed another man—and betrayed a vow I made as well. I was forced to remain close to her, but that only—increased the torment. Finally the guilt I felt because of my own feelings grew so strong that—"

He shook his head.

"I can't properly explain it. Something—broke in me, that's all. I had to get away." He smiled sadly. "At your age, Elain, I imagine you hardly know the meaning of that kind of desire."

She averted her head. "I know it well, my lord. Ever since you came to my father's house."

Then she grew red-faced. "Forgive me. We had better go back—"

She turned, a graceful, lovely figure etched against the brilliant light. Again Lancelot felt those odd stirrings, then shame.

Elain walked to the steep stairs built in the face of the wall. She started down, Lancelot close behind. All at once he shot out his hand:

"Mind the broken place—!"

One of the great stone stairs was split by a wide crack. The girl had been about to step into it, as if she didn't see it. Only as he grasped her hand did Lancelot realize that Elain's eyes were filled with tears. She leaned against him, head down to hide her weeping.

"This woman you love—" the girl murmured. "Was she married?"

"Legally. But never—physically."

"You know that for a certainty?"

"Yes. She told me with words and—in other ways. The man to whom she's wed understands her feelings for me and—refuses to touch her. A thoroughly wretched situation," he finished, making a bitter face.

They stood gazing into each other's eyes, tiny figures on the immense stair. Suddenly Elain closed her hand on his arm:

"Perhaps one woman could make you forget the other, my lord."

His smile grew still more bitter. "For an hour—"

"Lancelot—"

He saw her shyness burning away in the fire of intense emotion. She touched his face.

"An hour would be enough. Surely you must know I love you."

"And you must know my feelings—my gratitude for your tenderness. But—that's all there can ever be, Elain."

With false gaiety she stretched up on tiptoe and kissed his rough mouth.

"We'll see! When one woman is near and another far away a man changes—"

She kissed him again. Almost unconsciously his arms slipped around her waist.

The feel of her skin sent excitement coursing through him. Despite a warning voice far back in his mind he grasped her hand eagerly as they hurried on down the great stair to a small grove near the base of the wall—

xiv

The apple grove was littered with fallen fruit, and the scent was sweet and heady. Like fermented cider—

Elain's mind was *intoxicated* with it; she tugged Lancelot along behind her.

A favorite playground of her earlier youth, the group of shady trees now was the quiet retreat of her young womanhood. Its gently arching tree limbs gave her solace in times of troubled thoughts, and many a time had the soughing of the wind in the leaves lullabyed her to restful ease. Sparrows and linnets would serenade her here, and often she would hear in their songs the voice of the lover she knew would be hers, the true and only one, promised to her as Christ had been promised to the world.

And now he was here.

Lancelot, of the smooth foreign accent. Of a land beyond frothy sea breakers. A land of mystery and promise. She squeezed his hand and felt his answering squeeze, full of self-assured strength.

"The wall affords many such havens," she said, gesturing with her free hand at the shadow-damasked lawn. "This is my favorite." She motioned to the bole of a tree. "Sit. Savor the softness."

Softly he let go her hand and plumped down to rest in the place indicated. Leaning back, he closed his eyes as though to *experience* the wooden bower through senses other than sight. He took a deep breath and said, "Ah, the air is tart with apple and grass and the boughs nod most tranquilly. Yet smell I only a most sweet lass, taste only her essence of beauty."

"Silly," she said, laughing delightedly. "You rhyme most poorly." She lay down in the cushion of grass, her head spraying its long yellowish hair into Lancelot's lap. His hand dallied with her tresses, delicately yet enticingly.

"But it is not fair to be a critic, who cannot be criticized!" His voice was of a rich timbre and now was full of good humor . . . and a deep wanting that she'd not heard before.

"You don't need flattery, Lancelot," she whispered with breathy expectation. "You have my heart already. Have I not told you?"

"Nothing to do with flattery, Elain." She stared up and found his haunted ocean-blue eyes staring up at the shards of lesser blue through the tree limbs that were the sky. It was a gaze that had always been his, from the moment she set eyes upon this fevered soul. As though pain of the spirit was his lot in life.

Oh, she thought, with girlish intensity, *let him worship me with his pain soon. And may the pain melt into fulfillment and happiness with the application of my love. . . .*

For she had that in abundance.

Staring up at his finely chiseled features, she felt as though she had known the lines of that face all her life. Known this man and wanted him, always. The Latin prose and poetry that were the heritage of the long-gone Romans, she had devoured with longing, and now she understood the powerful emotions behind the longing words of poets.

He was silent for a while, and his eyes lost the look they got when he stared at her body. It was time that he be reminded of her presence, lest she lose this moment. She was never one to shirk opportunity, not to pin the blame for one of her harmless pranks on servants, and certainly not in winning this brave captain.

"Hey, up there, remember me?"

"Oh," he said, speaking softly. "I was just thinking about this wall." He pointed casually. "Walls are built to keep things out. I wonder what."

"Or to keep things in. I've felt a prisoner of this wall all my life." She raised her slender arms. "I want to be a bird and soar away. Visit lands like your home. Be free and alive."

"You have enough life for two women," said Lancelot. "I thank you for lending me some for my healing."

"I have more to give, dear Lancelot." She nuzzled her nose lovingly in his thigh. "Oh, you were like a broken-winged falcon when they brought you to my father's house. I feared for your life."

"Your warmth and your companionship healed me, Elain. Knowing that in my sea of insanity I could reach out to an island of security."

"I've not asked you this before. Was it very terrible, wandering so?"

"I remember little of it to be truthful. First, I merely wandered, dazed but not mad. And then a kind of fever took hold. The first face I remember seeing was yours."

"And what, pray tell, was that like?"

"Like waking to find my disregarded Christian heaven true and me in it, eye to eye with an angel."

She sighed. "Ah, I wish I were sure your heart were in your words, Lancelot. I have grown to love you so."

With a burst of spontaneity she pulled herself to her knees and mashed her lips against his. The stubble of his beard was harsh, and the woolens he wore were rough. Yet all she felt were the lips . . . at first unresponding . . . then suddenly alive, returning the kiss with vigor.

They parted for breath, and Elain's arms flew desperately around his neck, pulling his hairy head gently into the valley of her breasts, stroking his back softly and tenderly.

His presence seemed so unbearably intense, yet so rapturously sensual that she could barely control herself. It was a scene from the softest fantasy, sunbeams streaming like bars of silver through jade leaves, dappling the ground with light, depth, and texture.

Drunk with desire, she pulled impatiently at his jerkin. His sheathed dagger probbed stiffly on her abdomen as she moved. He chuckled throatily, eyes owning a peculiar haze, distancing them. "Here, calm yourself. You are inexperienced. It is not good if it is fast. It must be slow."

She nodded, an obedient pupil.

Pushing her back gently, Lancelot commenced to remove his clothing. First, the belt with its hardwood hilted weapon that clanked dully upon an exposed root. Then the dun leather tunic. The jerkin beneath, released and bulky, could not hide the fine form.

Elain swallowed, hardly noticing how dry her mouth had become. A twinge of fear moved inside her. What had she gotten herself into? It was one thing to dream—but to live out her dreams . . . well, that was something altogether different. Like when she had first climbed that expansive old oak on the forest's verge and had thought, how sublime to fall through the air like a bird. She had done it, not reckoning with the bruises and bumps that accompanied the jump. What awaited her beyond *this* plunge?

Lancelot seemed so big and overpowering, almost threatening. And yet simultaneously with her trepidation came a thrill of anticipation and of bold desire.

Hands on the bottom of his woolen jerkin, about to pull it off, he suddenly stopped as he noticed her entranced stare.

"You're supposed to take off yours, too."

She blinked.

He chuckled, head flung back with mirth. "Ah, my sweet young girl. You're too innocent for me, I fear." A mischievous glint in his eye, he reached down again for his tunic.

Elain protested. "I am *not*! I'll have you know that my cousin Boric and I have explored each other thoroughly in this selfsame spot!"

"How old were you?"

"What difference does that make?" She looked down, pouting. Grudgingly she murmured, "Nine years old."

"And he younger, I dare say." With casual, patient warmth he came to her and held her close. "I will take what you offer, for my soul has shrunk and needs the love you have in abundance." From the corner of her eye she could see his mouth twitch. "And in return I promise to give you what little love I have remaining."

"That is all I can ask, all I do ask, Lancelot," she replied sincerely.

"Then shall I help you with your apparel, my dear damosel?"

She smiled up at him brightly. "If I may help you with yours!" A note of eagerness crept into her voice. He laughed softly and nodded assent.

He let her pull the jerkin from his torso.

It slipped off like a tight glove, leaving his chest bare. She fingered the worst of several scars there, cooing with sympathy. At the sight of his partial nakedness desire swept her up in a cool fire.

Not that she had not seen him unclothed before. In nursing him and in bathing his fevered body she had seen him unclothed many times. But now—now his body was vibrant with life. Every movement was pure Lancelot, and to her he was the mystery and challenge of fulfillment.

With deft skill he removed her bright berry-red outer gown, leaving only her ankle-length under-tunic. The rubbing motion inflamed her, and it was but the work of a moment for her to kick off her leather shoes, fling off the gray tunic, and stand before him, proudly nude.

He bit his lip as his eyes wandered down the sleek roundness of her body. He saw what all the young male servants had hoped to ogle, all the lecherous men who lived within her sphere had tried to touch in their unwelcomed embraces.

As for Elain, seeing the soul of this wondrous man

come forth, she knew total love. She gloried in the desire that showed in his expression.

Lancelot slipped off his boots, his breeches, and, still standing, he held her, long and loving, almost melding with her.

In a few moments, the thought came to her that somehow Lancelot had not removed his dagger. When she looked down and discovered the true reason for the hardness against her thigh, she felt giddy astonishment.

Murmuring in his enchanting native language, sweet loving words, he lowered her onto the grass atop her long full tunic. "Are you cold, dear one?" he asked, reaching for his tunic to cover her with.

"No," she responded. "No, your warmth is enough."

He smiled easily at that. Covering her body with his broad strong body, he covered her neck with light kisses that sped shivers down her back.

She sighed and filled his curly hair with kisses. Gently she nibbled upon his ear, and his pleasured sound of response trebled her own pleasure.

Passion soon roughened his considerate touch and heightened the intensity of her need. Need for *what* she was not certain, but the ache was excruciatingly exciting and demanding. Sensing her pitch of excitement, Lancelot propeled it further, nibbling at her large breasts, nipples long since hard and receptive.

His hold was firm yet pliant, demanding yet considerate, rough yet subtle enough that the nuances of his love art were not lost upon her.

If there had been any reserve before in her young self, she lost it now, rapidly. Surrendered it, to his skillful manly caresses.

Any fear she'd owned rapidly turned to ecstasy at Lancelot's ardor. His was a busy mouth, a rapid and insistent pair of hands; loving eyes and cooing words flowed like warm water.

He hardly needed to guide her hands and mouth to the places that pleased him, for they went their way willfully and hungrily.

When the moment neared for their joining it was Elain who cried out for it, demanded it, pleaded for it, guided her lover's instrument to its final destiny.

As he plunged into her she felt a brief moment of exquisite pain, and then she was back into the rhythm of their duet. Her heart hammered. The liquidity and ease of their love matched the silent movements of the puffy clouds in the sky. A robin fluttered in the swaying leaves that echoed the rustle of her muted gasps.

Under Lancelot's skillful thrusts and pauses, her sensations suddenly began to draw inward, centered on his point of entry . . . and then exploded outward through her body.

She gazed up, certain that this marvelous man was spent; yet still he continued, eyes half-closed in concentration. And once more the cresting commenced, and she wrapped her arms around his strong neck and began to answer his movements with her own.

Much later, when they were finished, she lay resting in his arms. He dozed lightly, his passion subsided into gentle snores.

She lay there, awake and aware in his encompassing warmth. A tear slipped down her cheek.

It had been so wonderful, but then, at his moment of ecstasy, Lancelot had uttered a name that was not hers.

"Guinevere!"

In that moment she had tried to steal the pain from him with the delight she gave him, but failed.

She smudged away the tear with her hand.

The next time, she promised herself, the name on his lips would be Elain.

XV

The melting of summer into fall was long and liquid.

Suddenly, for Elain, the land of her birth owned the element it had lacked. The beauty of the rolling land had been a beauty without structure, without soul. But with Lancelot as the frame through which she viewed it, with his spirit and laughter and melancholy as context, the countryside became a masterpiece.

The two of them, hand in hand, took long walks, and Elain named each tree and flower and animal they saw. They bathed in cool streams and lazed in the warm sun for long hours. They picked gooseberries and jammed them for picnic bread. They talked endlessly.

Something great portended with this man; Elain felt truly one with him. All seemed right with this man from Gaul; he fitted into Britain as he fitted into her.

One day, while she was dreaming amongst a garden ledge, her father found her. His mouth was firm beneath his white-spiked beard. "You have been seeing much of Lancelot, child."

She gazed out dreamily to where her lover helped prepare for the coming harvest. "Yes, Father."

"I like him," the King of the Wall said. "There is a greatness in the man. But he is not one of us, Elain. He is of a foreign land. He thinks differently. He is not rooted to this earth as we are. Do not become too attached, Elain. He is recovered now. There is no telling when he will depart."

"Father," she said, looking at him directly. "There is something in Lancelot beyond our comprehension. Beyond his greatness." She gestured out to the fields. "He is a harbinger of things to come. Can I but be drawn to him?"

Ulric sighed and placed a fatherly hand on her shoulder. "I have always let you have your way, and in this way have I been weak. I wish I were not so." He looked out to the fields. "I wish he had not come."

A haze riffled the distance. The sun was mellow bright. It shone in Elain's eyes. She shaded them with a small hand, searching for Lancelot in the distance. Waiting for his return. . . .

No. He was her life now. She felt her abdomen. Something greater than the two of them was forming within her, beyond her understanding, but not beyond her awe.

Life would be meaningless without her Lancelot.

xvi

Some two months later Lancelot was working in the smithy at Ulric's fort, when the red-bearded king sought him out.

The young Gaul was bare to the waist, dripping with sweat from the heat of the furnace. He laid a glowing red bar on the anvil, then put down the tongs and hammer he had been using to work the metal into a blade. The physical labor was helping to restore his failed strength. It also took his mind off Elain, whom he had much guilt about. Despite all his warnings, she still believed she might win his love—

"There's a messenger from the high king," Ulric informed him. "The Saxons have pushed north and west of Londinium again. Arthur needs every man."

"I've told you before, my lord," Lancelot said. "I won't go back."

"*Every* man," Ulric repeated.

Lancelot shouted, "*No*! I couldn't face—"

He broke off the sentence. A sense of despair overwhelmed him, akin to that which had brought on his mad flight from Cam. In his mind he saw Excalibur shimmering—

"We will ride in the morning," Ulric said quietly.

His face lined with pain, Lancelot said, "I will need a mount."

xvii

In the clamor of the courtyard Lancelot found Elain and drew her around the corner of the buttery for a moment's privacy.

How tall and splendid he looked! the girl thought, hiding her sadness.

"I never thought this hour would come," he told her. "But I realize I was wrong. Years ago, in Gaul, I made a pledge to fight at the high king's side whenever he needed me—"

"I understand. I also know there's another reason you're going back. I've thought a good deal about what you told me that day at the wall. There's only one woman who would be out of reach of a captain as famous as you. It's the queen you love, isn't it—?"

"Don't." He kissed her quickly. "I've loved you too, Elain—"

"But not in the same way. Never in the same way." Her voice breaking, she cried, "God keep you safe—!"

She ran, disappearing around the corner of the building.

A short time later she watched from a window of the long house as a hundred mounted men rode out. Her father's white-shot beard caught the sunlight, there beside Lancelot so strong and splendid in his new mail and leather armor—

One of Elain's women, a toothless, palsied old creature with melancholy eyes, slipped to her side.

"Mistress? Did you speak to him about—?"

"The child?" She shook her head. "I could never put that kind of chain on him. For a week or two I really thought I could make him fall in love with me. Then I realized the hope was false—"

She whirled. "But when the child is born, if it's a male child, I want it sent to him, so he can be proud of our love."

The old woman blinked. "You speak as if you won't be here to see to it yourself, mistress—"

Elain turned away. Her eyes misted as the last of the mounted men galloped through the gate.

"Childbirth is difficult," she whispered. "There is no knowing what could happen."

CHAPTER 11

Elain

The battle was dying.

The fierce war cries and clankings of sword and shield faded into silence. Groans of the wounded sounded from time to time.

Lancelot's sword swung at the Saxon.

The duel-dulled metal chopped a slice of wood from the bloody man's shield. With his own nicked sword the Saxon thrust toward Lancelot's chain-mailed chest.

The fighting had started when the sun had been high and hot. Reddened now, as though with blood, the sun neared its setting.

Lancelot parried. The enemy's sword tip scraped the chain mail, ripping a link.

The Saxon wheezed with exertion.

As usual Arthur's men had been outnumbered. The Saxons, in a large, unruly band had been driving toward Mount Badon. If allowed farther inland, important centers of commerce would have been overtaken, ruined. It was their most concerted attack yet from the lands they owned in the South.

But the barbarians rode puny horses. Horses, as often as not, without saddles—and even the saddles had no stirrups. A light tap tumbled them to ground.

Arthur's well-trained force, however, was mounted

upon the well-bred horses descended from the noble steeds the Celt leader had obtained from Gaul.

Determination, and King Arthur's tactics of attack and retreat, attack and retreat, contributed toward the wearying but successful halt of the invasion.

But the battle had not ended: the blood-crazy Saxons did not seem to realize they'd been soundly beaten.

Lancelot gritted his teeth and swung his sword with all his might. The stench of death had filled him with anger. He wished to be done with this for the day.

Caught off guard, the Saxon had barely time to hoist his shield. Even so, Lancelot's blow was only slightly averted. The flat of his blade thwacked across the Saxon's temple. Stunned, the Saxon staggered a moment, then tumbled.

Lancelot checked the final cut. He had killed so many men today. He did not care to raise the tally. His philosophy had changed much since his early days of battle by Arthur's side. The softness that Guinevere and Elain had placed in his soul halted the blow a younger Lancelot might deliver.

Bloodshot eyes staring up in challenge, the half-conscious Saxon stank of sweat and fear.

The tip of his sword pressing against the warrior's belly, Lancelot leaned over and addressed the man.

"I should slice you in half, villain."

The Saxon gave a half-hearted snarl of defiance. "We do what we do. We are what we are. Now kill me and I will join my fallen brethren in the halls of the gods."

"Where you fight every day?" laughed Lancelot humorlessly. "What a life. Or death. No, cur. You are to be a prisoner. We will civilize you if we have to beat the notion into you." Lancelot gestured at the gore-soaked plain. Nearby, a headless body sprawled, abuzz with flies. Ripped limbs lay scattered. "This island is sopped with spilled blood, barbarian. Blood is no good to it unless still in a human body. One day we will be one nation, Saxon. No more swords will be raised except in play." He gazed about again. Defeated, the last of the Saxons were making their retreat.

Lancelot reached down and pulled the man up. "Come. Your bondage will not be so bad. We should try to understand one another."

The Saxon spat in contempt. But still he gave himself up to Lancelot.

Astride a black charger, Arthur himself rode up. His spurs jingled. Excalibur was sheathed in blood. The great king's back was stooped. His eyes owned a deep sorrow and resignation.

"We have won a great victory this day, my lord," cried Lancelot. "The tide, perhaps, is turning!"

The king nodded wearily. "Let us pray so." He perked up and reined in, steadying his fretful horse. "But what do you have here, my friend? A live Saxon, in your hands? You have changed, dear Lancelot. You generally only cart back the heads!" The king's face brightened, and his eyes for the first time showed a trace of hope.

"I did not think it necessary. We should take more prisoners." He shook his head and gestured to the south. "They are too many to destroy or drive away now. Perhaps it is time to tame them. Make them a part of our dream." He grabbed the Saxon by his shirt, shook him slightly. "We could learn some of their stubbornness, no?"

Arthur's head flung back, and he gave a good long laugh. "It is good to have you back again, Lancelot. Good indeed." He leaned over confidentially. A gleam shone in his eye. "But do I detect the hand of a woman in your heart?"

Taken aback, Lancelot blinked. Did he mean Guinevere? But no, of course not. The gleam was of humor.

"I do admit that I have met someone who has expressed interest, Arthur." He cleared his voice. "In the lands of Ulric."

"Yes. Ulric did mention a comely daughter." Arthur sighed deeply. Then surveyed the ruins of battle. In the midst of the havoc the dragon banners, though tattered, still flew, fluttering in the eventide breeze. "We must take stock of our losses and rally for tomorrow's drive. Take this young Saxon to Gawain. He'll find some useful work for him. We have earned a hearty meal, Lancelot. I will see you 'round the night's campfire to share it with you."

Spurring the horse, Arthur rode away to where his warriors were regrouping.

At swordpoint Lancelot prodded the Saxon toward the Celt's encampment, through charred underbrush burned by Saxon torches. He himself was smudged with smoke, smelled of it.

The sullen Saxon remained silent.

Lancelot thought back upon what Arthur had said. Had he indeed changed? Fatigue heavy on his bones, he ached for Elain's soothing touch.

Elain. He had used her ill, he knew. He did not love her, nor could he love any woman after Guinevere. As the sinuous, sensuous memories of Elain's touch and love unwound in his mind, though, he yearned for them again, despite the guilt that he felt about her.

The Saxon tripped and fell headfirst into a briar patch. Lancelot helped him out carefully and for the first time noticed the blood oozing from a wound beneath the man's arm. The man could barely walk with his weakness. And he had fought like a madman, with that wound! Lancelot had to admire his bravery.

"We'll have to see to that cut, soldier," he said. Thoughts of Elain retreated. As long as Arthur needed him, he would fight . . . he could not shirk his duty. Not for the sake of some woman. Not even for the sake of himself.

He slipped a gloved hand under the Saxon's arm to help him along.

ii

She walked the Roman wall in bright sunlight, almost a year after the time she had come here with Lancelot and then taken him to the grove.

Her heart breaking, she thought of the babe in the cradle. She'd kissed and touched the child before slipping from the fort at dawn.

The boy was strong. He squalled endlessly, a sign of a bold, manly character. She had christened him with a brave name too—Galahad. The old woman would see to his delivery to her beloved captain. According to couriers reaching the district, Lancelot had recently fought alongside her father and the high king, successfully turning back a Saxon tide.

Slowly Elain moved to the edge of the wall. Far below, great blocks lay tumbled—the remains of another stair that had collapsed. The blocks looked tiny. But she saw the countless sharp corners thrusting up—

She stared at those blocks but saw only Lancelot's face. Thank God he was still alive. For a brief time she had even hoped he might come back to her—

Foolishness. Vain foolishness. But when his son was brought to him, he would know, for all time, how deeply she had loved him.

Elain closed her eyes. The wind on her cheeks was almost like his caress.

She closed her eyes so that she could hold his image until the last instant. Her face bright with tears, she stepped off the edge of the wall above the cruel rocks.

iii

The sun set upon a land smeared with blood.

Lancelot kneeled by the gurgling river, close to the ford where King Arthur had made his stand. He splashed water over his face, washing off the blood. He would have liked to drink long and deep from the river, but much fighting had occurred. Bodies bobbed in the shallows. Severed legs, hands, and heads floated slowly downstream. The river was pink with blood.

Sighing, Lancelot squinted at the coming night, wrapping the landmark of Mount Badon in its cloak of dark.

He had never seen the like of this battle. No, not in his many days of fighting.

It had been Arthur's greatest victory.

The Saxons had been woefully tricked. Thinking that Arthur's army was complete in its encampment by the river ford, they had attacked full force.

Immediately the armies that had once been King Lot's, and the army of King Ulric swept down from their various hiding places amongst those rolling hills, outflanking the Saxon force and finally surrounding it.

The numbers were approximately even, but under Arthur's well-worked-out strategy and superior position the British armies had won the day.

But it had been a long and bitter struggle.

Lancelot ached. Oh, God, he ached. How many times had his sword swung this day?

How many hairs did a man have on his head?

He struggled to his feet, pulling himself up by bracing upon his bloody, dulled sword. Yearning to find the warm campfire that would surely be built soon and longing to fill his belly with some sort of food, he staggered through the body-strewn field.

Yes, a great victory, Lancelot assured himself. The Saxons had been routed. Destroyed. It would take years for them to reform . . . and by that time Arthur's strength would be such that their threat could be easily turned away.

Years of peace awaited, thanks to the great battle of this day.

Thanks to King Arthur.

But a deep sickness lay in Lancelot's belly. He could not believe that at one time he had gloried in battle. Welcomed it like he had welcomed his many lovers. Now he hated it. If he did not raise his sword again, he would not be sorry.

Picking his way clumsily over the dead and dying, the hopelessly wounded, the men, Briton and Saxon, gurgling their lives into the rich sod, Lancelot could not stanch the tears of weariness from coursing down his cheeks.

If he were forced into one more duel, he knew he could not bear up. He had been cut five times this day, once seriously. Blood soaked his tunic.

Etched in stark relief on a rise just ahead, stood a figure. A man, serenely surveying the scene of the great slaughter, perched upon a horse.

Lancelot recognized the breed of horse. It was descended from the lot that Arthur had purchased in Gaul. How long ago all that seemed. Years and lives away. They had just been boys then, he and Arthur. Strong-headed, willful boys, unaware of the pain and tragedy that would mark their lives.

How blissful had been that ignorance.

Spurred on by the refreshing memory Lancelot trudged up the rise, ignoring the stench of the foulness around him. He stared at the figure before him, and he recognized it.

Not by the man's helmet, not by his tattered cuirass did Lancelot recognize him. Not by the features, blurred in the descending mist. The posture of the man was slumped, speaking of a great burden, a surmounting weariness.

But firm and straight in his hand he held his weapon. Sharp and ready as always, it jutted up in his grasp over the battlefield, proclaiming this proud victory, like a staff of life and death transforming into the scepter of this isle.

It was by the sword that Lancelot recognized the man. As he drew near he cried, "Arthur!" It was a strong but ragged gasp—a clutching for the foundation of strength to be had in this great man.

King Arthur turned troubled eyes toward him—and those eyes brightened perceptively. "Lancelot! Man, are you well?"

"I confess, a few swords have tasted of my flesh," answered Lancelot, drawing up to his side. "But I will mend."

Arthur reached down and put his hand upon his captain's broad shoulder. "Lancelot, but for your presence I do not think we could have fought so hard. Your fighting was example to us all. Your courage stirred our hearts. I thought when the first wave of Saxons assaulted our line that the men would break and retreat. It was a fearsome sight." He shook his head, smiling a small smile. "What made you break file and rush to meet them single-handedly?"

Lancelot placed his own hand upon Arthur's and held it firmly. "I wished to get this business over with, my friend."

"And so it is, Lancelot. We have won a staggering victory this day." Arthur looked up into the coiling fog, burnished with the reds and yellows of sunset. "We have routed the cream of their men today. The rest of our country will flock under my command, now, seeing this victory." Vigor and pride filled the voice. "We will have peace for a long while, Lancelot. A good long while, thanks to this day. The light will remain!"

"It is an honor to serve you, my lord."

Arthur stared down at him sternly. "We serve a greater master than ourselves . . . or each other, Lancelot. We serve our glory and our honor as Britons. We serve what we have built up in the cruel and bloody world—a monument to the dignity of mankind."

A sort of transcendent pride filled Lancelot's breast. A joy beyond comprehension. Something filled his throat. A tear dripped from his eye.

They had worked and suffered so long for this day, and now the victory was theirs!

Overwhelmed his legs weakened, and he sank to his knees, head bowed. "I kneel not to who you are, Arthur," he said in a choking voice. "But to what you represent."

"I would that Merlin were here to see this day," murmured Arthur. "More than anyone else it was that determined druid that made the spirit of Britain endure to this day . . . and beyond it."

A solemn stillness swept over them.

Awe awoke in Lancelot as he stared out over the misty moors, the dewy green of this island. A fierce love burned in him for this, his adopted land.

He stared out upon the field, manured by the blood of Saxon and Briton, and saw that great things would grow from this day. It would be called the battle of Badon Hill, and it would be a hallmark of history.

The sky darkened with the absence of the sun. The fog bank grew heavier, blanketing the scene of the battle like a swathe of warming wool. It moiled and wisped in the valley below Lancelot's eyes, a thing of mystery and profundity.

A man walked out of it, toward them, streamers of mist spiraling away from him as he climbed the hill. In his arms was a small bundle of what appeared to be blankets. His measured step told the gravity of his mission.

Lancelot stood, hand to his sheathed sword. Called out: "Who approaches?"

The man did not answer. His steady march up the hill did not hasten or slow. A hood concealed his features.

Lancelot unsheathed his sword. "Halt. Come no farther without telling us your mission."

The cowled man stopped some feet away from Lancelot and Arthur. Slowly he uncovered what he held in his arms.

A baby.

The child slept peacefully, his face mild and beatific. A serenity hovered about him, a palpable feeling.

"Who is this child?" asked Arthur, his voice showing how moved he was with the baby's beauty.

The dark-robed man pronounced the name with reverence. "His name, sire, is Galahad."

Unable to halt himself Lancelot drifted toward the

man and the baby. As he approached the baby awoke and stared up with wondering, intense blue eyes. Lancelot lifted his hand to its face. The baby grabbed his forefinger in a strong, possessive grip and gurgled with a joy that shone in its eyes.

"He is a wonderful baby," murmured Lancelot.

"You may hold him," said the man.

He handed over the bundle of baby and blanket.

"Whose child is this?" asked Arthur, peering closer to see the child better in the fitful light of a nearby torch. "Is he an orphan of this battle? If so, he will have a home in my home."

"No, my lord, he is no orphan," said the man. "He was brought from the north this day to be with his father."

Lancelot, involved with gentle play with the bairn, said, "Why is this?"

"His mother has taken her own life."

"Come, come, man," complained Lancelot sharply. "You speak in generalities. Who are this baby's parents?"

"The mother, my lord," spoke the man solemnly, "was called Elain. The father is yourself. It is your child, my lord Lancelot. *Your* child."

The baby burbled softly, holding up its arms toward Lancelot.

A shudder ripped through him—a cold that penetrated his very soul. "No," he said, staring down at the babe in disbelief. "No." And then he saw Elain in those loving eyes, saw her soft features in the face. Sudden tears blurred his vision.

"Oh, God, no!" he cried, clutching the baby up in his embrace, burying his shame in its little body. Galahad wrapped his arms about Lancelot's neck, almost comfortingly.

"The women at Cam will look after him, Lancelot," said Arthur, dismounting to try to assuage the grief.

"Elain!" murmured Lancelot. "Why? Why didn't you *tell* me!"

He looked up again to entreat the cowled man to tell him that this news was not true.

But the man was gone.

Dark, consuming mist folded into the place where he had been, like floating grave shrouds, falling.

CHAPTER 12

Galahad

Lancelot stood in the stables, admiring the sleek new colt that one of his mares had foaled. A wonderful beast, full brown with one dove-white spot over its left eye. He saw that its mother, nickering over her new son, had a full portion of feed. She had provided his son Galahad a fine stallion to ride upon.

And speaking of Galahad, he thought, *where could the lad have gotten to?* He'd done a pretty slipshod job of brushing down the twenty horses that Lancelot kept in this stable at Cam, adjoining his own newly built home. Lancelot would let it pass this time. But he did want to impress upon the eleven-year-old the importance of grooming a fine horse. "Son, if they know you're taking care of them correctly, you've a lifelong companion. Horses have made the kingdom of King Arthur what it is. Horses and trained riders. Thus have we beaten back the Saxons!"

Although Galahad thought that truly fine, he seemed to take more interest in the odd things that went on in his head than in the hard realities of life.

A clopping of feet sounded outside the wall.

"To the hills, men! The fairy princess must be saved!" called a voice cracking with approaching adolescence. "And don't forget the magic swords!"

Lancelot shook his rough shock of slightly grayed hair. That boy. He'd better go catch him before he frightened a bunch of sheep again and Lancelot had to answer a fresh batch of complaints from distressed shepherds.

He paced out the door through the spread hay, kicking up spumes of straw dust. The homey smells soothed his nerves, adding to his sense of well-being.

If he had not had Galahad to raise, his life would have been one of pure despair. But the boy saw so much in the smallest things . . . it had revived Lancelot's sense of wonder in this barbaric world. Gave him some hope for the future of humanity.

All the same, the boy was as exasperating as they came.

Lancelot leaned around the wooden door. There was the lad, sidling away against the wall, holding his chipped wooden sword. His hair was a light brown, with blond highlights. He moved with the grace of a speeding turtle, thought Lancelot ruefully, although he did take to sword lessons well. It was that extra fat on the lad. He liked food as much as he liked tall stories.

Sneaking up behind him, Lancelot grabbed him by both arms. "Got you!" he roared.

Galahad flailed, crying out, "Never, foul Green Knight. No torture will unleash the secrets within me!"

Lancelot let the boy go. Galahad wheeled around, sword at the ready.

"So, my friend. Who is this dastardly Green Knight?"

"The bane of Arthur's round table!" proclaimed the freckle-faced boy. "He inhabits an enchanted fort to the north and keeps three beautiful women to do his bidding. Gawain is there now, but I can't figure out what's going to happen to him. You know how Gawain likes beautiful women, Father. They might conquer him with their charms and leave him at the mercy of the Green Knight. What do you think, Father?"

"Hadn't you better consult Gawain on that subject?

I'm sure he would not appreciate having tales made up about him and beautiful succubi while his wife still wields a heavy blow."

"Oh, Father, don't spoil it! Don't you see?" His eyes bulged enthusiastically. "I'm using the essences in these stories. I'm sure Gawain would rather be remembered as a lover and a fighter than as the hen-pecked husband he is."

"And you would rather live in your dreams than with the truth!" accused his father, shaking a finger. "You've caused no end of trouble with your stories about Merlin. And Excalibur! Taken from a hand sprouted from a lake? What absolute nonsense."

Galahad stamped his foot, face red. "How do you know? You weren't around then, Father. You were off in Gaul then."

"No, I was there by King Arthur's side. Not fighting sea serpents, which is the story you like to tell."

"Sea serpents—no! You were saving beautiful kidnapped women from the clutches of evil kings," Galahad declared.

"Ah, Galahad, you know well that those beautiful maidens would be in more danger from me than from anyone."

"Is that how I was born, Father?" Galahad asked innocently.

Lancelot sighed. "Yes. Something like that, Son." He tousled the lad's hair fondly. "So. What are you doing today?"

Galahad shrugged. "Looking for adventure, I suppose. Things have been a bit boring since I killed that two-headed giant last week."

"Ah, yes!" pronounced Lancelot, nodding his head sagely, playing along. "The one that didn't die until you'd chopped it into little pieces."

"Yes, sir. This island is crawling with monsters, dwarfs, fairies, and magic. It's a lot of work being a great hero."

"Well, great hero," said Lancelot, patting the boy's shoulder. "Make sure you're back by sunset. Magory tells me that that's suppertime."

"Not mutton again, I hope. That's all she cooks, Father! Can't we get another servant?"

"One that doesn't mother you so much, eh?" Lancelot smiled. "Maybe I'll be able to scare up some wild game for tonight's pot. I'm thinking about going for a hunt. Like to come along?"

Galahad shook his head. "No."

"You're going to have to start hunting sometime if you don't want mutton all your life. You just can't dream up your dinner, Son."

Sighing, Galahad said, "I handle weapons well enough."

"But you need practice on things other than beasts of your imagination."

Galahad pursed his lips, taking this thought in seriously. "I suppose you're right. But not today." He turned and strode away, his wooden sword slung over a shoulder. "See you at supper, Father."

"Watch out for monsters, Son."

With a gay lilt to his step Galahad departed for the wilds surrounding the fort upon the river Cam.

Spring had taken the land fully, drawing up dandelions from the grasses, trilling song from the birds, soft warmth down from the sun.

This was the golden and green time that Lancelot loved most of the seasons of Britain. There was such a lush richness here to spring that lasted longer than in Gaul. The colors were deeper, more vibrant, as though the residue of late winter fogs had watercolored them painstakingly.

The years since Badon Hill had passed slowly and for the most part peacefully. Arthur had consolidated his position as high king. Now the majority of Britons and Celts of the British Island called him king and prospered in the peace that he had brought.

It had been a golden time.

The Saxons seldom troubled the borders to the east and south. The Picts still raided the north from time to time and the Scots the east from their wooden ships. But these were only minor annoyances.

Now the Britons, under their King Arthur, had faith in themselves and in their land. A faith that burned in the warriors that beat back the barbarians time after time after time. So strong was the record of success that the attacks had diminished greatly, giving Britain time to grow and to become more powerful—a single nation.

Surely the dream of King Arthur—and of Lancelot—was very close.

But there had been a price to pay for Lancelot and Arthur—a dear one.

Lancelot had sacrificed to Arthur what Arthur could never have—and the subject of the sacrifice surely suffered as much as both of them.

Lancelot still saw Guinevere on occasions. But only public occasions when other people—particularly Arthur—were able to note how controlled were their actions toward each other. How placid, how civilized. And yet they could never know the torture of sitting next to the woman you loved at some banquet, chatting with her amiably . . . and knowing that she was not yours, could *never* be yours despite the great passion between you. Each gesture she made resounded in his soul, recalling the short days they had been true lovers. Each tilt of the head, each soft moving of those exquisite lips. . . .

If anything, Guinevere was more beautiful now than she had been when she had first given herself to Lancelot. In maturity her soul had bloomed. Lancelot found it almost unbearable to gaze upon her person—and yet could not help himself. He was a moth to her flame, and although he burned he could not help but revel in her light.

Lost in his thoughts he stared dreamily out upon the fields. It had been upon such a day as this that they had last made love. . . .

Lancelot closed his eyes, and the sensations of memory crowded in once more upon his senses.

The taste of her breasts.

The sound of her sighs, soft as breezes through the grass that was their bed.

The arch of her back.

The feel of her tender skin.

The depths of her eyes that swallowed him up in their gentle gasping love.

A lover's bittersweet memory: that which once had could never be had again.

Yet the agony was that, although the possibility of love fulfilled was dead, the lovers were yet alive, flesh and blood ghosts of desire to each other.

Lancelot bit his knuckle, hard, and fought back the tears for yet another time. *No,* he thought. *No good remembering. No good. . . .*

"Afternoon!"

The voice startled Lancelot.

He opened his eyes and looked around.

Before him stood a young girl of perhaps twelve years old. Her eyes were a piercing, endlessly questioning blue. She had quite long red hair—so long that it stretched the length of her back and then some, worn loose. Her face could have been of some precocious baby—or of a young woman.

"Good day to you, Ellanie," Lancelot said.

"Why are you sad?" She wanted to know.

"You are wise for your age," he said, feeling a little upset that the girl had glimpsed the agony he took such pains to conceal.

"My father says I'm a little pain. I suppose I say things I'm not supposed to."

"Are you looking for Galahad?"

A delighted smile of astonishment lit her face. "How did you know?"

"Oh, a little bird told me."

"I never heard of a bird talking. But yes, that's why I'm bothering you. Is he about?"

"He's off on one of his expeditions."

"Looking for monsters?"

"Or elves or dwarfs or fairies."

She shook her head. "I wish I could be around when he finds them. I never am, and he tells the most astonishing things about them."

"I dare say." Lancelot pointed. "I think if you headed out that way you might be able to spot him. Don't know if he'll want company, though."

She shrugged. "That's okay. He never does. But he needs it. Thank you."

"Tell me if you find any monsters," said Lancelot as the girl skipped away in the direction he had indicated.

"All right!" she called back.

Smiling, Lancelot turned back to look again upon his new colt, the memory of Guinevere pushed from his mind.

ii

What a *lovely* frog it was!

Modred peered over the top of the deep box in which he had placed the frog after his early morning hunting on the verges of his favorite pond. How he had searched for a fat, big bullfrog such as this one—one with a croak like froggy thunder, like Gawain's burp after a flagon of ale. And green as the fields of Britain. How appropriate!

But he'd gotten his breeches muddy in the process, sloshing about in the swampy fen. Modred did not care for getting wet. No. Someone would pay.

Yes, it would be the frog!

The bastard son of Arthur squatted behind one of the fort houses of Cam. The site afforded quite a wonderful view of the coursing river Cam, of the sweeping lush forests, of flowers and fields. But Modred was too attentive to his new prisoner to pay attention. The slim, well-dressed thirteen-year-old crouched enthusiastically over his prize, ready to embark on one of his many secret pleasures.

The bullfrog stared back at him with its usual stolid expression, bugged eyes moving not at all. Stupid frog! thought Modred. You'll be moving in a moment.

Quickly his hand darted down, grabbed the creature around its thick middle. It thumped against his hand, trying to get away, but Modred's grip was firm. He hefted the thing out. It squirmed delightfully, kicking its muscular legs wildly. Now *that* was more like it.

"Hold still, frog, and take your punishment!" Tongue protruding from his lips with concentration, Modred managed to slip a noosed end of some long twine about the juncture of the frog's webbed foot and its mottled leg. He pulled it tight, leashing his new pet. Then he let the bullfrog dangle from one leg, twirling most ludicrously.

Modred laughed.

He let the frog drop to the grass. It tried to hop away, but it could only get so far before Modred dragged it back. "You see, frog, I am destined to rule men! See my powers. I shall be a better king than my stupid father. But wait! The church says that before the true fun starts you must be cleansed of your sins. *Anomi domoni*, let the cleansing begin!"

Dark eyes brightened with malicious glee, he pulled the frog up into the air and walked with it to where he had built a small fire. Smoke twirled up from clutching flames about faggots of wood. "For your crimes, Lord Frog, for muddying my boots and pants, for not swearing allegiance to your most high king, Modred son of Cornwall, for profaning God with your blasphemous croaks, I sentence you first to a scourging of your sins by fire!"

The frog struggled, upside down, as though it understood what awaited.

Modred dipped it into the fire . . . (and so, Father, will *you* pay!) briefly.

The beast trebled its thrashings.

The sound of sizzling. A momentary stench of burned meat.

"The cleansing is finished. Your soul will fly to God upon the destruction of your body. Amen."

He lifted the frog out of the flame to inspect the damage. It was still alive; there was no question of that: it thrashed most lustily.

Its left forearm was oozing. The left eye was singed shut.

Glorious. "Praise the lord!" chortled Modred. "Another soul, saved to croak praise before your throne!"

He put the frog back down on the grass, where it sat, stunned, ballooning with deep breaths. Modred stared at it, frowning. "I know you hate me, frog. You all hate me. My father. His damnable men who whisper 'bastard' beneath their boozy breaths. His ugly, ugly wife who will not touch me. And all these stupid slovenly people of this pigsty! All despise me because I am different. I'm just smarter than you all, and you envy me. You torture me with your barbed words, your looks, and your contempt. But now I will torture *you*. You will pay for your lack of respect for Modred, your better!"

Giggling slyly he tugged on the twine. The frog shuddered, then hopped a fine hop. Gritting his teeth, Modred tugged hard on the leash. A tiny pop sounded: the bullfrog's leg broke. It flopped on the grass, rolled, then lay still.

"Don't die, frog," growled Modred. "I'm not finished with you." He leaned over, prodding the frog with a finger, screaming, "Don't die, damnit!"

The frog jerked spastically.

"That's right, Lord Frog. We have further games to attend to." Modred stroked his narrow chin, contemplating. His finger smote the air, aimed at the frog. "How would you like to die for the sins of all frogs, like Christ died for mankind? What? You've not heard of Jesus Christ? He was a very good man. But the Jews didn't like him. So they had the Romans do a very awful thing to him." Modred grinned, showing a fine white set of teeth below his thin, well-defined nose. "They crucified him. Now, I'm afraid I haven't got a cross, so we'll just have to improvise!"

He tugged up on the twine. The frog was pulled up in the air, twitching.

Modred sped to the wall of the wooden building. "Now, usually the Romans tied the victims to the cross with ropes. What? You don't know who the Romans were? They are the great race who civilized the Celts, whom my father worships. Yes—such wonderful people they were, raping and killing with much more efficiency than Saxons. Yes, that's right. They left us their written language. Latin. Just be glad I don't torture you with making you learn it, froggie. You really are most fortunate."

His eyes roamed about in search of proper materials. "Hmm. We'll just have to hang you upside down, like St. Peter."

He slipped out his dagger and stabbed it into the wood. It held. He wrapped the twine around the blade, letting the frog dangle against the wall.

"There, Lord Frog. Now I shall tell the rest of the story. First they stoned him." He picked up some pebbles from the ground. "No. Wait. Maybe they didn't." He shrugged. "Well, since I don't feel like getting you a crown of thorns, I'll just substitute a stoning. Any objection?"

The frog was quiet, thumping limply against the wall.

"I didn't think so."

Modred tossed pebbles at the frog, striking it as many times as he missed. "Now," he said. "They just let him sit for a while. To contemplate things."

Modred sat down beside the frog and sighed. "You know, you might not think so now, but I'm doing you a big favor. Life is pretty terrible. I wouldn't mind getting out of it myself."

He sighed deeply and covered his eyes with his hands. "I'm sorry, frog. I can't do this to them, so I've got to do it to you."

He was about to kill the frog with the dagger to end its suffering. But it was stiff and still.

Quite dead.

"Well, you'll make a good dinner for my dog," said Modred, taking the twine again in his hands to place the frog back in its box.

At that moment Guinevere walked around the corner.

"Modred," she said. "What have you got there? What have you been doing?" She wore a woolen walking dress, intricately embroidered, of robin's egg blue. A look of horrified consternation engulfed her face as she spotted the dead frog hanging in Modred's hand.

"Good day, Mother!" he piped with false cheerfulness.

"I asked you not to call me that, Modred," she said, attempting to control her temper. "What in God's name have you been doing behind this house?"

"I found a dead frog and thought fit to dispose of it. So as not to touch it I bound one leg in a noose and will now deposit it where its stink will not offend my lady's nose." He gave her a curt bow of the head.

Her eyes roamed around the fire, the dagger stuck in the wooden wall, stopping finally at the mangled, burned frog.

"You've been torturing innocent animals again, haven't you, Modred." Her eyes softened into a mixture of contempt and pity. "What is *wrong* with you, Modred, that you do such things? Why are you so spiteful of living things?"

"You jump to conclusions, Guinevere."

"No. No I don't. Your father will hear of this. He will do something to halt this . . . this atrocious behavior of yours."

"My father will do nothing!" snarled Modred. "I am the child of his loins. To admit that I am lacking in the qualities he would have in me is to admit to his own lacking. He is too proud for that, Guinevere, and you know it!" He sneered at her victoriously.

"I cannot believe that you are Arthur's son," exclaimed Guinevere, disgust marring her beautiful face, only slightly traced with wrinkles. "You act like a son of the devil!"

"Blasphemous witch!" cried Modred, upset. "How dare you!"

He flung the dead frog at her. It landed squarely on her shoulder, smearing the blue with bright red.

Horrified, Guinevere cringed, then, recovering, she gave Modred a look that turned his insides to fire.

"I will pray for you, Modred," she said simply.

Then she turned and walked away, remaining calm. She was going to tell Arthur, the foul bitch. And Arthur's temper might temporarily eclipse his reluctance to punish Modred.

That would be bad.

He knew what he had to do. An absence from these parts for a few days would allow Arthur to cool.

Hating Guinevere with a fierce passion, Modred jerked out his dagger, checked to see that his faithful pouch of gold coins was still on his belt, and then headed away toward the forest.

iii

Galahad swung his sword fiercely.

A gash opened in the troll's arm. Green blood geysered. It growled fiercely, rolling eyes the size of apples.

One more strike would destroy it!

"Galahad! Galahad!" The voice cried insistently from behind him. "What do you think you're doing?"

His attention diverted from the tree stump that had momentarily been a clutching nasty troll preying on local shepherd's sheep, Galahad's fantasy dissolved.

He turned. Oh, Lord. Not her.

Ellanie was running toward him, her long red hair billowing behind her, eyes wide with wonder. "Why in the world do you hit tree stumps with wooden swords,

Galahad?" Her sweet clear voice held genuine question. It was a voice that was used to questioning.

"Practicing," returned Galahad begrudgingly. He swiped at a bit of jutting tree fungus, snipping it off neatly. "See. I'm pretty good."

"What good are swords made out of wood?"

He shook his head, exasperated. "Silly. They're for practice. When I get my own sword, I'll know better how to handle it. Father doesn't like the idea of me carrying around a true sword yet."

"That's smart. You might hurt yourself."

"Who told you where I was?"

"Your father. Why shouldn't I know? You're not doing anything special."

"I am. I'm looking for adventure."

"Oh, good! Can I come along with you?" Ellanie asked. "I'm all through with my chores, and I've got nothing better to do."

"Adventures don't happen to girls," declared Galahad.

"How come?"

"They—they just *don't.*"

"But what about all your stories about princesses in towers, held prisoner by evil giants."

"Do you want to be held prisoner in a tower, Ellanie?"

"No."

"Then you shouldn't look for adventures."

"Can I come and watch then?" Her expression was sincerely hopeful. "I want to see one of your colored knights. The Black Knight sounds the most interesting."

"Absolutely not." He didn't care to let her in on the secret that every one of these encounters he had boasted of had been purely the product of his fertile imagination.

"I'll let you in on a secret if you'll let me," she said, smiling slyly, evidently confident of her secret's power over Galahad's curiosity.

"What secret?" Galahad demanded.

"I was walking in the west woods, by that stretch of small hillocks," she began. "Father doesn't like me going out there, but I think it's pretty."

"So. I've been there too."

"I found a cave."

"A cave? So? I've seen caves before."

She shook her red locks, smiling mysteriously. "You don't understand. There's something *in* this cave."

"Animals, probably."

"No. It's a trunk. A heavy trunk. With a chain binding it closed. I can't get it open. That's why I wanted to see you, Galahad; it might be important, and I knew you'd want to find out what it is."

Suspicion about her motives was rapidly swept away by a surge of joy. What could it be? Treasure? *How exciting*, the young boy thought. *A true adventure.*

"Where is it?" he asked eagerly.

"Not until you make a promise, Galahad," she said scoldingly.

"Yes, yes. What promise?"

"That whenever I'm free and you happen to be free too we can go out looking for adventure. Or you'll spend time with me, telling me your stories."

"You're always around when I tell my stories, Ellanie," he said.

"No. You don't understand. I want you to tell them to just *me*." She smiled charmingly.

"Very well. I promise. Now, where is this cave? What kind of trunk did it have?"

"It looked very old. Rusted hinges, you know. There is some sort of writing on it."

"Latin, probably. I can read that a bit."

"I wish they would teach me," said Ellanie with a disgruntled tone. "They never let me do anything much."

She was the daughter of Gareth by an affable Welsh seamstress. Most of Ellanie's time was spent home, sewing and embroidering. She was a cheerful, animated girl, with a curiosity that knew no bounds. She was forever asking questions of Galahad about the most obvious things. "What's a king for, Galahad?" Eyes blinking innocently. And: "How come you're male and I'm female?"

The most exasperating aspect of it was that he often found himself lacking an answer. Rather than admit that he didn't know, he made them up, like he made up his stories.

But secretly he enjoyed her company even though he would never tell anyone. After all he did have his reputation as a lad apart, an individual, a philosopher, and, above all, an untouchable loner. When the other children were about he regaled them with stories as though they were truths and reveled in their marvel and admiration.

And here finally was the possibility of a true adventure!

This was simply too good to pass up.

iv

Guinevere, queen of the Britons, felt sick to her stomach.

She marched through town, toward where she knew she would find Arthur. Something *had* to be done about that Modred!

The town perched on the hill above the river Cam had become quite a fortress in the past few years. The town, at Arthur's instructions, had been modeled after the towns the Romans had built in Britain.

Arthur was now in the town's baths he had ordered constructed.

Normally Guinevere would not have interrupted his solitude there, where he relaxed, thought, and planned. Now that Merlin was no longer around to lend guidance Arthur had become an even more thoughtful and burdened man. He deserved his time of rest. His thoughts were important. They had led his people to this plateau of peace, after all.

The baths consisted of one building housing many rooms, all given over to the cherished Roman custom of bathing. Through a gardened courtyard, one entered the *apodyteria*—or dressing rooms, where clothes were discarded. Next came the *frigidarium*, the cold room that was actually the last stop on the bathing route, a place where one bathed in cool water to acclimate to colder weather outside. After this was the *tepidarium*, which was just warm, and then the *caldarium*, the hot baths. During the course of a bath, which often took hours, one's body could be massaged by attendants, splashed with oils, and scraped with strigils.

Arthur had tried to keep things authentic.

Those who were privileged enough to use the bath hailed him for returning this most invigorating—and clean—custom.

Just entering the courtyard by the latrine, Guinevere spotted Arthur leaving the building.

How dignified he looked. How grim. Her heart welled with more than sympathy and respect for the man she had lived with these fifteen years.

Her heart was filled with a peculiar and yet wholesome love, one that had grown from the kernel of friendship, sprouting through awe and companionship into something far more. Although they did not sleep together, they had what Arthur jokingly called a platonic relationship. Their thoughts and wishes and dreams, their troubles and uncertainties they bared to each other, leaving them far more naked than mere lovers sharing a bed of desire. Arthur seemed to have grown accustomed to the fact that she did not love him that way; that no longer caused any tensions between them. He was father, brother, friend, and more to her.

And yet. . . .

And yet for all the wonderful things he had accomplished, despite the fact that he was a stout, courageous soul, he had one failing that he saw as a virtue.

Arthur of Britain was a very proud man.

Often, when he had drunk too much wine or ale at

the many feasts of rejoicing he gave, he would talk of his achievements as though they were just the beginning. This was the kingdom, he proclaimed, that would be a model for the nations. A system and achievement that would echo down the ages, a landmark in the civilization of men. He promised his captains of the round table that their names would be sung with praise throughout the centuries to come. The captains—Gareth, Gawain, Bedivere, Kay, and the rest—drank it all in like heady drink. At their feasts it was their wont to sit around till dawn, drinking and gorging and boasting of their various prowesses and courage, citing Saxon encounters, Pict battles, and Scot entanglements that may or may not have been true. Guinevere rather doubted Kay's boast, for example, that he had taken on twenty wild-eyed Picts single-handedly and had carved them all up within minutes.

"But, Kay, how can you say such things without witnesses?" she had asked.

"Witnesses? I told you, I was single-handed. The only witnesses were the Picts, and they are now quite dead, I assure you!"

What could she have said to that?

Only Lancelot refrained from the tendency to boast. He merely smiled and generally excused himself from such sessions. He had quite changed since Guinevere had first met him.

The haunted aspect of his character had taken over. The chains about his soul had taken their toll. Life had tried to drag him down, and although it had failed, he showed the marks of the struggle.

They spoke seldom, Lancelot and Guinevere—and when they did they only spoke of inconsequential matters. Nevertheless they still enjoyed the exchanges, despite the fact that their intercourse was never sexual.

Nonetheless from time to time Guinevere would turn about quickly and catch Lancelot staring at her with the old passion . . . eye-fire bespeaking his continual yearning for her.

At these times Guinevere had to avert her own eyes, lest the pyre light again within her own body. No, this could never be. And yet sometimes her dreams were vivid with him.

In spite of this she was rewarded for her faithfulness to Arthur. Her dear father Leodegrance had died some years back, and Arthur had inherited his lands and holdings, to the benefit of the kingdom. The strength it gave to his enterprise alone was worth the sacrifice that she had made so long ago.

But there was more. Where Merlin had gotten to no one knew. Galahad, that somber but funny storyteller who made up such wild tales, claimed that he had gone off to a magical land to bring back tools of sorcery to further aid Arthur. Often the boy would recount Merlin's latest adventure. He received news of these, he claimed most seriously, in his dreams. With the absence of Merlin, Arthur sought out Guinevere's advice on most matters. He claimed that she saw things with a kinder heart than his knights and that justice without a woman's conception of mercy was useless. Thus Guinevere felt useful and important in the scheme of things. Her life had meaning that it would not have owned without her station as Arthur's wife and queen.

All these things she was aware of as she strode to meet her husband, emerging from his time of rest and peace. She was also mindful of Modred's prediction concerning Arthur's response to Guinevere's complaint.

"Ah, Guin," said Arthur, face lighting with a warm smile upon seeing her. "How good to see you. I'm sorry I was not at breakfast this morning. I had to rise early to instruct the builders on new battlements."

"Arthur, I must speak to you on an important matter," she said somberly.

Arthur caught her high seriousness immediately and adjusted his tone accordingly. "I see. Walk with me back home, and tell me of the matter."

"It is your son, Modred," she said as they walked the paved road back to their villa.

Arthur grimaced. "Up to his tricks again?"

"Tricks? They are crimes against nature," she exclaimed.

"Every boy has a certain amount of high spirits," Arthur said. "I myself was known to get in trouble once in a while as a lad."

"Just let me tell you this," Guinevere entreated, already sensing difficulty. "His attitude is terrible, and I have seen countless harmful examples of it. It is the most recent that I must call to your attention."

She told him of her encounter with Modred. Brandishing her dress before him, she showed him the evidence of Modred's spite.

Arthur's eyes grew concerned at that. He fingered the frog's blood upon her dress thoughtfully, stopping to do so in the middle of a byway.

"I shall have to punish him," he said.

"Arthur, I really think you need to do more than that. You must discipline him," she maintained vehemently. "You pay too little attention to him, and he resents it, I'm sure."

Arthur bowed his head slightly, sending a flop of grayed locks down to his eyes sadly. "The sight of him saddens me. But he is not a bad fellow. As a boy I too killed animals. There is some of the savage in all of us."

"But I dare say you didn't torture them," said Guinevere as they continued their walk. "Arthur, there is some deep streak of viciousness in him. An evil."

"No!" Arthur said. "How can that be? He is my son. Am I evil?"

"No, of course not, husband, but—"

"Then how can the son of my blood be evil, then? How could something bad come out of what is glorious?" His arms swept out, alluding to the fortress town that he had built, the kingdom he had constructed.

Guinevere opened her mouth to remind him of the circumstances under which Modred was conceived. But she thought better of it. Her reminder would cause him too much pain.

"Perhaps, Arthur," she conceded. "But nonetheless you will have to admit that the boy needs disciplining. Perhaps a stay to the north in my father's lands with my cousin Mael . . . a stern disciplinarian if ever there was one . . . will teach him something of what is expected of him."

"I shall decide soon," said Arthur. "In the meantime I should punish him."

"Arthur," said Guinevere, almost pleadingly. "It is not for me that I ask. I merely wish that you take measures to correct the problem before it grows larger."

He took her hand gently in his. "My queen, you worry much too much." He gazed down a lane. "Ah, yes. This is the way I must go. Parcifal tells me he has developed a new military tactic utilizing foot soldiers and cavalry. He wants me to stop and see his men. He's awfully good—we might even start remaking some of the Roman weapons of old." He brushed her cheek with his lips. "Don't worry. I will have Modred do extra chores or something. And I will reprimand him sorely."

Not waiting for any more objections from her, the king blithely strode down the direction he had indicated, answering the excited hails of loyal passersby with a wave.

Shaking her head, Guinevere turned and walked slowly away.

A canker dwelt within Camelot that Arthur would not acknowledge.

Guinevere just prayed that it would not be his kingdom's undoing.

V

The underbrush was knotted with briar. The thorns pricked and pulled at Galahad's breeches. He floundered up the incline, scuffling up dead leaves, tromping on dry sticks, making a dreadful noise.

"Oh, blast!" he spat, falling against the rough brown bark of an oak, resting. "Are you sure this is the way?"

Ellanie, picking her way skillfully behind, ever the expert threader, said, "Yes. Just a little farther to go. Oh, Galahad," she cried, pointing. "Are those blackberries over there? Let's pick some!"

"I've had my fill of thorns, thank you," returned Galahad sharply, scraping burrs from his longish brown hair. He continued his climb through weeds, over dead, wormy trees, under low-slung branches like grasping, gnarled hands.

Only narrow beams of sunlight sifted this far down through the thick forest bearding the hill. The wood was bursting with spring colors. Here and there amongst the vines and the moss wildflowers grew, spraying the forest floor with daubs of vibrant yellow, bold red, subtle gold. A miasma of scents lay thick on the air; honeysuckle and wild rose, fern and larch leaf—undergirded by the prevailing earthy smell of humus.

Galahad felt a trifle hot and damp. He unbuttoned the top of his gray tunic. "What were you doing up here, anyway, Ellanie?"

"Digging for herb roots. Mother makes them into tea. I like tea with lots of cream," she answered.

"You really ought to be careful in thick woods like this," said Galahad gravely as he pushed away from the tree bole and hurled himself into the strenuous task of climbing the hill once more.

A few more minutes of swatting back tree branches and stomping down weeds and brush and they broke into a small grass-fringed clearing fronting a vertical hole in the hill face perhaps a foot high.

"That's it," said Ellanie, pointing.

Galahad was fascinated. What wonders lurked in that thick darkness? What relics of the fabled past did it hold?

A troubling thought occurred to him. "We're not going to be able to see anything in there! No way sunlight is going to be able to seep in."

"I brought a candle," said Ellanie, producing a length

of tallow and wick. "And a flint box." She pulled that out of her pocket.

Soon a flame kindled atop the wax.

"You first," said Galahad, a twinge of fear moving in him. Such an ungallant thought, but anyway she knew the way.

Without questioning Ellanie got down on all fours and crawled into the cave, holding the candle before her. Dim light advanced into the darkness, lighting earthy walls, squiggled with roots. The floor was littered with rocks and pebbles, Galahad noticed as he followed the girl. They bit into his hands and knees most uncomfortably.

The cave broadened almost immediately into a small roomlike enclosure. It smelled of rich moist earth. There were no further passageways. This was all there was to the cave.

Against the back wall sat a trunk.

A Roman trunk if the Latin inscriptions told a true story. It was held closed by a rusted latch.

"I can't get that latch off," said Ellanie. "I need your help."

Galahad nodded thoughtfully, then tried the latch. It wouldn't budge. "Just as I thought. A spell keeps it closed."

"However will we be able to get *inside* then?" whined Ellanie anxiously.

"Not too hard if you know the right way." Without further explanation Galahad slipped the wooden sword from his belt and applied it to the back of the latch. "Magic sword, you know," he explained to the impressed Ellanie as he pried the latch open.

Together they knelt before the trunk. Pushed up. As the lid gave way, a long wrenching squeak issued. The candlelight flowed into the trunk's interior, illumining cobwebs and a single scroll of parchment bound with a strip of leather.

Galahad's eyes bugged. His hand darted down and grabbed it.

"Come. Let's get out into the light so we can read this," he cried enthusiastically.

Ellanie's eyes betrayed deep disappointment. "Is that all there is?"

But Galahad was too excited to answer. He wriggled through the cave opening and out into the sunlight.

Hands shaking with anticipation, he stripped the leather, cracked with age, from the scroll. The parchment rustled as he unwound it, held it to catch the sun.

It was a map.

A most ornate map, delicately rendered with all manner of colored inks delineating roads and landmarks, rivers and mountains. Penned with monastic care at the bottom of the long, wide map was a Latin inscription.

Ellanie, newly emerged from the cave, tugged at Galahad's elbow. "What is it, Galahad? What is it?"

"Sshh!" quieted Galahad, poring over the writing intently, pursing his lips. "This looks important. It's in Latin. Something about Joseph of Arimathea."

"Who?"

Galahad ignored her. He only recognized a few words. There, that was "Jesus Christ." And that word, was that "cross?"

Abruptly a shadow swept over the parchment map. Startled, he swung his head around.

Between himself and the sun loomed a figure.

Modred.

In his hand was a sword—a *real* sword—brandished before him menacingly.

"Oh, dear," said Ellanie, instinctively drawing close to Galahad.

Wearing a lopsided smile, Modred said:

"Why don't you give that here, Galahad?"

vi

The leather whip came down hard.

The snap was harsh, and the blow bit deep into Aethelfrith's back. He cried out and fell into the grass, the skin of his back welting and stinging.

"That will teach you to forget who is the father and who is the son," said the fierce, bearded man, his eyes red and inflamed with drink. The whip handle drooped in his hand, but it could be wielded again at a moment's notice. "You think you can forget your father while he is away?"

The fifteen-year-old Kentish Saxon struggled to rise. Pain speared through his body, but he fought to gain his feet nonetheless. To meet his drunken, raging father eye to eye. "But, Father, you were gone so long. We didn't know what happened to you."

The scraggly, black-haired man made woozy gestures at the rounded hut, the small makeshift barn, the recently tilled fields beyond. "Have you no faith in your sire, ungrateful wretch? Do you not think I can provide for you well enough?" The man thrust his hand into a pouch, drew out a handful of tinkling, glittering gold coins. "There. And that's just part of what I got. We dodged the British dogs most cleverly and snagged a hefty share of loot." Marthic growled with disgust. "You act like some peasant farmer, plowing the field, planting seeds, giving your mother and younger brother crazy ideas when I can take you with me to march against the Britons."

Biting back the smart of the whip's blow, Aethelfrith glanced over to the mud and daub hut. Three frightened faces peered out. Mother and his younger brother and sister. He turned back to face his father, who had arrived home late last night after months away and had been drinking ever since, letting his anger mount until this.

"This is my home, Father," he said. "I like it here. I will do what I care to do. It is a good land."

"What?" Marthic's eyes widened. His nostrils flared.

"That's right, Father. You heard me. This is the home I've known for years. This is where I want to live—in peace—the rest of my life. Not warring with the Britons . . . not plundering them, killing them. Living with them, Father. It was their land first. We are lucky to be here; we are fortunate to have discovered this land. You may go back, Father, but I intend to stay."

Bluish veins stood out in Marthic's face. His muscles tensed. He raised his whip. "By Wotan, you will stay, but buried in the ground!" Marthic made to strike.

But Aethelfrith struck first, digging feet into the ground, lunging under his father's grasp to strike a blow in the man's midriff.

Marthic groaned.

Tears sliding down his cheeks, Aethelfrith struck his father in the face with a fist.

The drunken man did not need much more to knock him down. Soon he lay in an unconscious heap at Aethelrith's feet.

"Oh, Aethelfrith," cried his horrified mother, running toward him. "What have you *done*? They will kill you now! Your father's companions will hang you from a tree and torture you!"

"I could not let the drunken fool hurt me further, Mother." Emotion welled in him, undercut by resolve.

"But what will you do?"

"Quickly, before he wakes," said Aethelfrith. "Pack me some food. Some clothing. I will take his sword." He stopped and picked up some of the gold coins that had fallen to the grass. "He can spare these."

"Aethelfrith . . . rob your own father?" she said, blinking.

Aethelfrith had to smile at that.

"Like father, like son," he said. "Right, Mother?"

vii

"No, he won't!" said Ellanie, suddenly brave once behind Galahad. "It's ours! *We* found it."

Lancelot's son spun around. "But *we* don't have a sword, Ellanie."

"Exactly," said Modred, feeling the edge of his sword with his thumb.

"Oh, stuff and nonsense," said Ellanie. "He's just trying to scare us, Galahad. He dare not harm us—and he knows it."

"I'd rather not find out what he *might* or might not do, Ellanie, if you don't mind," said Galahad.

"What? You fight monsters and you can't fight *him*?" said Ellanie.

Modred sighed deeply. "Come, come, children. I would *never* harm such sweet people as yourself. I just would very much like to see what you've got, if it's not too much trouble."

Heartened by this knowledge Galahad replied, "What are you doing around here anyway. Following us?"

"Follow you? What . . . to hear one of your ridiculous stories?" Modred raised his head with polite laughter. "Absolutely not. I come here often." He pointed up the hill to a copse of trees. "Sort of a sanctum sanctorum I've got there."

"Are you in trouble again, Modred?" demanded Ellanie, hands on hips.

"Who? Me, the king's son, example to you younger folk!" Modred pointed to himself innocently. "Of course not!" He waved a hand impatiently. "So. Just what is this mysterious thing you've got there."

"It's a map," answered Galahad.

"Oh. Indeed. A map. A map, pray tell, of what?" Modred's eyebrows rose with interest.

"We're not sure," said Ellanie. "The explanation on the bottom is in Latin."

"Ah ha, and Galahad's education in Latin has not yet run its course?" Modred stuck the sword point first into the green and leaned on it nonchalantly.

"Well," Galahad returned. "I can make out a few words."

"Let's have a look at it, children. I can read Latin very well," Modred said, holding his hand out.

Hesitantly Galahad held out the map for him to inspect.

Leaning over it, Modred pondered the colorfully rendered parchment.

"Most curious," he commented quietly. "Let me see . . . yes, I can read most of it."

Forgetting their wariness, both Galahad and Ellanie urged Modred to do so.

" 'Hear me in awe, o brethren,' " Modred intoned with appropriate dignity. " 'Know that upon the death and resurrection of our Lord, Christ Jesus, the benefactor of His sepulcher, Joseph of Arimathea, did venture forth to spread His gospel. Carrying with him the vessel of pure gold, crusted with jewelry, that did serve to hold the vinegar that our Lord drank upon the cross as relic of the Holy Agony, Joseph did journey as far as the Roman land of Britain, and there he did spread the word.' "

Modred paused, studying the remainder.

"Is that all?" demanded Ellanie impatiently.

Modred held up his hand. "Please. I'm trying to make out a few words here." He cleared his throat gruffly and began to read again:

" 'Know that upon the death of Joseph his vessel was lost. Only recently have there begun tales of its whereabouts. Tales that should a man chaste and true find this vessel, this Holy Grail, he shall be blessed with a vision of God, and his nation shall be blessed with glory.

" 'Know that this is the latest map of the Grail's location. It has been hidden here so that some meritorious individual might find it and immediately set out for this glorious quest that shall be example to all his people.' "

Modred looked up, some strange light in his eyes. "That's all."

Galahad could barely speak. "Read—read it again!"

"I think we should take this right away to King Arthur," stated Ellanie.

Smiling crookedly, Modred said, "And cheat ourselves of glory?" He leaned forward toward Galahad. "After all, *we* found this, didn't we, my friend?"

Wide eyed, Galahad seemed totally dazed. "Yes. Yes, we did." Enthusiasm welled in him. "We'd be great heroes if we found this. The Holy Grail!" The words upon his tongue were sweet.

"Galahad," said Ellanie in a warning tone. "You shouldn't get carried away. How can we find this? We'd have to travel a long way. We have no food, no weapons, no extra clothes. And our parents would surely *not* allow it!"

Placing a hand to his chin thoughtfully, Modred said, "Now what was it I heard that monk say was in the New Testament? Something about forsaking one's parents to follow the path of Christ. As to the other objections I'm quite sure that this—" he held up his sword—"and the several other weapons I have stored in my little private fort will do quite well. And food and clothes are no problem. I've plenty of those as well."

Galahad blinked. "Are you saying that we should go *now*?" A strange kind of joy suffused him. This was his chance to seek his calling! A hero he'd be if he found this relic. His country would sing his praises evermore. No longer would he merely be a simple, neglected weaver of stories and legends. He could become the truthful *hero* of one!

"And what better time?" said Modred. "If we return, how long do you think we could keep this secret? It's too exciting, too important. Why, every captain and monk will be tearing across the countryside to be first to see this thing! 'Children, you *must* stay home,' they'd say, galloping away. No. We must go now—or never."

Galahad turned to Ellanie. "What do you think?"

Ellanie crinkled her nose suspiciously. "I'm not so sure, Galahad. My father would be terribly worried—"

"But when we come *back* with the Grail," said Modred. "Why, the populace will be so excited they'll surely forgive us."

"He's right," declared Galahad. "This is our chance. We've got to take it. According to the parchment those that find it are called upon by God Himself to seek the Holy Grail."

"And if God is with us," said Modred, "who can be against us?" He speared Ellanie with a piercing glance. "Would you have us go against God, Ellanie?"

"Well, anyway, *she* couldn't come along," said Galahad.

"And why not?" said Ellanie, glaring. "I can do anything *you* can do, Galahad."

"Why not, indeed?" Modred said, supporting her. "Besides, if she goes back, she'll tell everyone where we're going. We don't want that."

Galahad sighed. "I suppose you're right." He looked up to the top of the hill. "If we're going, then we'd better get under way."

Absently Modred fingered his purse of gold coins. "Yes. The Holy Grail, all gold and jewels, awaits us." He chuckled as he turned and stalked away, expecting the other two to follow him.

A brief queasy, uneasy feeling tremored through Galahad as Ellanie grabbed his hand. But then the excitement of the quest returned, and the moment of misgivings was soon forgotten.

viii

The candle burning in the window eventually guttered out. Lancelot stared out upon the night-covered land, searching for movement in the fields. Fatigue weighed as heavy upon his eyelids as upon his muscles. They seemed to want to clamp shut and never open again. But he kept them apart by sheer force of will. He had to. Galahad was somewhere out there and he stared out into the night as though by sheer force of will his sight might divide the night in twain.

He had searched the surrounding countryside all day. With no sign of the boy or his friend Ellanie. If they did not return by tomorrow morning, he would strike out and search until he found them.

Gareth, sick with worry, had already begun the search. But Lancelot could not believe that his boy would have ventured farther than a few miles away.

Oh, God, he thought, despair clinging to him like some clutching hand from the grave. *Oh, God, if anything happens to him, I am a dead man.* He clenched his fists.

A dead man.

He sighed deeply and replaced the spent light with a fresh tallow candle.

There was a knock at the door.

Galahad?

Heart hammering, he raced to it, swung it open.

Framed by the doorway stood Guinevere.

"Any news?" she asked.

"No," he muttered over the surprise stopping his throat. "Nothing."

Guinevere. Here?

She stood there, a breeze rustling the simple tunic she wore, rippling her long hair. The candle and the moonlight lapped her with flutters of light. For a moment the years shed away, and Lancelot was seeing her in the doorway of her bedroom, letting him in for their nightlong loving. He had to stop himself from taking her in his arms, losing himself in her fragrance and warmth and softness. Nestle away from this cruel, harsh reality. . . .

"Lancelot," she said softly. "May I come in?"

He nodded and stepped out of her way.

She slipped inside gracefully, saying, "Arthur knows I'm here. He sent me."

"Sent you?" Lancelot's throat grew dry.

"He'll be along in a while. He wishes to speak to you."

"Ah. I'm glad I'm up to welcome you."

"We knew you'd be." She settled in a chair, stared

out the window. "They've been gone for two days now, haven't they?"

"Yes." He approached her, the bittersweet ache in his loins and heart become almost unbearable.

The touch of her tongue on his teeth, soft against hard. . . .

"Two days," he whispered harshly. "Ellanie, Galahad." Pause. "Modred."

Guinevere looked up sharply. "Arthur's son is not the best behaved young man around, but I'm sure he would never harm—"

Waving away the notion, Lancelot said, "No. Of course not. But the wildest ideas come to the concerned, Guinevere."

"Yes. Arthur is concerned about Modred."

"And who are you concerned about?"

"You."

He broke down. He fell upon his knees and let his head rest upon her lap. Tears sprang and he sobbed as though gasping out his very soul. "It is so hard, Guin. So hard."

She stroked his fine head of hair and said, "You love him very much, don't you?"

"Yes. And you as well. I've lost you. If I lose Galahad, now, I don't know what I'll have—"

"You'll have your precious honor," she whispered, slightly bitter. "You'll have Arthur and your dreams."

He clutched her thigh, as though to grab something real and solid lest he slip away into a morass of emotion. "You cannot *hold* your honor, your dreams, Guinevere. They do not keep the cold out of the nights."

"Was she very beautiful, Lancelot?" asked Guinevere.

"Who?"

"Galahad's mother. I have heard her called Elain by the gossips."

"Yes," breathed Lancelot, almost penitently, almost as though he kneeled before some father confessor rather than before Guinevere, the great love of his life.

"And young." His voice sighed away, vaporous despair.

"You still mourn her," she whispered.

"Yes."

He fought the tides of emotion sweeping him, more cruel than any barbarian's blow. The memory of Elain, bright and young and happy, lit a summer image in his mind that burned and scorched his soul.

No, he told himself. It is not manly, seemly to weep before a woman. I am Lancelot of Gaul, and I cannot fall apart like this.

But thoughts were poor weapons to hold back his feelings.

"And tell me this, Lancelot," she murmured, with no trace of emotion in her voice. "Do you mourn our love?"

It was like a physical blow. He moved back from her. "I'm sorry. I'm under great strain."

He stood and half stumbled, half walked to the window. He clenched the sill till his arm muscles bulged trying to numb his inner hurt with physical pain. He tasted blood and was suddenly aware that he was biting his lip.

Soft swish of skirts. That unmistakable fragrance wafted over him, the incense of the altar at which he worshipped: Guinevere's scent.

She leaned her head against his arm. "I'm sorry, Lancelot."

He turned slightly and laid his hand softly against a warm temple. "No. It is well that you speak the rancor. Otherwise it will continue to fester."

"And have you rancor for me, Lancelot?" she asked, a trace of pain quavering her voice. "Do you hate me very much?"

"*Hate* you?" Turning fully, he clutched her up in a warm embrace. "Oh, how could I ever hate you, Guinevere? Sooner would I hate all else, than you."

"I would never let you do that," she said.

"And that is why I love you so. I love you for all you are, even though what you are, your loyalty, nobility, and bravery, has kept us apart. No, my love has grown beyond what it was before. I cherish it, Guinevere, for our loyalty to the master of our dreams has made it sacred. In denying each other our bodies we make our love grow invincible. Sometimes, Guinevere, I am so full of love for you that I think that love has become me, and the wild, reckless Lancelot has been swallowed away, dismissed unmourned."

They held each other for a time against the window, lit softly by moon and star beams broken by scuds of clouds that sailed in the deep black sky. Holding her, Lancelot felt at one with eternity. This exquisite moment seemed a part of forever. He seemed vaulted into pleasure—not the intense ecstasy he'd known in their physical love, but the calmer, wiser love of two souls, full of caring, mingling.

Guinevere broke the spell. "And yet, Lancelot, I lay awake nights wanting you."

He let his arms release her. "No, Guinevere. We mustn't torture each other."

"Lancelot, I cannot live without you. My youth is drying into a worn husk without your love to fill me." Starlight sparkled on a tear, two tears, coursing down. "Arthur will not touch me."

"You want him to?"

"Of course not. He is a great man, and he knows I do not love him that way. But Lancelot, I am a woman, and I am dying without the love I need everyday. My soul shrivels like a flower without rain."

"Don't Guin," he muttered, turning away. "Don't tempt me. We would destroy everything we stand for. Everything that Arthur has built. Don't you see? By knowing each other as we did before, by loving, we will corrupt love."

"No!" she said harshly. She ran into his arms, wrapped him up in her desperation, as though she could suck him up, consume him. She kissed him hungrily, fiercely, and her tears were salty in his mouth. "I must have you, Lancelot. You are a part of me."

His head swam. Dizziness threatened to carry him away into uncontrolled passion. The textures and sensations of their season of love returned full force . . . and he knew that if he gave her what she wanted the old intensity would bring pleasure and gratification beyond anything he had ever known before.

His loins and his heart ached for release.

A rapping began at the door.

Guinevere quickly withdrew from him, patting back her mussed hair. "Lancelot, hear me now," she whispered low. "That will be Arthur. This is our last chance. We must begin again or I will die." She drew in a rapid breath. "Tomorrow morning, at dawn, I will be bathing unaccompanied at Diviner's Pool. If you love me, Lancelot, you will divert your journey in search of Galahad to meet me there. I will expect you."

Stunned, he could only stare at her. Then he heard the knocking again and realized he had to answer the door.

As Guinevere had predicted Arthur stood outside. As soon as Lancelot opened the door the high king stepped in and placed a brotherly hand upon Lancelot's shoulder. "You must not worry, my friend. Already I have sent out other search parties for the children."

"Thank you," responded Lancelot. "I myself intend to depart at dawn."

"Ah. Good. May I accompany you?"

Arthur had moved into a position in front of his wife. Guinevere shot Lancelot a meaningful glance over her husband's shoulder.

"I thank you, Arthur," returned Lancelot. "But I don't want to rob the kingdom of its leader. I will go alone."

Arthur shrugged. "As you like, Lancelot. Now that I think of it I suppose you do prefer traveling alone." He sat down in a wooden chair. "But that is not what I came to speak to you about, in the main. I sent Guinevere to express our concern. I have come to ask you a question. I know this is not a good time to ask you this, but perhaps it will divert your attention from your troubles."

"My lord?"

"Oh, come off that 'my lord' business, Lancelot. We're longtime friends. We can save that for when we're ancient and oh so formal. No, I must speak to you of Cam."

"Cam?"

"Yes. Today I toured the boundaries. It is a good town."

"I cannot but agree, Arthur."

"It is my pride and my joy, the apparent evidence of what we have been able to accomplish these years. But to give it so much of my attention is not good. It distracts me from the kingdom as a whole. I need to appoint a governor . . . someone whose responsibility will be solely to attend to the needs and concerns of our capital, Cam. Someone who will see to the meting out of justice, the building, the constant growth of its boundaries. I cannot think of a person whom I can entrust with this chore better capable than yourself, Lancelot. Will you take on this new responsibility, my friend?"

"I—I am honored with the offer, Arthur," began Lancelot, but he was cut off by the king's quieting hand.

"No. I will not take an answer now. I did not come to obtain one. I merely wished to plant the thought into your consideration. You have a great deal now to concern yourself with. I will ask you again when this matter has been cleared up."

Lancelot said, "I do admit I am most worried about Galahad."

"And Gareth about Ellanie, and I about Modred."

Lancelot thought, *Now perhaps is the time to broach that subject.*

"Arthur, let me bring you a cup of wine. I have something to ask you."

Arthur smiled broadly. "I am always in the mood for wine."

Guinevere volunteered to retrieve it if Lancelot would direct her to where it was kept. Soon they all held cups of red, fruity drink.

"Now. What is the matter, Lancelot?"

"This sudden disappearance of my son, your son, and the daughter of Gareth. I have no doubt that Galahad and Ellanie were together. I suspect that Modred was with them as well."

"That is the way it looks. Obviously they got it into their minds to take leave of this area for a short time."

"I pray to God that is the case. But neither Galahad nor Ellanie would ever do something like that on their own. I see the influence of Modred in this matter, Arthur. I think we should speak of Modred now that I have the opportunity and the inclination."

Arthur's facial muscles tensed. "You too, Lancelot? Is there no one who believes that the lad is simply in a mischievous stage?"

"You anticipate our discussion." Lancelot tasted the wine, contemplating what he had to say. "I only wish to warn you, Arthur. The boy is born of something beyond your power. He is not good for this land. He must be taught not to flaunt the power he has as king's son. And while it is not my place to give advice where advice has not been asked for, if I were you I would send the boy to some monastery, where the difference between right and wrong might be instilled into his stubborn mind."

"Are you finished?" asked Arthur, testily.

"You want to hear more?" said Lancelot. "I can recount the evidence of Modred's deeds that will bear my thoughts out. The incident with the dead cats. His treatment of the captured Saxon. His constant malicious pranks. And—"

Arthur held up his hand. "Enough! I will hear no more!"

"It is for your own good," insisted Guinevere.

"He is flesh of my flesh and blood of my blood. He is my responsibility, and I will see that he is corrected." A kind of glaze fell over his eyes. "But I will not hear his name—nor mine—slandered in such a way. I can recount many questionable escapades of *our* youths, Lancelot. Have you forgotten your former wildness already?"

Lancelot bowed his head. "No."

"Very good." The king straightened his cloak. "Then let's have no more about Modred. He is a product of my kingdom. And is my kingdom bad?"

"No, Arthur," said Lancelot.

"Then how can Modred be bad?"

"But Arthur . . . his connection with Morgan le Fay and Morgause . . ." Lancelot began, but he was stopped mid-sentence by Arthur's glare.

"You will never mention those two names again, *do you understand*?" Anger filled the man's face. He turned away. "Come, Guinevere. We must go."

"My apologies, Arthur," said Lancelot.

Arthur nodded vaguely. "I am confident that we will find the children soon. In the meantime I hope that you will consider my request concerning Cam."

"I will."

"Good night then."

The royal couple departed quickly.

Lancelot stood at the door watching the night swallow them up, feeling as physically and emotionally spent as he had ever in his life.

He went back into his home to seek the soothing balm of slumber.

CHAPTER 13

The Grail

The night was warm.

Nevertheless they had built a fire in a clearing of a forest. It was supposed to be Modred's watch, while Galahad and Ellanie slept. But they were all up, staring glumly into the fire, long after the sun had set.

Sometime toward the middle of the night the stranger arrived.

Later Galahad remembered this vividly because just a short while before that event Ellanie had commented on how long it had been dark.

"I'm not used to all this darkness," she had murmured, peering into the shades of late evening. "I'm usually in bed long before, and when I wake up it's bright again."

Modred chuckled lowly. "I like the night. A person can be alone at night. I like to be alone."

"I imagine you don't mind having us around now, do you?" said Galahad, feeding another twig to the glowing crackling pyre.

Modred shrugged nonchalantly. He let that suffice as an answer.

Swallowing, Galahad sat staring into the fire, holding Ellanie's hand, wondering why he had let Modred talk him into going on this foolish trip.

At first it had been a gay, wondersome lark. Even Ellanie's doubtful complaints had not dampened his enthusiasm. After all the map indicated that the site of the Holy Grail was not far at all from the fort upon the river Cam. Two or three days' journey by foot, no more, and then the vision would be his. He would be a true hero, at such a young age.

There had been nothing wrong with the map. It had guided them true thus far. Every landmark indicated upon the chart was represented upon the landscape. The map even hinted at the best way to ford streams, skirt mountains, climb hills.

It had not hinted at the doubts that would swell in Galahad.

It was the discomfort of the first night, spent by a gurgling creek, that had awakened Galahad to the real possibilities of the journey. His father had often told him of the small bands of Saxons that roamed the land, taking unprepared travelers and villagers by surprise. Galahad had merely absorbed these tales into his own gallery of stories.

But laying awake in the still night, every shrub seemed a barbarian, every shadow wanted his blood. Invested with the shaping of his imagination, the surrounding wood held all manner of otherworldly dread, from ghosts to ogres. Only the presence of the others stopped him from openly whimpering and seeking to return the next day. He had to dig deep within himself to find the courage and determination that he needed.

Ellanie snuggled closer. Normally Galahad would have objected. But somehow her closeness was now comforting rather than annoying. Poor girl. He should never have allowed her to come along.

Poor boy, he thought mordantly. I *should never have come along.*

Only Modred seemed at all composed about this quest.

There he sat now, staring into the fire, the flames dancing in his eyes. The fellow was a loner, no question about that. Galahad had begun to wonder what he wanted from this Holy Grail they were seeking. He had never heard the king's bastard voice much interest in things of God—at least sincerely. Oh, certainly he mouthed them glibly enough. But at his core he seemed to scoff at religion, as though it were beneath him.

No. Galahad felt uneasy about this whole business now.

The wind curled through the trees. Leaves flapped. Galahad drew the blanket closer, although it was not cold. He wished now that Modred had not burdened them down so with supplies. Blankets, dried food, knives, extra clothes—Modred had them all in his little hut atop the hill. He'd stored all manner of supplies there—like a squirrel. Small valuables, casks of ale, mead, and wine, and an array of weapons from knives to slings to full-length swords. A pet raven, perched in a corner, kept watch over it all. Galahad had not liked it at all—especially not the flag spread over one wall. A flag bearing a griffin—the emblem of Cornwall. There was no trace of any dragon flag. That, too, made Galahad uneasy.

Galahad scrunched down farther in his blanket, trying to shut the night sounds out: the hoot of an owl distantly reverberating through the quiet, the sough of the wind through the trees, the snap of a twig, as though stepped upon.

Stepped upon?

With the suddenness of the realization that *someone* was out there the figure stepped into the pool of firelight. Tall and brawny, he presented a most fearsome picture. In both hands he held a long sword—but it was lowered, obviously simply ready if needed.

The man spoke in a language that Galahad did not understand.

But before he could complete the sentence, Modred scrabbled up, his own sword in hand, and attacked.

Eyes wide, the intruder spoke a Saxon word that Galahad understood. "No!"

Ellanie, sitting upright, echoed the word: "No, Modred. He says he means no harm. He just wants—"

But Modred was already at the tall youth. Firelight reflected on metal. The sword swished through the air. It clanged against the Saxon's weapon, held up in defense.

With surprising swiftness Modred brought the sword back and heaved another blow. Galahad was astonished at the youth's skill—obviously he had practiced much with wielding a sword out by his private hut.

But the Saxon's brawn and tallness were too much. On the third swipe of Modred's sword the much heavier Saxon long sword caught it near the hilt, banging it from Modred's grasp. The sheer force of the blow knocked the slight Modred down.

The Saxon blade rose.

Ellanie cried out a single word.

The blade checked.

The Saxon responded with a guttural sentence. Ellanie returned a few Saxon words, then scrambled over to where Modred lay, stunned.

"Apologize, Modred," she said harshly.

In the light of the fire Galahad could see Modred grimace. "Never!"

"Modred! He might kill us all," said Galahad. "You should be happy you're still alive."

"Apologize to that ruffian?" spat Modred. "I'd die first."

Ellanie shook her head, then spoke a few brief words to the Saxon.

The youth nodded, satisfied. He put his sword on his shoulder and began to walk away.

Ellanie called out after him. The Saxon halted. Turned.

Ellanie spoke in a questioning tone.

The Saxon answered.

Ellanie seemed surprised by the response.

Standing up timidly Galahad said, "What did he say, Ellanie?"

She turned. "I asked him what he wanted of us. Some food, he said, and directions."

"Directions to where?"

"To the fort of King Arthur," said Ellanie. "He wishes an audience."

ii

They sat around the campfire for a long time, Ellanie listening attentively to the Saxon, then translating for the others. She had always had a facility for languages. It was fortunate, she thought, that her father had made sure that she knew Saxon, if not Latin. She could speak it fluently, liked the way the words felt rolling over her tongue.

Modred sat removed from the others, still pouting, but listening nonetheless, obviously interested. He had gotten over his hurt pride and was considering the value of having such a swordsman as this along on their trip.

Galahad, quite simply, was fascinated with the big youth. Particularly by the fellow's jocularity. The Saxon had wolfed down a healthy portion of their food and had washed that down with large drafts of Modred's wine. Modred had begun to complain about that but stopped when he remembered how effectively he had been struck down.

For her own part Ellanie was quite taken with the bluff blond Saxon. While he had the air of wildness he obviously enjoyed their company, was grateful for the food, and was anxious to join their quest, in return for being taken to meet King Arthur.

His name was Aethelfrith.

He told his story. He told of his love for the land and why he had to leave his family. He claimed that he wanted to live here in Britain, in peace, not as a Saxon, nor as anything else except a native of this land.

He wished to farm the fields, drink the clear stream water, find solace and happiness on this unique land.

"I can't explain it," he said through Ellanie. "I've been across the Narrow Sea, in the land where I was born. It is a land of strife and always has been. Warfare is constant as tribes and peoples roam and clash. There are many languages, much misunderstanding." The youth leaned nearer the fire as he spoke, and the light showed on his face as clearly as the fervor did on his expression. "Here, there is the possibility of constant peace. If the kingdom of Arthur spreads throughout this land, bringing quietude and peace to all his subjects, it will be an island of peace. And what better fortress to defend from encroaching war than an island?"

Modred was leaning toward the Saxon, fascinated. "Yes, yes," he said. "I've never thought of things that way before."

Smiling broadly, Galahad pronounced: "Yes. He will make a good Briton."

Aethelfrith shook his locks. "No. Not a Briton, not a Saxon. Something different. A member of the combined tribes of many lands."

iii

Night gave up the ghost.

The darkness fled shred by shred as dawn paled the horizon. A flock of cawing rooks, like departing specks of the night, winged overhead. The air was heavy with dew scent, and the morning was bitter in Lancelot's mouth.

He walked his steed from the stable, mounted it, then set its path parallel to the purling Cam's waters.

The sun's pink rays flowed like translucent mist over the landscape, rolling over the Cam resplendently. Lancelot stared into the dazzle kicked up and for a moment thought he saw the figure of Guinevere, bathing.

The illusion pushed the fatigue from his joints like a gentle touch of balm. The familiar sensation of undiluted love moved in him lightly, underpinned by the more powerful rhythm of desire.

He saw her in a blinding moment as he rode, upraised arms and hands dripping diamonds of water that splashed onto her perfect breasts and ran down her body, wrapping her up in shimmer.

The image, departing, left him breathless with awe and anticipation.

He knew there was no stopping himself. *Had* known it since Guinevere told him where she would be when dawn came upon the world.

He was drawn to her as surely as iron is drawn to a lodestone. There was no control to his passion anymore, no hope for escape. His loyalty to Arthur and his principles dwindled in comparison to his burning love.

They had denied themselves for so long. They had tried. But it was no good now.

The voices of their souls called out to each other, and there would be no peace for either until they merged into passion and love that was not merely memory.

"Guinevere," he muttered, spurring on his horse past a clump of riverside weeds. Somehow the aches of advancing age and a sleepless night subsided as he thought of her in his arms again, finally. After all this time.

"God help me, but I'm coming to you."

The breeze was fresh and wild in his hair.

iv

When dawn found Galahad and his company they had already been traveling for some minutes.

Aethelfrith had roused at a most ungodly hour and had insisted that they immediately set out. He seemed as excited by the mystery of the Holy Grail as they.

Streamers of mist waved slowly from the valleys before them, evaporating in the dawning sun. The countryside had never owned so much color for Galahad. Deep hues of brown and green and red abounded, hazed by the shimmering unreality of the fog and the dew. The fresh air filled his lungs with life. With the comforting companionship of this big, strapping Saxon, he felt good again. He felt reasonably safe, secure.

God had seen fit to provide them a protector.

Long sword swinging at his side, Aethelfrith strode effortlessly before them, leading the way. Forgetting her preoccupation with Galahad, Ellanie tried to keep up with the big Saxon, chattering away in his language with gay abandon.

The youth merely grunted occasionally in response.

Galahad was partly amused and partly troubled. He realized that as irksome as it sometimes was he enjoyed the young girl's attention. Now all he had for company was the dour Modred, who spoke very little—and only when directly addressed.

In the two days they had spent together Galahad had come to understand the boy a little. But that did not mean that he liked him any better.

"What do you think of our new companion, Modred?" Galahad asked, needing a bit of conversation to make him forget the occasional quirks of pain in his limbs from walking.

"Who? Old Aethelfrith up there?" The boy walked smoothly and economically, with the grace of a lithe woman rather than a gawky adolescent. He smiled vaguely. "He is most handy with a weapon. I thought last night would be the end of me when he raised that long sword."

"He's just bigger than you are. Really," said Galahad, "you were quite brave to strike at him."

Modred raised his petite, narrow eyebrows. "I *was* on watch, dear boy, as you may recall. It was my duty."

"I never knew you so preoccupied with duty, Modred."

The youth stared away into the mountains, toward the south. Galahad could not see his expression. "Oh, I have my duties," he whispered harshly. "My responsibilities. I think I know my calling in this world." He turned around, smiling with a friendliness that Galahad had never seen before. "Just as you do. We are wrapped up in fate, Galahad. We must be what we are destined to become. What the hates and loves of our fathers and mothers have dictated that we be."

"But Modred," objected Galahad. "We all have choices. We must decide what our lives are to be, on our own. My father has told me that many times. Our lives are in our own hands."

Modred barked a derisive laugh. "Sprout wings and fly, then, Galahad. Touch us all with your fairy wand. Make us all happy as swilling pigs. I would like that. It's better than this life." He shook his head with something like disgust. "Don't talk about such things until you know that of which you speak. Until you come to grips with the forces that move us all, like dead leaves in a dark wind."

He moved ahead, obviously not wanting to talk anymore.

Aethelfrith the Saxon had talked long into the night, depriving them of their sleep. But somehow Galahad felt rested.

The big Saxon had talked of Saxon ways, which had been fascinating. Galahad had always visualized the people as the plundering maniacs their armies had presented them as; yet they had a structured life much as the Celts did. But most fascinating to Galahad were the myths and legends of the Saxons . . . the stories were wild and frightening, tales in which heroes did not always win but were often dragged down by the forces they opposed. The tale of Beowulf, which Aethelfrith had told just this morning as they prepared for their departure, was particularly striking—and haunting.

In his rough language, full of hard, matching consonants, the tale had flowed, its story matching the dissonant music of the words.

Even now Galahad marveled at its dark and bright beauty. What a tale of gallantry it was, the Saxon hero taking on two terrible monsters single-handedly, defeating them, and at the end dying in such sad glory. It appealed not to Galahad's love of stories but to his newly discovered sense of the dark side of life. These Saxons did not reject death but seemed to welcome it as a natural part of life. Theirs was an existence built around the thought of rising above the limits of life—and death. Heroic individualism seemed their ideal.

Galahad could understand that. And so he could sympathize with the Saxons for once. He could understand why Arthur did not object to the fact that they had settlements to the east, as long as they did not harry Celtic lands.

He found a sincere liking growing for the tall youth who led them on their journey now.

And only a tiny bit of jealousy that he should interest Ellanie so much.

They had been walking only a short while when they encountered the man.

Actually Galahad first thought he was simply a boy.

They were approaching the base of a low mountain, which meant their destination was near. The sides of the slope were green and brown with heather, redolent with the growth's smell.

From atop a boulder they were passing a head popped.

"You seek the Holy Grail," said the creature, in oddly accented Celtic. "I see the ordained map in your hands."

Surprised, they all stopped. Aethelfrith unsheathed his long sword. Held it ready.

But no threat seemed posed.

Modred was the first to recover. "Who are you?" he demanded.

The little man—and it *was* a man, Galahad could make that out clearly now—climbed higher upon the rock and sat down, draping his feet down its side.

"I am one of the People of the Hills," explained the little man. "You've probably never heard of us."

Recovering his tongue, Galahad said, "Yes, I have. The older folks talk of you. Small people living quietly off in the desolate, high places."

The little man nodded. "Quite so." He was small, and he was thin. Although not a midget or a dwarf, he was no taller than Galahad. His hair was uncombed and curly. His complexion was dark. He wore a straggly beard, although he did not seem very old.

"What do you know of the Grail?" demanded Modred.

The little person shrugged. "Only that all of our people of this particular tribe on this particular hill have been told these past years that some day a group of people would come seeking it. And, I might add, that it was our duty to take these people to the Grail."

"You know where it is, then?" said Ellanie. She didn't seem as happy at discovering this thing's whereabouts as she did at the notion that their journey would soon be over and they could all go home.

"Oh, indeed. And I have been instructed to show you where it is and to explain its importance," answered the little man.

Abruptly he stood.

"So, then?" he said. "Shall we go? We still have a distance to travel."

▼

The river Cam had several tributaries, streams and brooks that flowed into the sucking river.

Beside one of these, in a green glade, a small pool was formed, complete with waterfall and privacy afforded by the surrounding elms and beech trees.

Diviner's Pool.

Guinevere sat upon an outgrowth of slate by the waterfall. Misting droplets of water, spumed up by the driving water, threw a rainbow into the air. The sun glittered in the water.

Guinevere wept.

What had she ever done to deserve this sort of life, she asked God as she stared bleakly at the beauty of this pool. The fresh water smells were invigorating, blended with the scents of the water lilies, the poolside fronds and grasses, stirred by a kind breeze.

She had been terrible, last night, she told herself. Awful. Poor Lancelot was distraught with worry about Galahad, and she had troubled him with her silly feminine needs.

Sitting there on that hard cold stone, she was convinced that she was the worst woman who had ever loved a man.

It would serve her right if Lancelot did not come.

It would do her the justice she deserved if he never spoke to her again.

Bitter with herself she sat forlornly and thought about leaping into the pool, not to bathe, but to drown.

"Guinevere."

The voice was barely above a whisper. But she recognized it even as she recognized the voice of her own soul.

She swiveled around.

Stood, eyes wide, bleary. Face streaked with tears.

Lancelot stood on the verge of the glade, holding the reins of his horse. He dropped the reins and ran to her.

"Guinevere, love of my life," he said, wrapping her up in his warm arms. A comforting embrace . . . an embrace that gave meaning to her life. She buried her face in his tuniced chest to hide the tears that flowed freely down her face.

"I am here," he said warmly. "I am here, and I will always be yours. I reject all that I honor, all that I hold dear, save you. I challenge the promised fires of hell and the wrath of God to hold you so." His voice broke. "I cannot exist without you, Guinevere. You have shown me what a weak man I really am. I need you more than I can say."

He held her so hard and fervently that she could barely breathe.

She sniffed back her tears and said, "Lancelot, I do love you."

"Then we will leave this land," he said in a monotone. "When I have found my son we will make plans to flee. We will go back to my homeland. To Gaul. We will have such happiness that will cause heaven itself envy." He held onto her with crushing tenderness. "I have been a fool all these years. I should have followed my heart, not my head. I have wasted so many of your precious years."

For a time emotion so choked her throat that she could not speak. Her very eyes seemed to melt into tears, and silent sobs wracked her body. She wanted him so badly she felt she was dying.

When she had recovered enough she slowly drew in a breath.

"No, Lancelot," she said. The words tore the very fabric of her being. It took all of her will to enunciate them.

Lancelot did not respond immediately.

His grip on her slackened.

Taking the opportunity, Guinevere pulled away from him. She drifted to the edge of the pool and sat upon a boulder. She could not bear to look at him.

"No?" The word held all the hurt in the world and a terrible disbelief.

"No, Lancelot."

His words stumbled and stuttered: "But . . . but . . . my darling. Don't you understand?" A half-controlled sob broke from him. "I'm offering you . . . everything. You have my soul and more. I cannot give you more, Guinevere."

She shook her head. "No, Lancelot." She shut her eyes. "It is too late for us." She felt the heat of her tears upon her cheek. "It has always been too late for us. We must accept this, once and for all."

She felt his hand drop upon her shoulder. Not demanding, not questioning. Just there, as though to coax the rest of what she had to say from her.

"But last night . . ." he said.

"Last night I was a selfish witch. Last night all that was self-righteously evil in my heart took control."

"But Guinevere, our love is not evil. Nothing so beautiful could be evil!"

"No. To itself, it is the most wonderful thing in our existence." She opened her eyes and inadvertently caught his reflection in the still pool. His expression showed a man bereft of defenses. If she told him to leap into the river with her and die, he would do it without question. It was a terrible thing to behold, this power she had over him. She sighed, closed her eyes again, and thought, *Is this what lovers do to each other?*

She continued with her halting explanation. "But what are we, Lancelot? Two collections of blood, flesh, sinew, bone held together by frail souls. Each breath is numbered, each heartbeat drums our way to death. Only our values and hopes and beliefs separate us from the lowliest of animals. Oh, we are all the world to each other. And yet what is our love to others? Nothing. What will we achieve by treason? A few years of happiness? What is that weighed against what such a betrayal to our honor and our nation will mean?"

She shook her head. "We would destroy him, Lancelot. And with him, this kingdom. And with this kingdom, a candle in the night of the world."

He fell to his knees slowly and buried his head into her lap. "But . . . but what of our love? Are we to forget what we mean to each other? I am no more than a man, Guinevere. You are my soul's desire."

"And so it shall be to our deaths," she whispered. "The love we have between us will never die, Lancelot. We will keep each other in our hearts and know that in denying our love's physical expression . . . in sacrificing the pleasures of the moment for the greater good, we will keep our love alive forever.

"And who is to say what lies beyond these short lives of ours!" she continued. "We must cling to that, Lancelot. Cling and let it suffice that from our little miseries great meaning will sprout."

She stroked his long, soft hair, feeling her heart break.

After a time he stood. She looked up at him. There was strength again in his face. She loved him all the more to see it return.

"You are a brave woman, Guinevere," he said. "I have never glimpsed your life before and never will."

"You are wrong, Lancelot. We do what we must. That is all. That is our torture. That is our fate."

He turned his head away. "I must find Galahad."

Marching away briskly, he was soon gone.

Every part of her being screamed to run after him. But she did not. She waited until the sounds of his galloping horse died away into the distance . . . then she bent slowly down to the water to wash her swollen eyes, and her long brown hair draped down from her head like the branches of a weeping willow.

vi

As he rode through the sweeping beauty of Britain Lancelot felt unmoved.

All manner of sights availed themselves to delight the eye. Bright colors, exquisite shapes. Nature's bounty breathed varied perfumes, sounded sounds in a harmony of being. A bright yellow butterfly fluttered soundlessly above a dandelion-spotted greensward. Lancelot bounced in his saddle, empty of all emotion.

He felt as though his soul were dead now, his body just an animated husk.

He tried to bring himself to feel some sort of pain. Shed tears would be better than this *nothingness*. But he could conjure no emotion.

Perhaps he was beyond emotion.

Nothing seemed to matter anymore.

He traveled for hours that seemed minutes. Day dipped into the inkwell of night and emerged again untarnished, and still Lancelot traveled.

Exactly where, he was not sure.

On the late morning of the day following his meeting with Guinevere his horse would travel no farther.

He dismounted and fell, exhausted, upon a bed of dried leaves.

He dreamed that he stood upon a vast, featureless plain, the sun shining in the sky, wearing Guinevere's face.

A gigantic, dark hand emerged from nowhere and dragged away the sun.

The stars lighted. The moon rose, full.

Stamped upon it was the face of smiling Guinevere.

Like a geyser of blackness, the hand emerged again and took away the moon and the stars in one ghastly sweep.

No light was upon the plain now. He stood in total darkness. Fear began to collect in his bowels, grow hard and heavy.

It burst from him in a scream.

He woke and realized that it was still day. The light was still there, golden and bright, giving the world color and definition.

He felt the pain now, but he knew it was a pain he should cherish.

He was alive.

Somebody tapped him on the shoulder.

Startled, he swung his head around.

Standing before him was a short man. In his hand was a small but sharp sword.

Automatically Lancelot grabbed at his own sword. Something banged him on the head, hard, knocking him to the ground.

The black hand of his dreams reached for him, closing out the day, enveloping him in oblivion.

vii

They stood at the peak of a mountain.

The mountain stood amidst others but was taller. Its peak afforded the most spectacular view that Galahad had ever seen.

Perched upon its lofty brow, one could see beyond

this range of mountains. One could see to the east, to the west. To the north and the south. The day was clear. Galahad could see for miles.

He stood there with the others, staring in awe.

To the west, a deep blue ribbon of sea was visible. It sparkled and gleamed with the late afternoon sun. To the east, north, and south stretched the land of Britain, clothed in its fine dress of greens and brown, and more subtle shades, wearing a majesty of being that awed Galahad to his very soul.

He had never truly understood the concept of *big* before.

Nor had he known the tingling emotion of viewing such beauty.

Only Modred did not bother to gaze upon the sweeping landscape.

His eyes darted about like the eyes of a furtive ferret. "All right. We're here now," he said to the taller of the two Hill People who had shown them this place. "Where is the Grail? I want to see it."

Akes, the little man who had intercepted them, looked at his companion, Shere. The taller of the two shook his head wearily. Instead of answering, he asked of Modred a simple question.

"You wish to *have* the Grail?" The little man rubbed his clean-shaven chin thoughtfully.

Shere had only joined them a few hours before. He seemed very happy at their arrival, as though it was something that he had anticipated for a very long time.

"Of course!" declared Modred. "What are things for, other than to *have*?"

Shere looked over to Akes, who broke into a smile. They both began chuckling. Their mirth spilled over into outright laughter.

Modred was incensed. "What is the meaning of this? We are looking for a cup, a goblet. Gold, embedded with all manner of jewels. You said you knew where it was. I don't see anything. Why have you led us up this mountain if you've nothing to show us?"

"Oh, but we already have," said Shere. "And I pity you if you do not see it."

"Where?" demanded Modred, spinning about, feverishly. "I want it. I want it *now*."

"It is riches you seek, not the Grail," pronounced Shere. He seemed much older than Akes, a trifle stoop shouldered, with flecks of gray in his dark black hair. "Is this so?"

"I—" said Modred. "I seek the Grail as well."

Smiling, Shere gestured to the landscape. To the sea. To the rolling hills and the flat plains.

"This Britain," he said. "This treasured isle, this land of kings, this castle against sickness and war . . . this land guarded by the sea all around . . . this pregnant mother of glories to come . . . this is the Grail spoken of in the map you have. This is what the druid Merlin wished you who found the parchment to see."

"What!" bellowed Modred harshly. "What nonsense is this? We've been played for dupes!"

Akes turned to Aethelfrith, Galahad, and Ellanie. The children were standing still, serene, listening intently. "Yes. Some years ago a druid who called himself Merlin arrived amongst us. Our peoples had long been familiar with his efforts, his dreams. For they are our dreams as well. Our people have met your King Arthur. A long time ago, when he was not much older than you. We saw him fit for our purposes and Merlin's."

As the little man spoke Ellanie busily translated the story to Aethelfrith. The big Saxon looked on, clearly not understanding, a little embarrassed when the subject of marauding Saxons was brought up.

"When Arthur finally assumed the throne," the small man continued, underlining his phrasings with odd, quirky little gestures that might have some meaning to the People of the Hills but not to the others, "and some years passed into his reign, Merlin foresaw that he would not be around to guide things forever. Some device was necessary to reawaken the sense of purpose in Arthur's kingdom amongst the young, who might not remember the struggles of years past. He felt these generations might need a symbol to remember the goal of our peoples here on this island."

"Symbols?" cried Modred, aghast. "Remembrance?" He paced to and fro, frantically. "What utter rot! It's well known that the druid Merlin was a crazy, raving fool! Absolute nonsense." Clearly Modred was incensed that nothing of value was in evidence.

"Please," said the little man, folding his arms. "Let me finish. The druid did not lie. He spoke metaphorically." Pondering the horizon with slow stately sweeps of gaze, the little man paused in his speech. Finally he continued: "This land is the Grail of which Merlin spoke. The sea and rivers surround it like embedded jewels, which sparkle and shine. The land itself is a golden cup that will hold the wine that even now is being pressed. A wine that will never cease flowing, a wine of civilization. A civilized people to lead the world." He spread his arms out reverentially. "And so this Britain is the Grail. As for being 'Holy' . . . well, that is open for every individual's interpretation."

Shere smiled benignly.

Galahad realized that his throat was dry. He could scarcely breathe. He looked out upon the land of Britain . . . *his* land, *his* Britain . . . and he knew a love beyond words.

"Yes," he murmured. "Yes. We have found something beyond value. We do see a vision of God. But it's for all to see who look." He turned to Ellanie. "Tell Aethelfrith it's his vision, too. It's for all who see it . . . and everyone that *does* see it is united under a common bond."

Suddenly Modred was very quiet. He gazed again upon the landscape, and a small, sly smile appeared upon his face. "Yes. Yes, of course. How could I have been so stupid." A hint of glee shone in his eye.

Ellanie said, "I wish Merlin were still here. He'd be able to tell us more."

"What more do we need to know?" said Galahad.

"Why, I'll be able to get dozens of stories out of this." He smiled broadly. "And now I'll know their meaning."

Aethelfrith spoke a few guttural words.

Galahad immediately asked Ellanie what he was saying.

"He says that now that we have found what we were looking for," returned Ellanie, "please may we go, so he can meet King Arthur? He's ever so eager now to meet him . . . more than before."

"Certainly," said Galahad, "and we'd be glad of his company. Right, Modred?"

Modred had suddenly turned very affable. "Oh, absolutely." The youth seemed suddenly very pleased with himself.

Galahad realized that he was now acutely aware of all that surrounded him. The breeze that ruffled his long locks blew the fresh smell of the sea into his nostrils, mixed with the scent of the heather, the bracing chill of this mysterious, misty land. His perception of colors increased, as though the sense of purpose infusing him magnified his appreciation of everything.

He stepped over to Aethelfrith and put a hand on the Saxon's brawny arm. "You know what the Celtic word 'friend' means?"

Aethelfrith nodded. "Friend." He grabbed Galahad up in a strong bear hug.

Released him.

"Yes," said Galahad, recovering. "Friend." He surveyed the plains and rivers and ocean once more and felt one with this country, with these fellow human beings sharing the sight with him. "We must have a name for this land. Let's call it England." He tasted the sound of the name. Smiled.

Aethelfrith grinned and spoke in Celtic: "Yes, England."

"England," repeated Ellanie. "Yes, it has a pleasing sound."

The pattering of horse hoofs sounded from below a jutting cliff. They watched as riders came into view.

"Father!" cried an astonished Galahad.

"It's Lancelot," said Ellanie, disbelievingly. "How did he find us?"

Galahad wondered as well. But Lancelot's companions told the tale. Two horsed Hill People flanked the captain. They must have led him here. . . .

From the corner of his eye he saw Modred slink away, but he was too excited by the arrival of his father to think that the youth might be deserting them.

With a flourish of his cape Lancelot dismounted. His eyes held such relief to see his son that Galahad felt very bad. His guilt was assuaged when Lancelot grabbed him around the middle and hefted him up.

"I thought you were dead, you rascal," he said.

"Father," said Galahad. "We were on a quest."

Lancelot nodded sagely, a ghost of a smile appearing on his lips. "Yes. My friends here who showed me where you were apprised me of the situation. A very odd tale." He rubbed the back of his head ruefully. "These People of the Hills have odd ways of greeting travelers."

One of the small riders dismounted, wearing a crooked smile on his hairy face. "You went for your sword, Lancelot. We had no choice."

"We must go and tell Arthur," said Ellanie in a serious knowing voice. "And Lancelot. We've found a new recruit."

"So I see," murmured Lancelot, eyeing Aethelfrith suspiciously as he let Galahad back down to the ground.

The big Saxon stepped forward casually and clapped a gawky hand upon Lancelot's shoulder. "Friend?" He smiled hopefully.

"We'll have to see about that," replied Lancelot.

"Father, he's a good fellow. He wants to meet Arthur."

"A Saxon wants to meet Arthur?" Lancelot wiped his eyes as though to remove his incredulity. "Well, I've never seen one that wanted that save to spit the king with a sword."

"He wants to live in peace, Father." Galahad put his head against Lancelot's side. "Father, I understand everything now. It's all here. I know what Merlin wanted me to know."

"Yes," said Lancelot. "Even when the old devil's not around he still exercises his power." He shook his head. "But it is a good power, I suppose."

"Look, Father," Galahad said, pointing out at the land around them. "Just look."

Lancelot looked.

And he saw.

viii

King Arthur of the Britons sat upon his modest throne beside his round table. The attendance of captains was sparse this day. Only Bedivere, Kay, and Gareth. But they all sat enrapt at the story that Lancelot, Galahad, and Ellanie had brought back with them. They seemed a trifle leery of the brawny Saxon but pleased at his insistence, through Ellanie's translation, that he wished to be a faithful and true subject to King Arthur.

Modred was not in attendance. Indeed no one had seen him since he had stood with the small party atop the mountain. But no one seemed to miss him much . . . or worry about his absence.

Finally, when the Saxon was finished, Arthur stood, feeling proud. "These *are* great things that we hear this day. Reaching through the years, the architect of this kingdom, Merlin the druid, has reminded us all of our mission." He smiled, feeling a warmth at the memory of his teacher. "May the story of the Holy Grail be told to all."

He stepped around the table to where the Saxon stood. He put a fatherly arm around the lad. "But most important we have a sign of coming times. A symbol of hope for peace within this land. A hope that no more blood may be shed upon this treasured soil and that its several peoples may unite in a common friendship." He looked at the Saxon seriously. "Aethelfrith. You are a son of Kent, and you are a son of mine from this day forward. You will be given land on our borders. You shall help the Saxons to understand us . . . and explain your people's situation to us. You will be our go-between, so to speak. May many Saxons become like you. Let us just hope that more of your people see the wisdom of your choice. And may your family grow and prosper from this day forward, through the chronicles of time."

A curious feeling in Arthur told him that this Kentish lad *would* prosper, his family spread.

A sudden inspiration hit Arthur. He drew his shining bladc, Excalibur, and handed it hilt first to the youth. "Know that this is a gesture of my trust for you, Aethelfrith. Know that Excalibur, my sword, is symbol of my reign here in Britain. Just as it is in your hands for a moment, so it is in all the hands of my subjects."

He took the sword back. "Wield what it stands for with courage and hope, for I pray that one day this blade may no longer taste blood, but may bite into fertile soil and make a garden of our island."

He smiled broadly. "So then. Enough of the solemnity. It is time for drink."

Immediately servants brought forth mead and ale. Aethelfrith grabbed a whole pitcher for himself and drank heartily, to general boisterous approval. Arthur, feeling very good, took Lancelot aside. "What did I tell you, my friend. Everything has turned out well."

"Yes," murmured Lancelot, as though not terribly convinced. "Very well."

"So Lancelot. Every day I am more sure of the need for a master of Cam—and every moment I am more positive that you would be the best man for the job."

"I have decided, Arthur, that in this you are not being wise," breathed Lancelot. "You do not want an aging soldier like me in charge of what you hold dear.

No. I will not accept your offer, though I thank you for it."

Arthur was surprised. "But you have not had time to think about it! Have supper with Guinevere and me tomorrow night, and we will have a good argument on the subject."

A look of pain invaded Lancelot's eyes. He turned away. "No, Arthur. Tomorrow morning Galahad and I depart for Gaul."

"But Lancelot," said Arthur. "We need you *here*, still. This is your home now."

"I shall only stay a season or two. No more than a year, certainly." He looked at Arthur, smiled slightly. "You are right, Arthur. This is my home. This is the home of all who truly love it, this Britain, this England. You have made the dream bear fruit, and I love you for it." He breathed deeply, as though to gather force to push out what he had to say. "But never become too smug, too self-confident about what you have done. Never become too proud."

"But Lancelot. We all have much to be proud of!"

"In your education, Arthur," said Lancelot, after sipping his drink, "did you hear aught of the concept of Greek tragedy?"

"Certainly. Merlin taught me all he could. Something about the gods driving down men."

"Heroes, Arthur. Heroes with too much pride." He looked away. "I know nothing of Greek gods. I wonder how much I truly know of the Christian God. But I do know that a man who walks with his head in the clouds will trip." He turned and looked directly into Arthur's eyes. "There are forces in this land that seek to undo what we have accomplished, Arthur. Beware."

Lancelot squeezed Arthur's arm in a brief gesture of love and companionship, then stalked out of the room.

In leaving he passed Guinevere where she sat, and Arthur saw them lock gazes for just a moment. Guinevere turned away and refilled her cup.

A brief spasm of jealousy moved in King Arthur and then was gone, leaving only a dim resonance.

He looked about the room again, and the vague sadness that had filled him at Lancelot's words misted away into the fun and good feeling that surrounded him.

ix

Modred stood upon the mountain.

He could not get enough of the sight. He had been there for silent days, living amongst the sights and smells and tastes offered there as though he lived in a dream made real.

Eventually he decided that enough time had passed. He was about to begin the journey back to Cam and make amends to the court there. Let them punish him. He'd done nothing terribly bad. And in the future he'd be such a good fellow. Terribly good. He'd bow and he'd grovel before his father like a good son should. Oh yes he would.

His time had not yet come.

But when it did. . . .

He clutched his hand until his fingernails dug into the palm as he stared out upon the sun-filled land.

Yes, he thought. *When my time comes the end of* my *quest will be near.*

He looked out upon the land once more, wanting it, and then he walked down the pathway.

An echo of crazed cold laughter seemed to linger a moment in his wake . . . and then all was peaceful again.

CHAPTER 14

The Griffin

In seven years the fort on the great hill overlooking the river Cam had grown to immense proportions.

Its first defense wall had been torn down and rebuilt a dozen times, each time encompassing more ground. The walls presently enclosed a small city containing some two thousand persons.

New buildings of timber and thatch had been raised almost every year. The outer defenses had been continuously expanded as well. The main wall was now surrounded by four separate rings of earthworks. Lofty watchtowers had replaced the older, shorter ones. From the roof of each the flag of Pendragon flew in the wind.

From the platform of one of these towers Arthur surveyed the bustling, noisy community that had replaced the original, relatively modest fort. He was old now—or felt that way. His knee joints had begun to stiffen. In bad weather his healed wounds ached with varying degrees of pain. His hair was almost pure white. But an occasional glimmer of the old fire and enthusiasm sparkled in his eyes as he inspected the outer earthworks, being reinforced again by a corps of several hundred sweating men—

He strolled slowly around the platform to the inner side, gazing at the teeming life far below. Gardens grew between the buildings. Livestock grazed. The forges and the armory resounded with the clang of metal being hammered and the rhythmic shouts of men practicing foot drill.

In the large garden immediately behind the long house he recognized Queen Guinevere sitting with her women. Farther away, beside a barracks, he saw the familiar figure of Lancelot of Gaul, instructing his young, well-built son Galahad in the finer points of engagement with the spatha—

Young Galahad had fought valiantly in several engagements with the Saxons. He excelled in friendly competition with Arthur's remaining captains. The high king had watched the young man's progress with great approval, and although he realized that Galahad's primary allegiance would always be to his father, he made the boy a welcome member of the company of the round table. Galahad occupied the chair Merlin had called the Siege Perilous because Arthur had been so impressed with the vision of Britain that the young man had brought back from his quest for the Grail.

Weariness had become Arthur's greatest enemy. There seemed to be no end to the Saxon horde. The invaders were no sooner pushed back at one place than fresh shiploads landed at another, and he and his cavalry were again off and fighting—

Here at Cam things were not much better. He and the queen were still comrades, still friends, and still not lovers. Occasionally dark suspicions tormented Arthur.

He had never touched Guinevere in all the long years of their wedlock. But he found it difficult to believe that she and Lancelot had acted with similar restraint. When the worm of jealousy ate too deeply into his mind—usually at night—he couldn't rest. He imagined the worst about his queen and her outwardly polite and respectful lover.

The strange triangle, fraught with immense suffering for all, had produced another circumstance—a lack of heirs. Arthur was reminded of this by what he now heard climbing the stairs inside the watchtower. He could not see the new arrival. But he recognized the familiar snarling and growling of the huge hunting hound that always walked at his heels. His son Modred had sought him out again—

The young man appeared, splendidly dressed in an apple-green cloak and bright leather chest-plate. Modred bore little resemblance to Arthur. At nineteen he was slender, almost frail. His skin was pale, never seemed to color in good weather. His hair was close-cropped and quite dark. The boy's large, dark eyes reminded Arthur of Morgan—

Modred jerked on the rope leash that kept the hunting dog contained. *The boy seemed to derive great pleasure from controlling such a source of potential violence*, Arthur thought. Once, drunk, Modred had accidentally let the hound loose. It had attacked a small boy, bitten away half his face. Modred whipped the dog furiously afterward. Yet he had been unable to hide a smile—

As Modred's slippered feet brought him across the platform Arthur noted again—with annoyance—that the boy wore the spatha with the griffin of Cornwall engraved in its pommel stone.

"The emissary to King Ulric returned this morning, Father," Modred said.

"Did Ulric receive my messenger?"

"He did not. The King of the Wall shut his gates and wouldn't even look at your petition."

Modred jerked the leash of the straining, slavering dog. Dark hair fluttered against his pale forehead.

"Need I remind you that King Ulric is the fifth nobleman to abandon you in as many months?" Modred asked.

Arthur struck a fist on the rail of the platform:

"Why are they turning against me? That's what I can't comprehend!"

Modred shrugged in a studied way. "The question of succession can't be brushed aside forever."

Again Arthur shook his head. "But why now—after so many years? Who raised the question? I don't think it became a cause spontaneously—"

Modred gazed blandly toward the outer earthworks aswarm with men carrying buckets of dirt and fresh timber.

"Who can say why a fire ignites precisely when it does, Father? You know lesser kings and barons have always been jealous of your power. Perhaps one of them now sees himself as your successor. Especially since you've named no other."

No matter how hard the young man dissembled he could never hide his ambition. Disgusted, Arthur said:

"Nor will I— until the exact moment when I choose to do so. I am well aware of your interest in the issue, Modred. And I have told you before—straightforwardly: I see nothing in your behavior to indicate your capacity to wear this sword." He closed a hard, veined hand around Excalibur's pommel.

Modred went white. With a purse-lipped smile, he said, "I realize you consider me unmanly—"

"We need not discuss particulars."

The hunting hound began to growl again. Modred crouched down, stroked its sleek head. The dog grew quiet under his touch.

Fearing him? Arthur wondered. He feared Modred himself.

Through all the years of Modred's boyhood, Arthur had frequently regretted his decision to take the child into his household. Modred was a creature of shadow, not sunlight. Intelligent and resourceful, yes. But he lacked principles.

Perhaps it all went back to his rather frail body. Perhaps cleverness and connivance were required to compensate for a certain delicacy that Arthur found effeminate, even distasteful—

"Well," Modred said at last, "one thing's quite plain. To me—and to your followers. You'll never beget an heir from her—"

He gestured contemptuously at the figures of the women in the distant garden.

Arthur bristled. "You will speak of the queen with proper deference!"

"Speak with deference about a cuckolding whore?"

"Modred, your tongue's vile."

"I only tell the truth, Father. Do you think there's a king or baron or captain who doesn't know how she and Lancelot feel about each other?"

"That may be so. But they behave honorably—"

"In your presence, yes."

Arthur's eyes pinned the willowy young man:

"If you have evidence against them, bring it forth. Otherwise keep silent."

"I have no evidence—as yet," Modred said. "But that doesn't make such difference to your followers. *They* are convinced you're being cuckolded. *They* are convinced you'll never beget an heir—so the Pendragon flag will come down, finally. So one by one they're slipping away. Preparing for the inevitable struggle for power. If you would only name a successor, however—"

"Enough!" Arthur growled, stalking to a corner of the platform, away from the young man and his great fanged dog.

"Then at least put an end to the queen's treachery!" Modred cried. "This—excess of Christian compassion for Guinevere and her lover only makes you seem weak and foolish."

"You have great scorn for honor and mercy and justice, don't you?" Arthur said, not looking around.

"Yes! No matter what you think, this kingdom is not held together by—"

"But it is!" Arthur thundered, whirling. "Those are the linchpins of all we've built over the past years!"

Modred shook his head. "How deluded you are. The queen mocks your idealism—and you're blind to it. Just as you're blind to the real binding force that keeps the house of Pendragon paramount. It isn't mercy, Father. It isn't compassion." He pointed at sheathed Excalibur.

"It's force. Fear. I warn you again—the malcontents think you've grown too old."

Modred slipped closer to Arthur, dragging the hound by the leash. "If you would hold fast to all you've gained, you must convince your followers that you're still a strong king. The place to start is with the queen and her lover. Kill them."

"Leave me!" Arthur said, so shaken that Modred actually seemed frightened. "I'll hear no more of your schemes and your lies." His mouth thinned. He couldn't conceal his loathing. "If I was uncertain about your fitness to be high king before, you have removed all doubt."

Modred turned red. "I beg the king's pardon. I only attempt to serve—"

"Yourself."

Arthur spun away, trembling.

With an almost sickening sense of relief he heard Modred slip back into the tower and descend the stairs, his leashed hound panting at his heels.

For some time Arthur stood immobile. Then he returned to the inner side of the platform, gazing first at Guinevere in the garden, then at Lancelot, still shouting and laughing as he parried Galahad's thrusts near the barracks. The ring of steel drifted up to the tower—

For one dreadful moment he wondered whether Modred's accusations were true. Did the queen and Lancelot meet secretly—?

Ashamed, he put the question out of mind. But he couldn't shake off another thought quite so easily: Modred spoke the truth about the weakening of his authority. More and more men were drifting away from his standard. He already knew they were uneasy about his age, his lack of heirs. Modred clearly was not acceptable to them, any more than he was acceptable to Arthur himself. Therefore it was logical for them to reestablish themselves as individual rulers—prepared to assert themselves in the turmoil that would inevitably follow Arthur's death.

Dear God! If only things had been different, and he and Guinevere had been wed in more than name! If only they had birthed a child—

The longing suddenly turned to rage. There wasn't a man who would blame him if he executed Guinevere and Lancelot on suspicion alone. Modred said—such an action would show the malcontents that he wasn't weak, ineffectual—

The fury drained out of him, leaving a residue of sorrow. Even after twenty years men still saw compassion as weakness. It almost seemed that the whole struggle, undertaken with such high hopes, had been in vain—

Beset by problems he did not know how to solve, Arthur walked inside the tower and stood in the shadow at the head of the stairs, shivering.

ii

Seated in a relaxed fashion at a table in his quarters in the long house, Modred tested the cutting edge of his dagger on the ball of his thumb.

He felt oddly peaceful. The violent wrath of the morning was gone. From his father's lips he had heard the final denial of his right to the throne.

So the time for idle hope was over. It was time to act.

His eye fell on the pommel stone of his sword lying on the table. *Time to act.* The island-kingdom should and would be ruled by Cornwall, not Pendragon. Modred had always had a greater affinity for his mother's side than for his father's—

"My lord?" said a faint voice from the gloom behind him.

"You will not speak until I address you," Modred said, rising. In the corner the hunting hound growled softly, heightening the terror of the old man who had been awakened and dragged to Modred's quarters in the silence of the night. Men were always more easily frightened at night.

Smiling benignly, Modred walked to the kneeling man.

"Are you fond of your position in the household, Colin?"

"Aye, sir," the elderly man gulped. "I've been the master of the high king's kitchen fifteen years or better."

"And you take pleasure in seeing your children growing up?"

"Yes, sir, great pleasure."

"It would be a shame if they were—" Modred gestured with his dagger. "—cut down in life's prime, shall we say? Just as they're ready to marry—raise families—yes, that would be a pity. It would be equally sad if you were suddenly removed from your position and turned out to find your living as best you could."

"If either happened, I'd die, sir—God's truth!" Colin swore.

"Then of course you'll say nothing if I ask a boon of you, Colin." Modred smiled.

"What—what boon, my lord?"

"A simple one. You will introduce a certain substance into the high king's food at intervals I will specify—no, don't speak. The intervals will be infrequent at first, then closer together. You are in charge of the kitchen—the king in his Christian trust employs no taster of food and drink—it will be easy, Colin. Easy and free of risk. The only risk is that which will follow if you decide not to honor my request."

Blinking, the old man quavered. "My lord, I catch the sense of what you're saying, but—I can't do it. I love his majesty."

Suddenly Modred's right hand streaked down, touching the knife point to Colin's wrinkled throat.

"Don't you love your children more? And your life?"

Modred's eyelids barely flickered. Yet the hound caught the signal. Growling, it crossed the stone floor, its claws tick-tacking. Great yellow eyes fixed on the kneeling man. The hound's tongue lolled over yellow fangs.

The old man gazed at the dog in abject terror. Then: "If I refuse, sir, you'll—?"

"I don't say. I swear. Your youngest girl will be the first to go. Followed by the others—and you last of all. Each—passing—will be so carefully arranged that it will seem accidental. But the deaths will be painful, Colin. Extremely painful."

Almost weeping the old man covered his face. "All right—all right—"

A moment later he lowered his hands.

"What exactly must I put in the king's food?"

"Why," Modred said with a charming smile, "only a little pinch of poison."

iii

"And by securing these roads with our men—" Kay knuckled the parchment map spread on the round table. "—we should have ample warning of any new Saxon thrust from the east. I ask the king's leave to arrange for companies to take up the watch duty."

Kay frowned as his words dropped into silence. Nearby Modred sat in a chair vacated by one of the captains who had recently gone home with all his men. Modred appeared to be immersed in stroking the head of the hound sitting beside him.

Young Galahad said to Kay, "He doesn't hear you."

Sorrowing, Kay looked at Arthur's slumped figure across the table.

The high king's skin had taken on a waxy pallor. His half-lidded eyes seemed to glitter, as with fever. His hands, resting on the arms of his chair, were bone-white, almost lifeless.

"Majesty—" Kay began, louder this time.

Arthur roused, spoke with difficulty.

"Will you repeat what you said, Kay? I seem to be afflicted with drowsiness tonight."

"Begging the king's pardon," Bedivere rumbled, "but

we have all watched unhappily these past weeks while some kind of sickness weakened you. Perhaps a leech should be summoned."

"No—" Arthur hitched himself higher in his chair, slightly more alert. He blinked several times; his eyes were watering. "It's only a spell of the winter ague, I think. What was your comment about guarding the rivers, Kay?"

Miserably Kay mumbled, "The road, majesty."

Arthur's face convulsed, as if he felt excruciating pain. Gareth and Gawain exchanged glances. So did Lancelot and his son. On every face save Arthur's there was a clear indication of doubt about the king's strength.

But Arthur was adamant:

"Go on, I tell you!"

"Yes—well—to resume—"

Kay launched into a repetition of what he had already said.

Frowning in a concerned, thoughtful way, Modred studied the map as Kay spoke, his hand working excitedly back and forth over the hound's fur.

iv

"Captain!" the handmaiden cried, a moment after Lancelot thrust open the door from the corridor. Flushed and windblown, Lancelot shot a glance at the closed doors to the inner rooms.

"I must speak to the queen. It's most urgent."

"She's in her solar. She's not prepared to receive—"

Lancelot's left hand tightened on a rolled scrap of parchment. With his other hand he pushed the woman aside. He stalked to the right-hand door of the three and burst into the solar.

Guinevere, wearing only a morning robe, sat on the bench in front of a small loom. She whirled around:

"You know I'm not to be interrupted when—"

Then she recognized the man closing the door. In spite of herself she turned pink.

"Why have you come here? We agreed we must never meet alone—"

Lancelot's sun-browned face was confused. He held up the rolled parchment.

"I came because you bade me to. In the most urgent terms."

"But I didn't—!" She ran to him, snatching the parchment.

"The hand is yours." He pointed at the message she was reading, her face dismayed.

"Who brought you this?" she asked.

"One of the servants. I don't recollect which—"

"You must leave at once!" she cried, her dark eyes full of fear suddenly. "They've gulled you—look!"

She thrust the parchment at him. "Examine it closely. You'll see the writing is only a fair approximation of mine."

Instantly Lancelot's hands iced. The sunny solar became a chilled, forbidding place.

A culprit sprang to mind. Lancelot named him hesitantly.

"Is this some test of Arthur's? Devised to see whether we—?"

"*No, you cannot!*"

Lancelot spun when the woman in the antechamber cried out. He and Guinevere heard the thump of heavy boots, struggling, oaths—then another outcry, loud thud, as if Guinevere's woman had thrown herself against the door.

Lancelot's eyes slitted as he smelled the treachery. He thrust Guinevere back toward her loom, drew out his spatha. There were more sounds of struggle, then a voice he recognized:

"Woman, this is your last warning. Remove yourself from the door."

"Not until you lay up your swords! It is unseemly to come in here with—"

The sentence became a shriek. In horror Lancelot saw the reddened tip of a spatha crack through the door at waist level. The tip disappeared, withdrawn. The woman moaned. Run through—

By the fox-faced young nobleman who booted the door open an instant later.

Behind Modred, Lancelot saw a gaping Bedivere—and Kay and three others.

Stepping over the gutted body of the woman, Modred moved the bloody point of his sword in a small circle. "Why, this is a pretty sight! The queen in private chambers with a man who is not her husband. You're in disarray, madam," he said with mock horror, pointing at Guinevere's mussed robe. "Your lover was impatient, was he—?"

Lancelot knew the trap was all too real. Alternately he felt immense shock and immense rage. Modred's large eyes watched him, bright with cunning. What Lancelot read in the other faces he preferred not to recognize—

For a moment he felt an urge to swing at them with his sword. Then, in righteous wrath, he decided against it:

"Is it you who arranged this little entertainment, Modred?"

"I have no notion of what you mean, sir? A number of us were having a meal—and a servant whispered that you were busy in the queen's—chamber—" He gave the last word obscene emphasis. "I was not even the one who was told first. The servant approached—"

Bedivere started to confirm it, but Lancelot laughed. "That would be easy to arrange, good Modred—just as it would be easy to imitate the queen's handwriting after a little patience."

"I am still confused about your meaning," Modred retorted. "The evidence of my eyes is quite clear, however." He gestured. "Take him to the king."

Eyes blazing, Guinevere thrust forward. "No! Lancelot is innocent of your foul accusations—!"

Modred shrugged. "If that's true, the high king will perceive it." He glanced at the Gaul, then gestured again with his sword.

"Seize him."

"*Wait!*"

Guinevere snatched up the fallen parchment.

"Lancelot came here believing he had received this message from me. I did not write it!"

Skeptically Modred scanned the parchment. "It resembles your hand, my lady." He passed the note to Bedivere. Each man scrutinized it, resulting in more stares of concern and confusion.

It was Bedivere who spoke for them all:

"My lady, I doubt there's one of us who has ever seen your handwriting before."

"My husband has!"

The scent of danger was so overpowering that Lancelot growled his words:

"Illness has blurred the high king's vision lately. But perhaps my lord Modred is counting on that."

"Your defenses are very pretty." Modred smiled. "But they remain defenses. You have been caught. You are a traitor, a defiler of the queen, and you will be punish—"

Modred's words blurred into a shrill cry as Lancelot hurled forward, struck Modred with his shoulder, and bowled him backward against the half-open door.

Feebly Modred tried to thrust with his own sword. Lancelot was faster. The point of his blade caught Modred's wrist at waist level, pricked the skin, drew blood.

Squealing, Modred dropped his weapon, clapped the wound to his mouth.

The other men backed into the outer chamber. Crouched again, sword ready, Lancelot stalked them.

"You are my fellow captains. I have no wish to harm any of you. But it's for you to decide. I am going through that door."

Bedivere held up a placating hand. "We should let Arthur settle—"

"My guilt? But it's been settled! Or should I say arranged? Now—do you wish to fight me? Or will you open the way?"

"Christ's wounds, take him!" Modred shrilled, on his knees. The men facing Lancelot looked at Arthur's son. While their attention was diverted, the big Gaul moved again, throwing himself forward to knock Kay aside and scramble into the hall.

Lancelot's thudding footfalls died away as Modred gained his feet, snarling:

"Keep the queen under guard. She at least will go to the king for judgment—"

Like one demented he ran out, shouting alarms.

By the time Modred reached the outdoors a dozen men and women trailed behind him. He cursed as he saw the southwest gates swinging open while a horseman bridled his impatient mount—

"*Don't let him through*!" Modred screamed, dashing toward the gate. The creak of the great hinges and the stamp of Lancelot's horse prevented the gatemen from hearing until it was too late. Bent low over his horse's neck, Lancelot galloped through the opening.

Overcome with rage Modred stopped in the center of the yard. Beyond the open gates he saw Lancelot's horse plunge into the river and disappear in the beech woods on the other side. He spat oath after blasphemous oath.

A moment later he regained his composure, muttered:

"Well, one slipped the noose. But one remains."

He turned and walked briskly toward the crowd outside the long house. He regretted Lancelot's escape. But his real quarry—Arthur—was still inside the fort.

V

An almost sexual excitement filled Modred as he strutted before the dais, outlining the charges against Guinevere. The queen knelt on the paving stones by the lower step, her dark hair spilling over her shoulders, and her morning robe only partially concealed by a fur cloak someone had lent her for the sake of decency.

Arthur was slumped in his judgment seat. Excalibur rested across his thin, wasted legs. His pupils were tiny glittering points beneath his drooping lids.

The poison had worked well over the past few months, Modred thought. Theatrically he held up the parchment.

"A loyal man of the household brought news of the queen's immorality to the captains. To Bedivere in fact. We followed him to see for ourselves—"

The main hall was hushed, crowded with nearly every inhabitant of the hill fort. They packed against the walls and strained to hear Modred's words.

The young nobleman flung a hand at Guinevere.

"We found her as you see her—closeted in her solar with Lancelot, the evidence of their sin discarded on the floor in their flagrant haste to couple—"

Modred heard a sword clack partway out of a sheath. From the corner of his eye he spied Galahad, fire-eyed among the captains. The boy might be a problem. He would have to play the rest of the game delicately—

"I did not write that accursed note!" Guinevere said to Arthur.

"I—" The high king coughed. "I wish to see it."

"Of course, majesty," Modred purred, climbing the dais and slipping the parchment into Arthur's feeble hand.

Arthur unrolled the little sheet, held it at an angle. His eyes watered as he struggled to decipher the words in the light of bracketed torches burning above his chair.

"It appears—" He struggled for breath. "—it appears to be the queen's hand—"

Guinevere jumped up. "Your sight deceives you, my lord!"

"Beg pardon, madam, but you are the deceiver!" Modred cried. "The traitor. The whore—!"

A gasp ran through the hall. Arthur barely stirred at that last, damning word, Modred noticed. Good.

"There is not a man or woman within a stone's cast of this fort who has not heard of Lancelot's affection for the queen. An affection years old. An affection of consuming intensity—!"

Suddenly Galahad stepped forward, fingers curled around the hilt of his sword. Modred drew a quick breath.

"That may be so," the young captain said. "I'll not deny that much of your story. But at the same time every man and woman in this hall knows my father's character—including his loyalty to the king. My father never let personal feelings override that loyalty."

"Unless—" Modred began.

"Unless *what*, my lord?"

Modred swallowed. "Unless, after long abstention, the spurs of lust grew too sharp to bear—"

"You sneering clown!" Galahad yelled, sword pulled and glittering in the torchlight.

Modred whipped out his own blade, but the captains restrained the struggling young man.

"Release me!" Galahad shouted. "The note's a trumpery and so is his story!"

"If so," Modred thundered, "why did your father flee—instead of standing here and proclaiming his innocence?"

"Because he knew he wouldn't be believed!"

Modred waved. "More likely it's because he was not innocent at all."

Galahad lunged again, held back only by the exertions of Kay and Gareth. Modred pivoted away, terrified but pretending indifference. He approached the dais again.

"This wrangling is troublesome and unnecessary, majesty. I submit my case to you. Does the queen deserve punishment, or does she not?"

Arthur shifted in the chair, dabbing a spot of moisture that had seeped into the corner of his lips. *How pathetic he looked!* Modred thought, the ecstatic feeling consuming him again. Arthur raised an emaciated hand.

"I must ponder the matter a little—"

"Begging his majesty's pardon, what is there to ponder? The evidence is clear—!"

Modred leaped up two steps, saying in a loud whisper:

"Surely the king has heard the tales of Lancelot's affection—"

The answer made Arthur shudder with agony.

"Of course I have."

"What has happened today only confirms common knowledge!"

That set the men and women in the hall murmuring in agreement. Although it was still daylight, only a few weak sunbeams penetrated the high, narrow windows. Modred's torch-born shadow seemed to leap and caper as he played to the crowd's reaction.

"For months your loyal subjects have begged you to root out this foul growth staining the honor of the Pendragons. For years the culprits have laughed at you. And now, when they flaunt their indecencies—and are *caught*—surely you won't shrink from your duty. The penalty for royal adultery is known to everyone."

He whirled on Guinevere. For the first time she seemed cowed. Her dark eyes were fearful as she listened to a mounting grumble of wrath from the crowd. Only one voice, Galahad's, opposed it.

"The penalty," Modred shouted, "is *burning*!"

The words rang and echoed. Arthur grimaced. Then he glanced at Guinevere, his lidded eyes coming fully open for a moment. Were those tears of anger? Modred wondered. Tears of pity? Or only the rheum of a man slowly dying—?

"Burning is severe and final," Arthur whispered. "The evidence is not altogether conclusive—"

"I saw otherwise!" Modred exclaimed.

"Still—I oppose—"

Arthur swayed in the chair. There was a gasp from the crowd.

Arthur's head slammed back against the chair. His fingers constricted on the arms. He struggled for air.

Covertly Modred glanced at the captains—the key to this desperate moment. He nearly crowed at what he saw: consternation and dismay that reduced them to inaction—

Feigning alarm, Modred sprang toward them.

"Bring a litter! The king's sickness has overcome him. Until he is himself again—until he has the strength and reason to carry out his duties—"

Now Modred whirled, moving toward the dais. He saw Arthur's lips forming a word:

No. No.

Modred's heart thundered like a drum. This was the most dangerous moment of all. His success depended upon whether he had read Arthur's condition correctly—

He climbed to the dais, holding the crowd's attention by speaking as he moved:

"—the king must have a regent to serve in his stead. He is too ill to judge the queen's case. Too ill to take the field—"

"*No, no*!" the voice whispered from the chair. Modred barely heard it. He knew the others could not hear it at all.

He thought he saw Arthur's pupils glare with anger. The king realized what he was doing. But Arthur only raised one limp hand, then let it fall again.

Modred reached out.

Lifted Excalibur's sheath with one hand—

Drew out the great engraved blade with the other—

"Therefore—in the interest of maintaining the kingdom's strength and unity, I, his majesty's son, will serve in his stead until such time as the king is fit to resume his duties."

Fingers tight around Excalibur's hilt, Modred sweated and stared at the captains. A few were outraged by what they had just heard. But as long as they pitted no more than scowls against him—

"You see?" he said quickly, sounding compassionate as he touched the king's pathetically thin hand. "It's necessary. He cannot even speak."

Men ran forward with a hastily improvised litter. Modred said, "Bear the king to his chambers and fetch the leech from—"

Dreadfully strong fingers closed clawlike around Modred's wrist. He nearly shrieked aloud.

Arthur seized him with a grip whose tenacity signaled the king's ferocious struggle to exert his authority over the wasting weakness of the poison. The king was glaring at him. Unable to talk, gasping for air—but glaring.

Modred wrenched away. The thin fingers loosened. Only Arthur saw Modred's brief smile.

"He wearies," Modred said. "Bear him away quickly—"

As the litter carriers rushed to surround the king Modred returned to the foot of the dais.

"As regent I will pronounce judgment in his stead." He pointed Excalibur at Guinevere's white throat. "This woman is guilty of adultery. Seven days hence, when she has made her peace with the Almighty God, she will be burned."

Guinevere stared at the blade, her disbelief changing slowly to horror. Without moving his head Modred scanned the fringes of the crowd. Not a hand raised against him. *Not one*! His loin shook with unholy joy—

A joy marred by the sudden movement of Galahad, who stalked to the doors.

Passing the round table, Galahad paused at his own chair, the Siege Perilous. With a baleful glance at the king's regent he flung it over.

The chair struck with a great clatter as Galahad strode out of the hall.

vi

"*Kay.*"

The faint voice stirred the grief-stricken captain who kept vigil at the high king's bedside.

Kay glanced at the pale, sweating face illuminated by a single wick floating in oil. Clumsily Kay knelt, not even certain Arthur had spoken.

"*Kay—*"

The enfeebled hand sought his, closed. Arthur's lids flickered open.

For an instant Kay saw some of the old animation in Arthur's eyes. He responded by leaning close to the king's barely moving lips.

"What of—Modred? I have—a memory of him—taking Excalibur."

"That was four days ago, majesty," Kay whispered. "He has taken more than your sword."

"What—what do you mean?"

"Modred sent messengers to the kings who deserted you. Now the soldiers of those kings are *his* soldiers. They're pouring into Cam right now. Modred continues to claim he'll step aside when you recover, but—"

"I will never—" Arthur fought for breath. "—never recover in this place. I suspected—days ago—that I was not—sick from a natural sickness. I saw—the truth—in Modred's face—when he seized the sword. I think he—gave me poison."

Kay gasped. "Surely not, majesty. Not your own son—!"

"He was born—to destroy me." The feeble hand closed again. "We must get away from this place. With all the men still loyal to us. But it—must be done secretly. Else— he'll never let us go. Once I'm free of the poison—"

Silence.

Arthur was dozing off again, murmuring:

"*Free of the poison*—"

Kay stood, wiping a sleeve across his mouth.

"Majesty? In three days the—the queen will burn—"

Arthur didn't hear.

Kay hesitated only a moment longer. He slipped out of the room and boxed the ears of the sleeping boy supposed to keep watch in the outer corridor.

"Find Bedivere and bring him. And Gawain and Gareth. Quickly, boy. *Quickly*!"

vii

"*Poison?*" Bedivere raged. "We should have guessed it, I suppose—"

"The point is we must get him out," Kay said. The conspirators were meeting in the chamber where the king slumbered. "The time must be propitious—we'll leave by the north postern. We can easily overwhelm the two guards. But we can only go when the rest of the fort is occupied."

"Aye, the postern's the best way," Gareth agreed. "We'd never make it with an armed dash to the gates. Modred has too many companies of soldiers garrisoning the place now."

"You will arrange for the horses," Kay instructed. "Gawain, you'll carry the king. Bedivere and I—" He touched his sword. "—we'll open the way—and the throats—between here and the postern."

"When?" Bedivere wanted to know.

"At the only time everyone's eye will be elsewhere. Sunset three days hence—when Modred puts the torch to the queen's pyre."

viii

Roused from her prayers by a knock at the door, Guinevere slowly made the cross-sign over her breast and rose.

One of Modred's captains was waiting outside. He wore the livery of Ulric of the Wall, who had delivered five hundred fighting men back to Modred at mid-week.

The captain was nervous. Guinevere, by contrast, seemed composed.

"The monk has come to walk with you, my lady," the man said, standing aside, then going to wait in the hall. A cowled father shuffled into the outer room.

Guinevere nodded calmly. She was past all grief. Perhaps she deserved the fate that had come to her. She had betrayed the high king in thought, if not in deed—

"I am ready, Brother Abbot," she said, fitting the royal golden circlet over her hair. The monk apparently failed to hear. "I said—"

His back toward the outer door, the monk raised both hands, as if about to pray. He whipped one hand to his lips, brushing back the edge of his cowl as he made the sign of silence.

It took every ounce of Guinevere's self-control not to cry aloud.

Within the cowl familiar eyes watched her.

The eyes of Lancelot of Gaul.

ix

Modred had ordered the burning to be held well beyond the outer earthworks, so as not to endanger the towers and buildings. The pyre had been laid on the muddy shore of the river, opposite a thick grove of beeches that stirred fitfully in the light wind.

A thousand people or more had found seats on the earthworks overlooking the scene. All around the pyre itself, an armed ring, stood foot soldiers provided by the kings and barons who had returned to the Pendragon standard once word reached them about Modred's regency.

The sullen sunset sky cast a red pall over the area. On the watchtowers twin banners unfurled—the griffin and the dragon. Very shortly, when pretense was no longer necessary, the dragon would come down—

Hand on the pommel of Excalibur, Modred waited near a small fire being kept alive by a bare-chested smithy with a bellows. Impatiently the young man glanced past the soldiers surrounding the pyre—

There she was coming down the rude track that led up to the gates. She walked among four guards, a monk at her side. The holy man had reportedly come all the way from Tintagel to give her succor in her final hours.

Standing next to Ulric and several of the other kings who had returned to the royal standard, Modred found himself uneasy. He asked himself why. The answers robbed him of the feeling of total triumph he should have been experiencing.

For one thing Guinevere looked astonishingly calm. Her head was raised—almost proudly.

And Modred didn't see any of Arthur's most loyal captains in the crowd. He supposed it wasn't mandatory that they attend the execution.

What disturbed him most was the sight of Galahad, yonder beyond the soldiers guarding the pyre. Lancelot's young son was mounted. Why?

The fleeting fear of a rescue attempt disturbed Modred then. He dismissed the idea as an impossibility. But he kept fingering Excalibur's pommel stone nervously. He had erred in not eliminating Galahad—and Arthur. He would rectify that error before the night was over.

The soldiers parted to let Guinevere through the ring of spears. Modred frowned as the people on the earthworks fell silent. A moment ago they had been laughing and chattering. Now their faces were somber. Were they finally realizing what was about to happen?

Well, it was too late for the fools to regret anything. They had hailed Modred by not raising a hand against him when he seized Excalibur.

The monk came on slowly, one hand resting on Guinevere's elbow. A huge flock of birds went sailing across the western horizon, whose deep red light turned the purling Cam to a sheet of scarlet. Impatiently Modred snatched up a brand, thrust it into the small fire until it flamed.

He waved the flaming brand, exclaiming:

"We have delayed long enough, Reverend Father. Hurry—!"

Modred had difficulty seeing what happened next. The spitting torch blinded him a little. But he thought the monk had stumbled.

There was a clattering behind the soldiers on guard. A horse?—again the flame prevented Modred from seeing clearly.

He flung the torch away, his eyes astonished. Galahad had maneuvered his horse near the monk and the queen. He was dismounting.

One of the soldiers yelled a warning. With incredible speed the monk caught the sword Galahad tossed him. Sweeping Guinevere up in his other arm, he gained the saddle in an instant.

Modred screamed. "*Treachery!*"

That some madman would attempt to rescue the queen was beyond comprehension—until Modred heard another, louder sound behind him. Ulric seized his arm.

"In God's name, my lord—whose men are those?"

Modred whirled. Three columns of riders were pouring from the beech grove across the river. Swords winked in the sunset light.

Confused, some of Modred's soldiers raised their spears against the holy man, who held the queen. The monk shied his horse forward. Galahad's blade chopped in a flame-lit arc—

Two of the soldiers fell, cut open in a most unholy fashion.

Frantic, Modred screamed orders. The monk charged the horse at the ring of men. They scattered. The horse thundered straight at the unlit pyre, leaping over it in one immense bound.

The monk's cowl flew back—and Modred's mouth flew open at the sight of Lancelot.

In another moment the riders reached the near shore. They formed a mounted guard around Lancelot and the queen.

Ulric literally ran at his own foot soldiers, shoving them forward in pursuit. Modred kept screaming incoherently—

On the earthworks he heard a few yells of encouragement. He spun—saw Galahad slipping away—

"Kill that one!" Modred howled.

A quartet of soldiers doubled back and surrounded the young man. Galahad attacked, kicking and mauling with his fists until a spear gored his throat.

Modred saw Galahad fall. The young man's face was almost beatific. He seemed to be straining for a glimpse of his father, who was lost among the milling horsemen. Their murderous swords chopped fingers, hands, and whole arms from the helpless soldiers Baron Starkad of the North had ordered forward.

Starkad himself reached the water's edge, stabbed at the stallion of one of Lancelot's men. The man reared his mount out of the way, raised his spatha for a downstroke—

"No, spare him!" Lancelot shouted. The man didn't hear. His blade broke Starkad's skull and pitched him into the shallows. A deeper redness spread in the crimson water—

Storming toward the river, Modred shrieked and raged. The horsemen turned, hacking down the last few soldiers who had managed to reach them. They thundered back across the Cam, sending up immense plumes of scarlet spray. They plunged into the beech grove, lost in the shadows between the trees.

x

Not until the following dawn did one of the captains who cast lots—and lost—go to Modred and inform him in a trembling voice that somehow, during the lightning attack that had carried Guinevere away, Arthur had been taken from his sickbed by four of his captains.

When Modred heard the news he turned his hunting dog on the luckless soldier. The man fled through the corridors of the long house, the dog's bark and the regent's maniacal cries ringing out behind him.

xi

"Care for her well, Sister," Lancelot said.

It was just before dawn. Cool shadows filled the gallery of the nunnery of St. Sulspice, well east of the Cam fort.

The robed abbess compressed her lips, still not quite approving of the disreputable figure who had led a band of armed horsemen to the gates and was now parading himself in God's house in a bloodstained monk's habit.

The tall captain added, "I only ask a moment's privacy."

Grumbling, the abbess walked away.

"I won't leave you here unless you are certain—" Lancelot began.

Guinevere's face gleamed faintly in the starlight. "I'm certain, beloved. You gave me back life. But I have great penance to do. By loving you I betrayed the king, who loved me."

"We're equally guilty, I'm afraid," Lancelot sighed. His heart almost broke at the sight of the lovely woman clad in a coarse gown the abbess had provided. "And it's no consolation that neither of us meant to do him harm. We harmed him anyway. By raising doubts about his wisdom—his ability to handle the affairs of his own house. I'd go back to Cam and try to raze that accursed place—except there would be no purpose in it now. I doubt Modred will let the king live long. And my own son's gone—"

"That grieves me most of all," Guinevere said, tears like gems at the corners of her eyes. She touched him. "You lost him for me."

"Aye. But he fell bravely. And when we met in secret across the river to arrange the rescue he was as much in favor of it as I—"

Still, the words were gall as Lancelot remembered the bright, brave lad who had given him such joy as he grew and took his place at the round table.

"Where will you go?" Guinevere asked.

"To the seacoast, then back to Benwick. I've not seen Gaul since last Galahad and I crossed the Narrow Sea so many years ago. I'm old, Guinevere. Old and chilly, and my bones ache—"

He tried to smile. "Maybe that's age. Or seeing a dream pulled down to ruin."

He stroked the softness of her tear-dampened cheek. "Like you, I owe God—and Arthur—penance."

She shook her head. "You shouldn't feel such despair! You accomplished great things—all of you! The Saxons were held back—"

"Yes, we did win time for the island. And there are signs the invasions are slackening. In twenty years many of the Saxons who came here to pillage have made homes. Have become—" Again he tried to smile. "—good Englishmen, almost. Certainly as good as I am!"

"Think of the rest, too. The king's justice and mercy—"

"That," Lancelot said, "I fear Modred will destroy as if it had never existed."

Distantly a choir of nuns began to sing a morning prayer. The sweet, keening notes filled the gallery with ethereal sound.

"We aren't perfect creatures, Guinevere. But God knows the high king was as perfect a man as there has ever been."

"And I never loved him properly. Perhaps it's impossible to love a demi-god. Perhaps that's why I loved you inst—"

He stopped her mouth with one grimy palm. "We mustn't speak of that. It's done."

A man materialized in the shadows.

"Captain? The men are anxious to be gone to the coast. They fear capture if we dally—"

"I'll be there in a moment."

The man vanished.

"At least within these walls, Modred can't touch you. He hasn't gotten so powerful that he can flaunt the right of holy sanctuary."

"Kiss me before you go—?" she whispered.

He did, sweeping her into his arms for one long embrace as the choir pealed forth its praise of the Christian God and the daylight began to tint the eastern horizon.

But there was no light in Lancelot's soul as he left Guinevere without looking back.

She stood a long time, listening. She heard the clatter of his troop starting up and riding away. Then, uncontrollably, she began to weep.

The stout abbess appeared. She circled Guinevere's shoulders with a comforting arm, saying nothing.

CHAPTER 15

King Arthur

Goats bleated in the nunnery stable as Guinevere emerged, her novice's habit dusty and flecked with straw. She brushed a bit of the golden stuff from her forehead as she approached the bent, toothless sister who had summoned her.

The autumn sky had a lovely hazed gold look. The fall always made her melancholy. This year, though, she felt it less than ever before. Perhaps it was because her first months in the nunnery had brought her a true sense of fulfillment—

"You called me, Sister?" she asked in a suitably meek voice.

The older woman nodded, frowning. "Once again St. Sulspice has been disturbed by visitors. Making free with our well—clattering about with their weapons—"

Guinevere shook her head.

"I'm sorry, Sister, but I don't understand why I—"

"Because the captain of these ragtag soldiers asked for you. The mother abbess told him our novices were expressly forbidden to see persons from the outside. He demanded an exception be made. He's waiting in the chapel—"

With a skeptical shake of her head she added, "His soldiers carry shields showing the red dragon. The man claims to be their leader. The king everyone says is dead."

Guinevere's dark eyes widened when she heard that. Her heart began to pound. She gathered up the hem of her habit, exposing her sandals and her ankles. The elderly nun gasped her shock.

Like a stone from a sling, Guinevere shot by the older woman—in quite unseemly fashion, she realized as she reached the chapel that she didn't care.

The chapel blocked her view of the nunnery yard. But she could hear the stamp of horses: rough male voices. As she pushed the chapel door inward there was a tension, an expectancy within her that no vows of piety could suppress—

She saw him.

He was standing in the light that fell from windows above the altar. His long hair was almost white, his cloak ripped and filthy. An unfamiliar, ordinary sword hung at his hip.

A thrill of joy swept over Guinevere as she hurried forward. He barely resembled the man who had lain ill at the fort by the Cam. His waxy pallor was gone. He stood straight and his eyes were clear—

But his face was more seamed than she remembered it. His mouth looked stern, as if weariness and struggle had cast it forever in that mold.

Arthur bowed his head, an acknowledgment: "Sister."

"My lord—" She started to kneel. He caught her hand. The touch of his fingers communicated a tenderness that almost made her weep.

"You mustn't kneel to me any longer," he said. "You serve a higher lord now. With contentment, I trust?"

"With—great contentment, finally." She nodded. But the old guilt was beginning to clutch at her. "The folk who pass by here said the high king was dead—"

Arthur smiled then. But without humor.

"I would have been if I'd stayed at Cam with Modred. My son conspired to have me poisoned. The night Lancelot stole you away my captains seized the opportunity to spirit me out of the fort. We've been hiding in the great southern wood ever since. The effects of the poison are gone at last."

"How—how did you find me, Arthur?"

He gestured. "Why, it's no secret that the queen sought sanctuary with the nuns of this order."

"More than sanctuary." She forced herself to look at him. "Forgiveness."

"That's why I came here, Guinevere. To tell you—" He touched her again. "There is nothing to be forgiven."

"Yes there is! I betrayed you. I was never the wife you needed. My feelings for—"

She stopped, unwilling to speak the name.

"Lancelot?" Arthur shook his head. "I knew from the hour we were wed that you loved him and not me. But I forced you to live a marriage that was impossible from the start. The fault is mine. I came to tell you that and to say I feel no anger. Not against you—and not against Lancelot—"

As if sensing the question she wanted to ask he went on. "We haven't had word of him since he brought you here, then crossed the Narrow Sea to Benwick. I'm praying he can be found there; I need every sword."

"Then the fighting's not over?"

"Not quite. Modred won't sleep easily until he's certain I'm dead. Since my men and I have left our sanctuary in the wood, we've been seen frequently. My son will soon know I'm alive—if he doesn't already. I have no heir to take the throne. But at least I can prevent the succession of a vicious weakling who would undo all I've worked for—"

His face a study in pain, he paused for a moment. Then: "I took this chance to see you because I may not have another." Arthur gripped her shoulders in his strong hands. "I hope your days will be filled with peace and joy, Guinevere. Remember that whatever sins I committed against you I committed out of love."

Weeping, she clasped his right hand between hers. She pressed her lips against the scar between his thumb and first finger. She felt a shudder of release sweep through her. When she gazed at him again the cloud of pain in her eyes was gone.

"I have never received a greater boon than the one you just gave me, my lord."

In an almost fatherly way he caressed her cheek. Perhaps it was a trick of the light, but his eyes seemed opalescent.

Tears? she wondered suddenly.

"I'd best be going. The men are impatient. God keep you safe, Guinevere—"

"And you, Arthur. I'll pray He will."

Starting toward the small door beside the altar, he turned back at those words. "I'm afraid you'll pray in vain. My time's almost done. All I ask of God is a few more weeks—and Excalibur back in its rightful hand."

Eyes bleak, he bent and vanished through the doorway.

She lingered in the chapel until she heard him gallop off with his men. Then she approached the altar.

She knelt, her head bowed in a shaft of light. Silently she thanked God for the peace he had granted her.

ii

Campfires glowed around the standing stones, where Arthur's partisans were gathering. They had come on horseback in groups of ten or twenty, summoned by Gawain and Gareth, who had been in the saddle the better part of two weeks.

A few shabby weather-worn pavilions had been erected at the makeshift camp. In front of one a staff was planted. On it the red dragon flag hung limp in the chilly air. A fat autumn moon hung just over the horizon.

The camp was strangely quiet. Men moved back and

forth, seeing to their mounts and their weapons, but with no singing and little conversation.

Outside the king's pavilion, Bedivere, red-cheeked from a hard ride, confronted the sons of King Lot. Both of them were white-haired now.

"Where has he gone?" Bedivere demanded. "I must speak to him immediately."

"He's in there—" Gawain gestured at the moon-etched ring of stones rising from the darkening plain. "By the altar, I think."

Gareth said uneasily, "Communing with ghosts, no doubt."

"There are ghosts here to haunt all of us," Gawain said. "It was a happy time when I first saw this place. A time of hope—of promise."

Bedivere ignored the remark, stalked to the entrance of the ancient ring. After a moment the brothers followed.

Bedivere stepped inside. He spied the high king's solitary figure by the altar. With an eerie shiver he saw that Arthur's hand was resting on the crevice from which, years ago, he had drawn the great sword—

Bedivere clumped across the yellowed grass, making noise deliberately. Arthur roused, turned—

"You saw them?"

"Aye," Bedivere rumbled. "And turned back the moment I did."

"How many are there in my son's host?"

"Two thousand at least. A great many foot soldiers from the kings who deserted you—but that's not the worst of it." Bedivere's face wrenched angrily. "The whelp has companies of Saxons, too. I was hard put to tell whether it was an English army or a foreign one!"

Arthur looked stricken.

"The Saxons have come to his standard? How did he get them?"

"Recruited them from the farms where they've settled, I don't doubt. Modred's clever. He knows barbarian blood can't be transformed in a generation—nor completely tamed by the taking of a wife and the birth of children. Many of the Saxons probably lost kin when we first fought them. They'd be glad to help bring you down."

"Two thousand—"

Despondent, Arthur shook his head and leaned on the altar with both hands.

"And we have only eight hundred."

Gawain stepped forward from the shadow cast by one of the huge stones. "We can't risk an engagement here on the plain, majesty. We'd be encircled and destroyed in a space of hours."

The counsel was sound, and Arthur knew it. He began to pace, his thoughts speeding—

Suddenly he whirled on them, his old patched cloak belling at his shoulders:

"The coast, then. We'll go southeast to the coast—to the point where crossings are always made. Lancelot's sure to land there. And the terrain's rough. With our backs to the sea there'll be no way for them to circle us before Lancelot arrives."

"You're counting heavily on Kay's pleas being heeded," Gareth said.

"Kay will bring him." Arthur nodded. "Lancelot will come."

But Gareth still doubted. "Is that a certainty, majesty? Or only a hope?"

Arthur's worn face, half in shadow, half in moonlight, took on a severity that made Gareth ashamed. But the king answered truthfully:

"Some of both. Pass the order—the men are to have a good night's rest. At dawn we ride for the coast."

iii

Arthur slept badly, plagued by nightmares in which he saw his son, armored for war, leading a Saxon host. When he awoke he was trembling. Cold perspiration bathed his body.

He pulled up the hide blankets. They seemed to afford little warmth. All he could think of was Modred commanding the barbarians he had fought so hard to defeat and pacify.

But the longer he dwelled on the vision, the angrier he became. Modred was the darkness, the divisiveness and ruin that had been staved off at such great cost. Modred must not be allowed to win the final battle—!

In the shadows of his pavilion Arthur let a new thought surface. Until this hour he had laid his plans only in terms of defeating Modred's army. That, and reclaiming Excalibur, had been his chief aim.

Now things were changed. Modred had roused the pacified Saxons—repeating the same, fateful mistake of Vortigern. Years ago, Vortigern had admitted the enemy, only to find himself the enemy's victim. Arthur realized military defeat was not enough this time—

Modred, flesh of his flesh, must die.

iv

A wind of almost gale force beat against Arthur as he clambered to the top of the rock. He gazed despairingly at the foam of the surf far below, then out across the whipped waves of the Narrow Sea. A dull gray sky stretched from horizon to horizon.

At his elbow, shouting to be heard above the wind, Bedivere said, "Even if Lancelot were waiting to cross right this moment, he couldn't. The wind is wrong."

"But we can't evade them any longer," Arthur said, clutching the rock to keep from being buffeted off the cliff. He swung slowly, looking inland.

In the near distance, beyond the belt of coastal rock, the noon cookfires of his small army glowed. He saw tiny figures moving lethargically. His men sensed the desperation of Arthur's position—

Farther west, along the ridge line of the rolling hills, a vast black smudge stretched north and south for half a league or more. Modred's army, drawn up on the hilltops, had no need to hurry now that the quarry was caught. Arthur's scouts had already brought him word that escape along the coast in either direction was impossible. Modred had completely ringed Arthur's position and could move his main force quickly to block an escape attempt in either direction.

"With luck the wind might change in a day's time," Bedivere commented. "But we don't have a day. Modred will likely advance before nightfall."

"Then," Arthur eyed the white-capped water. "Then we must buy the day, Bedivere."

"Buy it? How?"

"Take half a dozen men and white banner." There was humiliation on his face as he swung around to the burly captain. "We will ask my son for a parley."

"Parley with that filth? *No*!"

Arthur seized his arm, his eyes furious:

"It's no longer a question of pride, captain! It's a question of survival! Set the parley for noon tomorrow. Tell Modred I'll come in person." Arthur grimaced. "He'll grant the request. He'll be pleased to see me humbled. I doubt he knows about Kay going to summon Lancelot. He probably won't suspect we don't want a truce, just a change in the wind—"

He clapped Bedivere's shoulder. "We'll have our pride back in full if we fight with Lancelot's host helping us."

Mollified, Bedivere clambered down from the rock. Arthur stayed, clutching the cold, wet rock and searching the murky horizon.

V

At noon the next day Arthur rode out of camp with Bedivere, Gareth, Gawain, and three other captains.

All carried their whitewashed shields with the red dragon device. But the shields were hung from their saddles and scraps of white cloth were tied around the hilts of their swords.

Bedivere and Modred's representative had agreed on the site: a declivity not large enough to be called a valley, equidistant from the hills and the rocks along the shore. The high king's men had taken up defensive positions in those rocks, in case Arthur's party encountered treachery.

Cantering along, Arthur felt gloomy. Modred's army covered the skyline. All night and all morning the wind had continued to gust out of the northwest. Even granting an immediate shift, open boats would take most of a day to negotiate the Narrow Sea. Thus Arthur's current hope was to stretch this parley into a second one. As many as necessary, in fact, until the weather changed—

Riding beside him, Bedivere pointed downward and to the left. A coppery snake was sliding out of sight among some large stones.

"That's the fourth I've seen," Bedivere called above the noise of the hoofs.

"Well, don't act rashly if you see another," Arthur cautioned. "No sword is to be drawn at the parley."

Bedivere spat. "I'd sooner converse with a snake than with your son. At least a snake gives a little warning before it strikes."

Arthur raised a gauntlet to cool the truculent captain. Gareth swung wide around the party, galloping to a position in front so that the flag whose staff rested in a stirrup socket could be clearly seen by the half-dozen men waiting at the appointed place.

As Arthur and his followers rode down the gentle slope of the declivity, his feeling of humiliation returned. Gareth's banner was ripped in four places. The edges were frayed. Mud disfigured the dragon.

Modred's banner was clean and new. It snapped on the staff planted in the ground, displaying its device—

The griffin of Cornwall.

Arthur scowled. The deceitful young man had revealed himself at last. He was no Pendragon. His aim was to revenge himself on the Pendragons—the house that had orphaned his mother and widowed his grandmother. How blind Arthur had been, never to perceive that while the boy was growing up—

In contrast to Arthur's cracked leather and ripped link-mail, Modred's war apparel was new and fine. As the high king and his men reined in, Arthur saw with disgust that his son had not even bothered with a sheath for Excalibur. The bare blade hung ostentatiously from a looped thong at his waist.

Arthur's knees ached as he dismounted. But he held himself erect as he walked toward the younger man.

Behind Modred, Arthur saw two captains he recognized as belonging to King Ulric. Modred had also brought three stocky, bearded Saxons, aglitter with arm rings from wrist to shoulder.

Modred smiled smugly as his father approached. The usurper was bareheaded. His close-cropped hair fluttered on his forehead. Campaigning outdoors had done nothing to deepen Modred's color. He was as pale as ever.

"Good morrow, Father," he said.

Behind Arthur, Bedivere swore. The king held out a hand for silence. Without taking his eyes from his son he said, "I expect to be addressed by my rightful title."

"But you have none!" One of the Saxons snickered, then ambled over to sit down on a large stone. He rested his war-axe on one knee.

"God's blood, I didn't come here to suffer insults—" Arthur began.

Modred shrugged. "You requested this parley, not I."

Arthur struggled against his rage, composed his face. "Yes, that's true. I wanted to see whether we could reach an accommodation—"

How bitter and false the words tasted on his tongue! But even as he spoke them he felt a subtle change in the air. He glanced quickly at the silver disc of the sun half-hidden behind clouds. Was it his imagination or was the wind—?

Yes, by heaven! The long grass in the declivity had

ceased to whip back and forth. If this was not just a momentary lull, but the beginning of a change—

"I hardly see any basis for accommodation," Modred said, flexing his right hand above the pommel stone of the royal sword. "Or any reason to talk, at all, if you want the truth."

"But if we could come to some agreement, then there needn't be a battle. Innocent men would be spared—"

"I doubt you'll find any innocent men under my standard," Modred joked. "Most of them were blooded against your horse-troops. They want a chance to repay you."

"Why waste breath on this sneering swine, majesty?" Gawain exclaimed. Modred flushed, seizing the hilt of his sword.

Again Arthur's raised hand held his captains in check. But he was having trouble with his own temper, too.

"What sort of agreement did you have in mind?" Modred demanded.

"Frankly I don't know yet," Arthur said. "We'd have to discuss the various possibilities at some length. Perhaps a co-regency—"

Modred chuckled. "Out of the question. I'm afraid you're not facing the realities of the situation, Father."

Turning, he indicated the men blackening the distant ridges.

"You are encircled. Badly outnumbered. I have no need to sue for peace—or for terms of any kind. Only you do."

Abruptly Modred's smile grew coy. "However—if you were to beseech me to undertake a discussion of what you call the possibilities—and if you were to do so in a manner befitting my new station—"

The dark eyes glared. "Shall we say kneeling?"

Arthur fought to hold his tongue. It was difficult. He heard his men grumbling.

"Well, Father? What's your answer?"

Modred's captains waited too, hands not far from

their hilts. By sheer will Arthur kept silent, trying to ignore his son's smirk. Arthur drew a breath, listening—

The wind had died. He must prolong the discussion. Even if it meant enduring the worst sort of insults from—

The Saxon perched on the rock let out a yell and jumped up. His war-axe flashed in the silver-gray light.

The move sent Arthur's hand to the hilt of his own weapon. Bedivere leaped in front of him. But Arthur glimpsed the sinuous copper body that had crawled from under the rock to startle the Saxon—

"*Gareth, don't!*" Arthur cried—too late.

Taking the Saxon's raised axe as a sign of hostility, the son of Lot had hurled himself forward. Gareth's spatha stabbed through the barbarian's throat.

The Saxon's tongue protruded. His eyes bulged. He hung impaled on the blade until one of Modred's captains cleaved Gareth's neck from the side.

Blood fountained, spattering Modred and the grass. Modred screamed, "Treachery! Damnable *treachery*—!" He fled on his horse up the far side of the declivity, then suddenly reined. He pointed at the shaken Arthur with Excalibur's long, shining blade:

"We'll do our parleying on the battlefield, whoreson!"

Roweling the horse, he galloped out of sight with his men.

Gawain ran forward, knelt, and clasped his brother's nearly decapitated body in his arms. Arthur left him alone.

When Gawain finally raised his head and walked back to the others, the face of the son of King Lot was bleak and ugly.

Arthur felt defeated. He had gambled for time and had lost. Even if Lancelot launched his boats at this very moment, it would be a day before he reached the English coast—

And already, from the western ridges, rhythmic thudding drifted out.

Modred's drummers—giving the signal for the army to form and advance.

The enemy officer charged his horse across the litter of human and animal corpses. A smirk broke the grime and gore that turned his face to a hideous mask.

Up came his spatha, its target a ragged, reddened man who had been giving succor to one of his own fallen captains.

Almost spent, Arthur let Bedivere's head loll. He staggered to his feet as the officer thundered toward him—

The man had come upon the high king in one of the pockets of rock along the shore. There, since early afternoon of the previous day, the battle had raged.

It was a battle whose savagery was almost beyond Arthur's comprehension. Through the late afternoon and most of the night, his eight hundred had resisted the onslaught of Modred's host. The enemy struck the natural fortifications of the rocks like endless waves from a savage sea.

The main action had moved up and down the coastline for almost a league. Now, as the officer spurred his stallion to attack, Arthur realized that the center of the battle had shifted again. He had gone to see to Bedivere, having glimpsed the burly captain toppled by an axe. In moments Arthur's troops had slipped away to other ground—

The area in which the officer confronted Arthur was a roughly circular open space walled head-high by slabs of rock. The hard ground, bathed in late morning sunlight, was a nightmare tangle of hacked limbs and severed heads, fallen men and gutted animals. The stench of blood and offal sickened Arthur as he blinked to clear his blurring eyes, preparing himself to counter the mounted man's stroke—

Sword clanged against sword. A chip of metal flew

from the cutting edge of Arthur's overtaxed blade. The impact of metal against metal staggered the king. The officer maneuvered his horse for another blow—

Arthur smelled the stinking lather on the horse's flanks, saw its huge eye rolling as the officer controlled it with savage jerks of the rein. He darted back as the officer's spatha whistled through the air, missing him narrowly—

His boot slipped in the slime of a dead Saxon's entrails. Gasping, he sprawled on his back.

The officer reared his horse, intending to let the animal's slashing hoofs crush the high king's head.

Sprawled on his left side among corpses, Arthur drove his right arm up. His sword tore into the horse's belly.

Arthur rolled frantically away from the murderous hoofs and the outpouring of warm blood—

Unhorsed, the officer scrabbled toward the sword that had been jarred from his fingers. Arthur killed him with a single stab in the side.

Arthur freed his sword with a wrench. He wiped horse blood from his cheeks. One thrust ended the pain of the thrashing animal he'd gutted to save his own life—

His cloak was torn away. His leather armor was ripped. His brown-streaked white hair was tangled and bloody. As he glanced one way, then another, he resembled an ordinary fighting man caught in the midst of an incredible carnage—

Where was the center of the battle now? he wondered blearily. He listened, heard drumming, shrieks, the ring of weapons in the rocks somewhere to the north—

Only those rocks had kept his force intact and fighting valiantly for almost an entire day. Hidden in the rocks Arthur's men had forced Modred's to come to them, to separate into columns that could penetrate the narrow defiles between the tumbled stones. With Modred's army thus divided, Arthur's had multiplied its potency.

His men fought more bravely than he had ever known Englishmen to fight. Yet he knew the inevitable end—defeat. Modred—whom Arthur had not seen since the aborted parley—simply kept replenishing the columns that assaulted the positions in the rocks. Arthur, with fewer men and three-quarters of those already fallen, could not hold out much longer—

Operating more by instinct than by reason, he began to work his way northward through the stone corridors. He came across hideous sights: friend and enemy lying together in the final, bloody communion of death—

He passed between two jagged stones and emerged on a short ridge that afforded a more general view of the area. The ridge itself had recently witnessed fighting. Here and there, men flopped and floundered, pleading for help or praying for God's forgiveness in their last moments.

Gasping for breath, he stumbled along the ridge, hardening his heart to the pleas of the wounded. He must be at the center again. Only he could keep his men from breaking under the onslaught of the fresh companies that were marching from Modred's encampment far on his left—

All at once he felt wind against his face. Sea wind, salt-tanged. He stared out over the water—and almost wept with joy.

The northeastern quarter of the sky was darkening, indicating a storm blowing from the continent. But closer in to shore he saw sails—six—eight—ten of them! The great sails were blazoned with the lion of Benwick. The ships were black with the tiny figures of fighting men.

God be praised. Lancelot had answered.

Elated, the king felt a little of his strength return—

"*Father?*"

Arthur whirled. Riding up the slope on the west side of the ridge was Modred. Excalibur swung at his hip.

For a moment Arthur couldn't puzzle out what bothered him about Modred's appearance. Then the answer came. His son's leather armor was spotless. His pale face showed neither dirt nor blood.

"So," Arthur panted. "You've let others fight for you all day—"

Modred smiled. "A prudent general commands from a distance. Spares himself for greater accomplishments than dying. I was just informed your army was routed—"

Arthur flung out an arm from which links of broken mail dangled. He pointed his nicked sword northward.

"You were misinformed, whelp. They're still fighting. And now they'll win!"

Laughing hoarsely, he swung the sword seaward.

"Ride up here and look, Modred. There are ships from Gaul below. They'll beach within an hour. Lancelot has come from Benwick."

"Liar!" Modred screamed, spurring forward as Arthur dodged out of his way.

Seeing the sails bearing toward the beach, Modred mouthed frightful obscenities. In the north the sky blackened. The wind began to whip Arthur's hair again. Full flickers of lightning lit the sea.

"Did you come to find my corpse, Modred?" Arthur called. "A little prematurely, I think—"

"I was told you had fallen." Modred was white, almost frothing at the lips. "I was told."

Arthur shrugged wearily. "In battle one man's easily mistaken for another, and I've been cut off from the main fighting for some time—"

The lightning glared, casting an eerie radiance on the grotesque tangle of dead and dying. But the devastation was no more horrible than the sudden gleam in Modred's eyes.

He slid from the saddle, smiling a mad smile—

"You're an old man, Father," he said, slipping and stumbling through the bloody mounds of flesh. "Your time to die is long past. I'll give truth to that false report—"

Modred's right hand clenched. He lifted the engraved

blade. Excalibur caught another flare of lightning and shone with a chilling radiance.

"*With your own sword.*"

vi

They fought savagely, two figures in a landscape of the dead.

The darkening sky was brightened occasionally by lightning. It flamed white, showing Arthur the animal fury in his son's eyes. Thunder paled, reducing the clang of the swords to a small, bell-like sound.

Each parry of Modred's slashes was given at great cost. Time and again Arthur nearly lost his footing. Modred pressed him steadily backward along the corpse-strewn ridge. Each blow of Excalibur against his own blade sent great jolts of pain down Arthur's sword arm. A sharp hurt in his chest testified to his weariness—

His son seemed to have demonic strength, now thrusting, now leaping aside to avoid Arthur's feeble lunges. Arthur realized he was being driven to the rocks at the southern end of the ridge. How far behind were they? He dared not look around—

He feinted. Modred turned sideways in response to the thrust that never came—

Instead of striking, Arthur twisted; the rocks were closer than he had thought. Modred had nearly backed him into a stone cul-de-sac—

Lightning forked across the black heavens. Arthur pivoted back to his adversary again, sidestepped as Modred lunged. Excalibur whistled by Arthur's ribs. He hacked downward with his own nicked blade.

Modred jerked back in time. Arthur's cut missed.

Modred swung at Arthur's head. Desperately the high king thrust his sword almost straight up to block the stroke. Excalibur hit his blade. Bluish sparks spurted as the metal edges raked each other—

Hilts locked, Arthur and Modred stood no more than two steps apart. Arthur's despair was deepened as he stared into his son's huge, maddened eyes—the eyes of a crazed beast—

Without warning Modred spat in Arthur's face.

Laughing shrilly, he retreated a pace and kicked out. His left boot slammed into the high king's belly.

Arthur gasped and dropped to his knees—onto a dead man's torso. His mouth filling with sourness, he whipped his sword up to parry Modred's arcing, whistling cut—

His blade whined and rang at the impact. It snapped a hand's width from the hilt—

The forward end of the sword fell away. Lightning blazed. Modred's face was a leering mask as he saw his father kneeling helplessly.

The light died. Arthur flung the useless hilt away, scrambled backward toward the rocks. Modred's two hands brought Excalibur down viciously. Arthur was gone; the only victim the blade claimed was the man already dead.

Another sword! Arthur's mind cried. *Another sword or I'm done—!*

Three long steps brought him up against one of the great stones at the end of the ridge. In the windy, howling darkness it was difficult to see the fallen men and horses—let alone find a discarded sword. Modred sensed his advantage and came running. Excalibur rising over his head, still held two-handed.

Once more Arthur slipped. He fell sideways as the engraved sword streaked down—

Without conscious thought Arthur wrenched his shoulders aside. Excalibur rang like a great bell, striking the rock and skittering downward—

Driven into a cleft where two stones pressed together.

Modred jerked. The hilt slipped from his hands. He screamed, spittle-lipped.

He twisted and tugged. Excalibur was securely wedged.

Arthur clambered up. For the first time since the terrible contest began there was an almost happy look on his face—

Perhaps Modred's palms were too slippery to pull the great blade loose. Whatever the reason the high king's son whirled wildly and began to root through the corpses, hunting another weapon—

Arthur went rigid. He leaned his head back and closed his eyes, letting the full force of the wind buffet his face. He seemed transfixed in some silent plea—

The thunder crashed, deafening. A lightning bolt sizzled straight down toward the ridge. Arthur felt droplets of rain on his eyelids.

He didn't cringe from the fiery bolt that seemed to be coming straight toward him. Again there was no conscious thought—only a sudden leap of his hands for the hilt of Excalibur protruding from between the rocks. A strange, almost supernatural shudder ran through him as his aching fingers took the hilt—

Lightning burst around him, making the scarlet dragon within the crystal pommel stone shimmer—

Terrified, yet filled with an ecstatic sense of power, Arthur gripped the hilt while the thunder tore the world. When he opened his eyes again—

Excalibur was free.

The red-spattered pain of his face changed to an expression of almost holy joy. There was no fear in him now. None at all.

He released his left hand as the downpour started. Through the rain Arthur saw his son running at him with a blade snatched from among the dead—

Eerily, effortlessly, Arthur's right hand seemed to float forward, the great length of Excalibur like a mighty extension of himself. Too late, Modred shrieked and tried to stop—

Modred's expression of insensate fury changed to one of utter agony as he impaled himself.

He gazed down in astonishment. Then he uttered a howl of pain. Instantly Arthur's feeling of power was gone. His tears began to mingle with the rain on his cheeks.

Modred's mouth opened. But it was not a cry of hurt that came forth; it was the shriek of a wounded beast.

And then as Arthur stood with his sword arm extended, Modred took a stumbling step—

Another—

Pushing himself forward so the blade drove deeper into his bowels—

And deeper—

Modred's face convulsed at every step. Disbelieving, Arthur felt the awful shudders of Excalibur as his son strained forward.

Modred's right arm raised. Too late, Arthur realized why his son was doing this. Gutted, he couldn't reach his father first.

Now he could.

Hanging midway up the great blade, his belly leaking blood, Modred struck—one swift, sure stroke that slid beneath Arthur's leather armor, into his vitals—

Arthur bit down to keep from screaming. Modred dropped his sword. His pupils rolled upward in his head. Rain streamed from his chin.

Shrieking again, he tried to grasp Excalibur. Arthur released the hilt and toppled forward, clutching his dying son's shoulders for support.

Locked in a strange embrace, father and son crumpled slowly among the dead. The lightning guttered out. The rain fell furiously in utter darkness.

vii

When Lancelot saw the place to which Arthur's soldiers had carried him, his face wrenched with sorrow. What kind of pavilion was this for a high king—a half-dozen spears stabbed into the ridge, with several cloaks snagged over the butt ends to form a canopy?

Lancelot reached the makeshift structure at day's

end. His mail and leather were red from an afternoon's fighting.

A leech and a pair of captains guarded over the still, white-faced figure lying on a pallet of cloaks. Arthur's right hand rested on Excalibur's blade, which someone had laid atop his body.

Sheathing his sword, Lancelot bent and crept under the canopy that dripped rain.

The storm had lasted no more than an hour. But the sky was still misty. Now and again, over the distant crash of the surf, wounded men cried out. Otherwise the field of battle was silent. Captains and soldiers slipped through the murk, searching for friends, phantom figures—

"Is he—?" Lancelot began.

The aging leech shook his head. "No, there's a little breath left in him. I have bound him up as best I could. But I fear the wound's mortal."

"Who killed him?" Lancelot asked.

One of the captains said, "Modred. We found them lying together."

Heartbroken, Lancelot dropped to his knees. He touched the waxy face. With an immense effort of will he whispered, "Majesty?"

In the silence rain plopped on the ground. Lancelot couldn't escape the dreadful conviction that he had somehow strayed into the realm of the dead. The bent figures of the searching soldiers and the dimly perceived rocks had a grotesque, sinister aspect—

He inhaled sharply. The high king's eyes were open.

Lancelot bent to hear the feeble voice:

"I—knew you would come. What—what of Kay?"

Lancelot shook his head. "He fell while my soldiers drove Modred's army from the field. They scattered like chaff once word spread that their leader had fallen. I was also told that Gawain was killed. It seems you and I are the only ones left to carry on the round table—"

The sad, forced smile on Lancelot's face faded. Arthur was moving his head from side to side with great effort:

"I will—follow the others—soon enough."

"No!" Lancelot cried. "You must live! Rebuild—!"

"I cannot," Arthur whispered. "It's done. We—held back the dark—as long as we could. Perhaps longer—than other men—might have done. Because—"

The thin hand lifted from Excalibur, touched Lancelot's.

"—because I had great captains. Now—you must give me a boon—"

"Anything!" Lancelot vowed softly. "Only promise me you'll hold the will to live—"

This time it was Arthur who tried to smile. The smile became a grimace as he arched his back and groaned.

"I—might have the will. But—the strength is gone—"

The hand crept slowly back to Excalibur, the fingertips resting on the engraved inscription.

"Take this—and—cast it into the sea—so that none can use it wrongly—"

"*No!*" Lancelot burst out again, unable to hold back his tears. "Majesty, you will recover—"

"I will—not."

"You must keep the sword. It's the only symbol of hope the people have—"

"You are wrong. They—have their own—strength. The truths—I tried to teach them. The—travail they endured. They—have lived through the worst of—the Saxon night. There—may be more darkness—but—never as deep—as it might have been—if we had not—held it back a little—"

Suddenly the dying king's eyes seemed to clear. Lancelot thought that he gazed at the young Arthur, fierce-willed and sure.

"I *command* you. Take the sword to the sea!"

Then, by some miracle of strength, the high king closed his fingers over the hilt just below his throat. He raised Excalibur so Lancelot could grasp it.

The captain from Gaul hesitated, glancing to the others huddled under the rain-soaked cloaks. They wouldn't look at him.

"*Take it*," Arthur whispered.

Broken, Lancelot gripped the hilt, touching Arthur's fingers. How icy they felt—

Stumbling, the tall captain made his way from the pavilion and started down the seacoast side of the ridge. Oppressive dread overwhelmed him. Sinister shapes moved soundlessly nearby: soldiers prowling, hunched and ominous—

Presently he left the worst of the carnage behind. He emerged between two great stones at the edge of the bluff. Far below, half-hidden in the mirk, he glimpsed his moored ships. There was no horizon visible, only a lifeless blending of dark water and mist. The last light was fading from the day, just as hope was fading from his heart—

Slowly he lifted Excalibur and stared at it, thinking of all it had represented. All the hope and courage and dedication—

With a growl that was half rage, half misery, he raised the mighty sword over his head and whirled it in the air once.

The air seemed to sing softly.

Twice—

The sword gathered momentum. The high, piercing note grew louder—

On the third swing he let go.

Excalibur arced upward, as if straining toward heaven. Then it began to descend. The moment seemed suspended, timeless, as Lancelot blinked back tears again.

God's name—was it a trick of his battle-weary mind—?

Or was that some great, spectral hand bursting upward from the misty sea beyond his moored vessels?

Down and down the sword tumbled. Vast cascades of water fell silently from the upraised, waiting hand—

The hand closed on the hilt of the falling sword and held it aloft a moment; then slowly, majestically, drew it beneath the gray water.

Everything blurred as Lancelot tumbled backward, the vision burning in his mind as his body surrendered to the exhaustion of battle and of grief—

An hour later, a wandering soldier found him lying unconscious and bore him back to the high king's pavilion.

viii

Arthur lived through the night, although he didn't awaken. Lancelot kept vigil in the chill wind that slowly drove the mist away and revealed the stars. Just at dawn a halloo from the seaward side of the ridge brought him sleepily to his feet.

As he staggered toward the bluff he noticed men pointing out toward the east, where roseate light was coloring the Narrow Sea.

Lancelot drew nearer to the curious band along the cliff. They were not all soldiers. He saw an elderly woman, two small peasant boys—

His voice showed his anger.

"What are these people doing here?"

"Why, captain," said the old woman, "we live a little way to the west. All through the night Modred's soldiers were running by. They said the high king had destroyed him and was dying. We came to see."

To the soldiers, Lancelot growled, "Keep them away from the king's pavilion. *Well* away!"

"Aye." The man nodded. "But look down there, sir. That's why we called you."

On the beach below a small skiff had dropped its anchor stone between the high bows of Lancelot's vessels. By the flaring orange light of a watch-fire built on the sand he could just make out the stout figure of a boatman leaning against the skiff's mast—and three black-clad figures speaking to one of his soldiers.

Celtic nuns— Lancelot could hardly believe it.

He ran among the stones until he reached one of the precipitous paths leading down. Moments later he arrived breathless beside the snapping fire. The three nuns, two quite young and one in her middle years, greeted him with polite nods.

Lancelot's anger seethed again. Farther down the beach he saw two raffish men approaching. Fishermen, by the look of them. Apparently there was to be no end to the arrival of the curious—

Lancelot's anger vented itself on the nuns:

"What do you want here, Sisters? No prayers can help the king."

Undismayed by his severity, the older nun said quietly, "We have brought our little boat from Avalon, captain. The island of the apples—"

"I have heard of it but have never seen it."

"We maintain an abbey there. We were instructed to come and take the king to it so that he could rest safely."

"Instructed?" Lancelot snarled. "By whom?"

The nun's calm eyes made him ashamed.

"By a voice that spoke at the darkest hour of the night, captain. To me—and to these sisters as well. We all heard it, so we have come for him."

Lancelot was on the point of speaking, when she added, "You must let us take him. God has commanded."

Lancelot bowed his head in silent assent.

ix

Soldiers bore the high king laboriously down to the shore. There, at his own insistence, they raised him upright.

The beach was brightening with the golden radiance of morning. Still annoyed by the crowd of onlookers—farmer folk, mostly, perhaps thirty in all. Wretchedly dressed and coarse faced, they gazed in awe at the sight of the great king garbed like a common soldier and stumbling in obvious pain between the two captains supporting his arms across their shoulders.

Several of the peasant women wept. The boatmen waited in the purling surf. The three nuns had already gone aboard.

Glancing at the crowd again, Lancelot noted two additions he hadn't been aware of before. Holy men, one with his head uncovered and his hair cut in the Celtic tonsure. He was a red-nosed, venal-looking fellow.

The other was not of the same order. Lancelot couldn't see his face; his cowl hid it. But his plain wool gown was of a different cut than the first monk's. And the runic brooch pinning up his cloak at the right shoulder was definitely no Christian emblem—

Lancelot's gaze traveled on. Massed at open places on the bluff, literally hundreds of dark, motionless figures stood. Soldiers watching.

Suddenly the captain from Gaul could bear the pain of the moment no longer. Unashamed, he dropped to his knees in the sand. He clasped his hands, murmuring a prayer:

"God give him the strength to live. The land needs him—and his captains too—"

He thought he heard a reedy voice speak his name. He opened his eyes, saw the three-figured shadow on the sand in front of him. He looked up—

Arthur seemed to tower against the cloud-puffed heavens. His brown streaked white hair fluttered in the sea wind. His waist was bound with great swathes of linen, dark with drying blood—

"I will live, Lancelot," the high king whispered. "I will rest at Avalon and come again when the need is greatest."

The wind seemed to die, bringing total silence. Arthur said, "I promise you that—"

Pain welled in the high king's eyes then. He hid it by averting his head for a moment.

Lancelot said to the two captains, "I will carry him."

They offered no argument. Carefully Lancelot gathered the king's body into his arms. Then he turned and strode into the surf, his heartbreak almost unbearable.

Off to the east the sun had cleared the surface of the sea. Searing light blinded Lancelot for a moment—

The boatman clambered aboard ahead of him. Lancelot handed Arthur up into the skiff. The boatman carried the high king to the stern. With a gentleness unusual in one his size he laid Arthur on a pile of blankets, then arranged his cloak.

Unable to watch any longer Lancelot stumbled through the white foam to the beach. Standing apart from the crowd, the cowled holy man was using a stick to draw in the damp sand, just above the reach of the tide.

The boatman called good-bye and began to hoist his sail. The two younger nuns hauled up the anchor-rope like experienced hands. Lancelot shielded his eyes against the blaze of the sun as the skiff put about, caught the morning breeze in its sails, and moved slowly away from shore. Soon it was difficult to see. It seemed to be vanishing into the center of the radiant sun—

"What was that he wrote? He wrote something. I saw him!"

The rasping voice of a fisherman brought Lancelot around. Some of the watchers were clustered at the place in the sand where the cowled man's stick had moved. Of the man himself, Lancelot saw no sign.

"I can't read it," a child complained.

"Because it's the old church tongue," his mother said.

The venal-looking monk shoved his way into the circle. "I can read it."

He gazed at the scrawled inscription. "*Rex quondam—rexque futurus.*"

In a moment, after the watchers were suitably impressed with his erudition, he translated: " 'The king who was—the king who will be again.' "